800
O/P

FIREGROUND TACTICS

About the author

Emanuel Fried joined the New York City Fire Department in May 1936. He rose through the ranks and retired in 1958 as Deputy Chief of Department. After serving some two years as consultant and as Chief Instructor for the Mount Vernon, New York, Fire Training Conference, he assumed the position of Chief of Hinsdale (Illinois) Fire Department. In 1968 he was appointed Chief of the Chicago Heights (Illinois) Fire Department. Chief Fried has written numerous articles for fire service publications and has lectured for state and national organizations, including the Fire Department Instructors Conference and the International Association of Fire Chiefs Conference. He was Staff Instructor for the Illinois Fire College, Lecturer for the New York City Fire College, and he holds several teaching certificates including one from the New York State Education Department. He has conducted private schools for firemen and officers and has served as consultant and investigator. In 1947 he was awarded the Franklin Delano Roosevelt Medal and Department Medal of Honor for meritorious service at extreme personal risk. He is inventor of the Pry-Axe forcible entry tool. In May 1970 Chief Fried retired from active firefighting duty, although he continues to remain active as lecturer, instructor, author, and as a consultant. He is Consulting Editor for FIRE CHIEF Magazine and is instructor for the FIRE CHIEF Magazine Firefighting Tactics Seminars.

FIREGROUND TACTICS

Emanuel Fried

William Randleman, Editor

H. MARVIN GINN CORPORATION
CHICAGO

FIREGROUND TACTICS

Library of Congress Catalog Card Number: 70-184809

First Edition: 1972

Foreword

I am quite pleased to write the foreword for this book. Chief Fried saved my life years ago when he was a Lieutenant and I was a fireman in Ladder 120 in the Brownsville section of Brooklyn (New York City). He did not save me by a thrilling rescue; rather he did it by an almost instinctive judgment of fire behavior that saved us both by a matter of seconds.

However, I am not writing this foreword out of gratitude. Quite the contrary: I am writing it because the book will fill a great need—the need for better knowledge of firefighting tactics. The author has two assets which make this book as good as it is. One is his wealth of varied experience. He worked in several sections of New York City, including being Chief of the 44th Battalion, the busiest in the world. Then he was Chief of the fire departments at Hinsdale and Chicago Heights, both in Illinois. The first is essentially a residential community; the second is highly industrialized with a variety of large, high hazard industries. Therefore this book is one that is written by a man who has been through most of what he writes about.

The second asset is the author's willingness to be specific. He is not content to confine his writing to principles and generalities. These qualities will make this book a valuable contribution to fire service literature.

WILLIAM E. CLARK

Ocala, Florida
November, 1971

Preface

Some of you who have listened to my lectures or read what I have written may have noticed that at times I poke a little fun at the fire service, or call attention to some of its shortcomings. This is not done with malice, but rather with affection. It may be likened to the loving father correcting his errant son by citing some related bit of folklore humor, or the husband jesting with his wife of many years to explain a point.

The fire service has been good to me and my family. It has provided us with security; and in addition, for me, it has been a most challenging work all my life.

The beginning was neither tranquil nor secure. Come back with me in time to the Thirties and those terrible depression years. Like millions of others, I was caught in the maelstrom—no work to be found, and little hope of any to come.

In my case I was fortunate enough to have a gentle, concerned brother who urged me to try out for the fire department. He took the trouble to bring home the application, filled out the information called for on the form, and cajoled me into signing it. He then coaxed me into taking the examination. I was appointed to the New York City Fire Department on May 16, 1936. The success that I now enjoy is due to many. I will always remember the people who taught me the art. Their teachings are an integral part of this book.

EMANUEL FRIED

Tierre Verde, Florida
November, 1971

Acknowledgments

My special thanks

—to a good friend, Bill Randleman, editor of FIRE CHIEF Magazine, whose long hours of competent editing made this book a far better work than it would otherwise have been.

—to a dear friend of 30 years, Bill Clark, Director of the Florida State Fire College, who reviewed the book and was good enough to express his generous sentiments in the Foreword.

—to my gentle, wonderful brother, David, who guided me toward the fire department so long ago. It was he who got and filled out the application mentioned in the Preface.

—to not only a dear brother, but a contemporary as well, Julius, who served with me in the fire department for over 20 years, retiring as a Battalion Chief. He was kind enough to give me carte blanche in the use of his voluminous notes, much of which I used generously in this book.

—and to slightly change the old cliché (I use it because nothing expresses my sentiments better), last but the "mostest" to my lovely Becky, who for the 35 years I put in this business helped me study. She did my typing, listened with patience to my griping, cheered me up when I needed it, and applauded me when I didn't deserve it. She often restored my flagging spirits, and in better, younger days, even helped me drink some of them.

EMANUEL FRIED

Contents

Contents—Continued

Section III—Specific fire problems

Section IV—Solving firefighting problems

Section V—Conclusion

Introduction

FIREFIGHTING HAS a dual objective: saving lives and conserving property. To accomplish this objective as efficiently as possible, a sequence of operational practice has been developed over the years. An analysis of past and contemporary techniques shows that the operation generally follows this pattern:

1. Pre-fire planning.
2. Fireground sizeup.
3. Firefighting steps: (a) ventilation, (b) operation of hose streams, and (c) overhauling.
4. Post-fire analysis and study.

Although there are many more firefighting facets than those mentioned above in point 3, such as forcible entry, ladder work, search and rescue, these are basic skills that are amply covered in many excellent training texts and are not properly a part of this book.

Under the heading of firefighting, specific fire problems as well as general ones are dealt with in this volume. Generally, good ventilation practices are much the same in most buildings. So rather than treat the subject of ventilation in a hotel fire, in a multiple-dwelling fire, and again in a factory fire, ventilation is given detailed attention as a separate and integral part of this text. Where there are problems in an occupancy that vary from the norm, the differences are noted and discussed. Except for a few sample exercises, the same reasoning prevails for sizeup, which is handled as a separate topic and covers most fire contingencies. Special consideration is given to unique problems. In the same way, the subject of partition fires is handled in the chapter on concealed fire problems.

If a particular fire requires elaboration because of an unusual problem or involvement, this is done. Otherwise, such practices are not discussed separately for each situation.

Naturally, saving lives in fires always is given priority over saving property, and this book emphasizes that. It makes the important point that, under extreme conditions, where many persons are trapped; all men may be used to rescue them. Ordinarily, this would delay other operations necessary to fighting the fire, but it is important to note that the judicious use of a hose stream or certain acts of ventilation may save more lives than raising ladders to rescue persons visible at the windows.

To illustrate these two points, consider first a multiple dwelling with a fire involving the stairway. Three or four people are screaming from windows on the upper floors, smoke is pouring around them. The natural tendency would be for all hands to rush to place ladders to save those people, particularly if you are short-handed or if only two units rolled in initially. What is not obvious, however, is that a dozen or more people may be cut off from trying to get down the inside stairway and are trapped in their apartments on the sides and the rear of the building. In such a case, the rapid advance of the hose line up the stairs would extinguish the fire, prevent its spread to the apartments in which people are trapped, and save more lives than raising ladders would do. In the same case, if the engine company could not advance up the stairs because of smoke and heat, removing or opening the skylight or scuttle on the roof over the stairs could well save lives.

If a ladder company arrived first and found the conditions described above, immediate ventilation over the stair shaft would pull the smoke and heat straight up, preventing it from involving the apartments on each floor. Thus a ladder company could effectively channel the fire away from persons trapped in their apartments pending the arrival of an engine company.

Decisions on the proper technique in fighting any fire will depend on many variables. Probably the most important is experience, which helps one to make the right judgment. However, because of the relative infrequency of large fires, many firemen—even officers and fire chiefs—sometimes lack such experience.

That is the principal objective of this book—to provide specific, detailed information on the most effective firefighting techniques, information that I have gathered first-hand in my 35 years of experience.

I have tried in this book to avoid generalities and to deal with real situations, many of which I have encountered.

EMANUEL FRIED

Fundamentals of firefighting operations

Chapter 1

Basic rules of firefighting strategy

WHAT ARE THE basic elements of firefighting strategy? What are we trying to accomplish? In seeking the answer to these questions, we find that the subject breaks down conveniently into 14 general areas. I call these the 14 basic rules of firefighting strategy. They are:

Rule 1. The highest priority is to determine the degree of danger of the building's occupants. This is particularly important where the occupants are old, infirm, or held in legal custody.

Rule 2. Where the fire poses an actual or probable threat to the safety of people, they should be removed.

Rule 3. If fire threatens to cut off the escape route of the occupants, you must direct a hose stream between the threatened egress and the fire. There are exceptions to this rule: where a ladder company is first to arrive, where there is a less dangerous route of egress for the people, or where it is physically impossible to do this in time.

Rule 4. The occupants of a building in which a fire department is operating, or is about to operate, should not be disturbed—provided the danger to which they are exposed can be eliminated. The prime reason for this rule is that people rushing through smoke-charged halls and down stairs impede firemen in their work. That could result in permitting a fire to "get away" that normally could be easily handled.

Rule 5. Countermand any previous order that is contrary to good fire tactics. Company officers are nearly always the first to arrive, and each officer, having his own company to direct, is not in a favorable position to direct firefighting according to a general plan. Good strategy therefore often demands that operations undertaken before the arrival of a chief should be varied. This may require countermanding orders. Chiefs sometimes seem unwilling to do this, but they shouldn't be. The disadvantages under which company officers labor in directing large operations are so great that they should not be held responsible except for good faith, obedience, a reasonable display of energy, and proper command of their own companies.

Rule 6. Cover the exposures first—attack the fire later. Exposures by which fires threaten to spread should be covered by streams before engine companies are assigned to positions from which an attack on the seat of the fire may be launched. In subsequent operations, exterior streams which are merely protecting exposures should, where possible, be redirected to a point where operations can not only protect the exposure, but also attack the fire.

Rule 7. The safety of men operating at a fire should not be dependent upon a single line of hose. There are exceptions to this rule: for example, when men are engaged in rescue work or when no other additional lines or men are available.

Rule 8. As soon as it becomes evident that the water is not reaching the seat of the fire, men whose sole egress might be cut off by an extension of the fire should be withdrawn. An exception should be made where new positions are taken from which the fire can be reached.

Rule 9. Whenever it is necessary to withdraw a line from a position rendered untenable by the extending fire, keep the stream in operation until the men get out safely. The exceptions to this rule are spreading liquid fires, and fires spread by explosions or falling floors, walls, roofs, or large heavy objects.

Rule 10. A building seriously involved by fire should be ventilated promptly and thoroughly.

Rule 11. With a fire reaching a shaft, stairway, or other vertical opening which extends to the roof, the duty of a ladder company is to ventilate directly above such openings. There seem to be but two exceptions to this: (1) Where the service of a ladderman is required to rescue persons in grave danger of being cut off by fire, and (2) where the risk involved in going to the roof is too great.

Rule 12. Don't let the natural impulse to attack a fire induce you to do so in such a way as to spread the fire.

Rule 13. If you are a chief, don't try to take over the duties of a company officer. Stay outside on the street where incoming units can reach and report to you. Keep a picture of the whole fire in front of you. Cover the sides, front, rear, top, and bottom of the fire.

Rule 14. Assign junior chiefs to these vantage points and maintain liaison with them.

Chapter 2

Engine company operations

THE FUNDAMENTAL techniques for engine company operations break down into 20 categories. Here are the 20 basic rules:

Rule 1. Select a source of water supply that is sufficient for the job intended. The nearest hydrant may not be the best choice if it is on a small main and there is a large main nearby.

Rule 2. Use a proper hose layout. Give thought to friction losses and the volume of water needed. Your hose layout should not only allow for current water needs, but should take into account the possibility of the fire growing. One suggestion would be to place a siamese connection between the first and second lengths back from the nozzle. This would take only a short time. Go to work on the fire as soon as you get the water. If it be-comes necessary, a second line can be filled into the siamese, thereby cutting your friction losses more than 75 percent (see Figure 1).

Rule 3. Get the line inside—to the seat of the fire whenever possible.

Rule 4. Don't open the nozzle on smoke. The smoke will lose its buoyancy, making ventilation more difficult. You will also cause more water damage.

Rule 5. Open and close the nozzles slowly. With a nozzle closed no water is flowing, thus there is no friction loss. If the pumper shows 200 psi on the pressure gauge, this is the pressure at the nozzle with no water flowing. Opening the nozzle suddenly releases this 200 psi instantly. The reaction may tear the nozzle from your hands. Closing it too quickly will cause a water hammer that can burst hose or damage the pump.

Rule 6. Don't charge the line before going up a stairway or ladder. It will be extremely difficult to advance under such conditions. Wait until you are in position before charging the line.

Rule 7. Don't open the nozzle directly on the fire (particularly inside a house). Bleed off the entrapped air first or you may scatter burning embers with a jet of compressed air.

Rule 8. If your hose line is under considerable pressure, straighten it out behind you. This will help you to hold the nozzle with less effort.

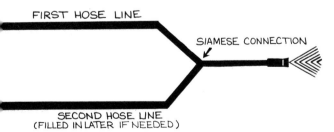

FIRST HOSE LINE

SIAMESE CONNECTION

SECOND HOSE LINE
(FILLED IN LATER IF NEEDED)

FIGURE 1. *Two-way siamese inserted in hose lay one length before nozzle. Water can be started and the clapper will keep water from backing out of the unused siamese connection. The second line can be filled in at any time without having to shut down. The friction loss in the siamesed hose will be reduced by about 75 percent.*

FIGURE 2. *Second man is holding line at waist height and Number 3 man is holding it almost chest high. To aim the stream upward the nozzle-* *man must kink the hose. The second man is crowding the nozzleman to the point where he is having difficulty even holding on to the nozzle.*

Rule 9. When advancing a line up a stairway fire, don't try to move up with the nozzle all the way open. As you lift one foot to step up, back pressure may throw you down the stairs. Handle a stairway fire by darkening the fire ahead of you. Direct the stream up the well hole* for an instant, then partially close the nozzle to relieve the back pressure. Now move up to where you are ready to open the nozzle fully again.

Rule 10. If you are trying to make a tough cellar or long hall, make sure your spare hose is pulled up (not kinked) just outside the cellar entrance or hall so that when you start to move you don't have to stop in the middle of the stairs or hall (the most murderous part) to pull up more hose.

*The well hole is the space between the stair banister and the side rail of the floor landing and hall above. If you stood on the lowest hall floor and looked up, you could see all the way up to the top floor. This opening is called the well hole.

Rule 11. Don't stand in front of a door to the fire area before it is opened. Step to one side and crouch low. When the door is opened, the combustion products and heat will pass over your head. Wait a few seconds to give the fire a chance to light up or "blow" before you move in, then move in with your charged line. You don't want to get caught in the middle of the hall when the fire lights all around you. You will also be able to spot your target much more readily.

Rule 12. Don't crowd the nozzleman. Give him room to work. Give him enough space to hold part of the hose under one arm while the other hand holds and guides the nozzle. If he wants to aim the stream toward the ceiling, his supporting crew should hold the hose line behind him, down toward the floor. If the nozzleman wants to aim the stream downward, his supporting crew should elevate their hold. Otherwise they are contradicting each other's efforts and making the job more difficult. (See Figure 2.)

Rule 13. If you can't spot the fire because of heavy smoke, crouch down low and listen. Keep everyone quiet. The chances are you will hear the crackling and can then move toward the fire. If the fire covers a large area, you will generally be better off to direct the stream in a sweeping arc against the ceiling, which will act as a huge deflector, giving far greater coverage than spot stream delivery.

Rule 14. If you are at the nozzle and having difficulty breathing, remember all streams carry some entrapped air. Put your face as close to the nozzle as possible and you will be able to get a few breaths of air.

Rule 15. In extremely difficult, hot, smoky conditions, crouch low—if necessary, lie on the floor and inch your way forward. Heat and smoke tend to rise. Therefore some fresh air will come in along the floor to replace the heat and smoke.

Rule 16. When you are ready to take your hose line down from upper stories or ladders, disconnect at the first hose butt outside the building. This will relieve the hose line of the weight of the water and you will be able to get down with less effort.

Rule 17. Don't bend hose that is frozen. You will break the fibre and seriously weaken the hose.

Rule 18. When you get back to quarters and have had your second cup of coffee, examine your hose carefully for possible damage. Inferior or suspect hose should not be put back on your fire truck. If hose breaks in a fire building, you may be cut off by fire and lose your life.

Rule 19. If you are an engine company officer, keep a list of your men with you. As soon as you have backed out of a rough position, count heads to see whether anyone is missing.

Rule 20. An engine company operates as a team with a single mission to perform: the control of fire. This function is quite different than that of ladder companies.

Chapter 3

Hose line placement at fires

THE MATTER of proper hose line placement at fires is a subject that deserves considerable exploration. To judge its importance one should examine the fire problem in some detail. Fighting most fires is a relatively simple procedure. Small grass fires, mattress fires in bedrooms, fire in an upholstered living room chair, or similar situations may require only an extinguisher, a booster line, or less frequently a 1½-inch line for a few seconds. Admittedly, the mattress or upholstered chair fire can make you uncomfortable for a while. But the techniques are basic: a dash of water, the opening of windows, and the problem is controlled.

If most of our fires require such academic procedures, one may question the need or justification for expensive and elaborate equipment, intensive training, and the time-consuming organizational details in anticipation of the large fire. The answer is that fire departments should not only be able to handle complex fire problems, they should also be prepared to handle more than one major fire at a time if the need arises. In all too many cases they cannot do so with the required efficiency.

To substantiate this premise, let's look at some statistics. The American Insurance Association* says that less than half of one percent of fires are large enough to require powerful stream equipment. Even fewer require

the use of ladder pipes and elevating platform streams. The inference here is quite clear: we lack sufficient practice in the techniques of handling large fires which call for heavy stream appliances.

Another study** shows that of all the alarms we respond to, 75 percent of the fires are out on arrival or easily extinguished by booster lines; but that less than two percent of the fires cause most of the loss of life and 70 percent of the damage. Less than half of one percent of the fires produce losses or more than $10,000.† But this half of one percent causes 25 percent of our fire loss. *Municipal Fire Administration*†† says that firefighting involves a large number of fires which are relatively simple to handle and a few fires which involve many complex factors. Some are complex because they are large and some because they involve hazardous processes, materials, or both. As a result, our fire departments usually are proficient in handling simple fires, but weak in handling complex ones. The plain fact is that we do not have enough large fires to develop, through experience, sufficient proficiency to handle the more serious fires.

The inevitable conclusion must be that our performance is good on the average fire, but certainly questionable on problem fires. If we concede that our problem is that of the

---

*Bulletin 148.

**A.I.A. Bulletin 229.
†A.I.A. Bulletin 109.
††Published by the International City Managers' Association, 1313 East 60 Street, Chicago, Illinois 60637.

FIGURE 3. *Time is 4 A.M. Fire starts in abandoned building at left. Fire is threatening occupied residence structure at right. First line should go to the threatened apartments. Second line covers the floor above if necessary, or to the original fire building.*

FIGURE 4. *The time is 4 A.M. This time the fire is in the residence and is threatening to extend to the abandoned building. Line placement should be the same as given in Figure 3. This is because life safety is always the determining factor.*

larger fire—the one requiring three or more lines—how do we go about line placement? Do we have valid reasons for placing hose lines in certain positions, or are we really guessing? Unfortunately, in many cases we do just that—guess. Is the term "science of firefighting" justified? Is our job a science or one of skill and judgment based on practice and constant observation?

A science is exact—results should not vary from time to time. The very word science connotes precision. Is our job such? I think not. If our job is one of great skill, why cannot we serve some form of apprenticeship, learn it well so that firefighting becomes largely a matter of applying what we have learned? Actually, this is partially the way we do train our men.

Is there then a general procedure to follow at major fires? If so, can this procedure be applied to all fires? It would be helpful if the answer was simple and constant. The difficulty, again, is the lack of similarity in fires. Because fires are different, they require adjustment of techniques to deal with the problems at each particular fire.

Procedures need constant revision

Commanding officers often guess at fires because they are not sure what to do. They become even more confused when incoming fire companies press them for assignments. Primarily to relieve inner mounting tensions, the commander will quickly position a company because he feels a decision is demanded of him. Such a decision may be a serious mis-

10

take because once a company is positioned, with lines laid, it is difficult to change the assignment quickly. There may be a crucial need for this hose line elsewhere only moments later. If the commanding officer is not sure where to place a company for the moment, he should simply tell the company officer to stand fast while he reviews the situation. Men respect such calm, reasoned judgment and are quick to sense indecision. If you shout, they will know you do so from tension. Therefore refrain from shouting and remain calm. This attitude also will help junior officers to retain their composure.

The three phases of firefighting

If procedures need constant revision, can there be some over-all plan to guide the commanding officer in his line placement? The answer is yes. The basic purpose of a hose line is to extinguish fire or protect someone or something from fire. This is academic. But there are other purposes for hose lines, such as: (1) ventilation (breaking of windows by hose streams or fog nozzles), forcible entry (fire boat streams on pier siding), and washdowns (spilled flammable liquids).

There is a logical sequence to firefighting, and it includes three phases:

Phase 1. Locate the fire (not always an easy job—too many men still use water on smoke).

Phase 2. Confine the fire (head it off and surround it).

Phase 3. Extinguish the fire.

If we understand the basic purpose of hose lines and the logical sequence of events in fire fighting, we then can establish some guidelines for planning proper hose line placement.

You will notice that extinguishment is listed after confinement in the three phases of firefighting. There is a reason for this: the original fire still exists and must be confined. If you concentrate on the extinguishment phase first, the fire may spread, involving adjoining or adjacent structures. You now may have two or more fires on your hands. So your strategy should be to head the fire off—don't allow it to go any further. One should not wait until fire shows up in an exposed structure and then stretch a line to cover it. A

hose line should have been placed in anticipation of such an occurrence. Once this has been accomplished, then move in to extinguish.

What do we mean by exposure? There are two types: internal exposure—that which the building offers to itself—and external exposure—that which the building offers to another structure.

Note that in most cases Phase 2 (confine) and Phase 3 (extinguishment) are synonymous. If you extinguish the fire in most cases you have stopped its spread. Actually if you stop to think about it, most fire tactics follow these three phases.

First consideration is life safety

Unfortunately, the principles just stated may be a dangerous over simplification. We do come across situations where placing a line in one position may be correct, yet the same fire in the same building might require different techniques under different conditions. The principle is this: regardless of strategic dictates, the safety of human life should always be the strongest motivating factor in the placement of a hose stream.

Figure 3 shows a fire in an abandoned building extending across a narrow shaft into an occupied apartment. Assume the time to be 4 A.M. Please realize this sketch is an over simplification of the problem. If the drawing were to include the usual amount of smoke and fire, the details for purposes of explanation would be obscured. The first hose line should go to the fire extension point, the occupied apartments. Line 2 should cover the floor above (if any) or, if this were not necessary, to the abandoned building.

Now look at Figure 4. All conditions are the same except that the fire originates in the occupied apartment and extends to the abandoned building. The hose line placement would be the same as for Figure 3. The reasoning in both cases is that the protection of life takes precedence over any other strategy. Time and time again, the judicious use of a hose line has proved to be a great lifesaving factor. In both fires, the third and additional lines would go into the abandoned building.

Figure 5 shows people escaping from a

FIGURE 5. *Fire is in the cellar. People are leaving safely via the fire escape. Hose line is being advanced into cellar. This is correct line placement.*

building on fire by way of the fire escape. The fire is in the cellar. The entrance to the cellar is from the inside hall under the stairs. There is another entrance to the cellar: a pair of folding iron doors outside and level with the sidewalk. Line 1 should try to make the cellar from the inside hallway. If this is not possible, back the line out to the hallway and close the cellar door. This line must remain here to protect the upper stairs in case fire should extend from the cellar or start to run the sidewalls.

Line 2 should be sent down the front cellar entrance through the folding outside doors. Make sure people are off the fire escape before you open these doors or they will be terribly exposed. If Line 2 can't make it, stretch another line and have Line 2 and Line 3 try it together (sometimes both lines abreast may cool the fire sufficiently to knock it out). If Line 2 and Line 3 can't make it, then back them out. Put Line 2 into a cellar pipe, cut the floor over the hot spot, and shove the cellar pipe down. Line 1 should cover any superficial extension at the baseboards and Line 3 should be kept ready to move to the floor above if needed.

Once people above have been evacuated,

open the door to the cellar in the hallway to provide ventilation for the lines trying to make the cellar from the outside, but make sure the first line is ready in case fire starts to come up the cellar stairs.

Now this, in my opinion, is the proper line placement under the conditions outlined. But suppose that Line 1 was being advanced into the hallway at the moment the people were coming down the front fire escape; and right then the fire blows out the front windows under the fire escape (see Figures 6 and 7). I think we would all agree that if nothing were done to protect the people on the fire escape they would fry like meat on a griddle.

Is there anyone who would deny that the proper use of the first line right now is to throw a protective shield of water between the fire and the endangered people; if possible, to drive the fire back into the windows until the people can either get down or back into the apartments above and away from the lethal flame? So again we see it is difficult to establish a set rule in this matter of line placement. The fire officer must be able to think fast and be ready to change any prearranged plan to fit the situation.

How much water is needed on a fire?

We all know that to put out a fire we must advance the line until the water from the nozzle can impinge upon the burning material. How much fire can one line handle? When shall we stretch a second line? Here again the answers are not simple. The fireground is no place for the slide rule, so you will have to rely on experience backed by good judgment. Here are some guidelines to follow:

Residential fires. For the average residential structure, a 1½-inch line discharging between 75 and 100 gpm should be able to handle up to two rooms that are well-involved. This should be backed up with another 1½-inch line and a third line to the floor above. Of course, if there are adjoining exposures, they must be covered in similar fashion. There should be three men per 1½-inch line; one at the nozzle, another about five feet behind, and a third man about 10 feet behind, lightening up on the line and pulling surplus hose as needed. If you are "making" a stairway, you will need a fourth man.

If the fire is beyond this size, then all back-up and covering lines should be 2½-inch lines.

Industrial fires of any consequence call for all interior lines to be 2½-inch lines. This requires two men at the nozzle, a third lightening up behind, and a fourth man pulling surplus hose. If you are "making" a stairway you will need a fifth man.

Exterior streams, if required, call for a minimum of 3-inch hose, siamesed into heavy stream appliances. It is possible for two men to operate these heavy stream appliances except when it is necessary to shift the appliance to another position. In nonurban areas where 3-inch hose is not common, you must rely on 2½-inch hose. In such cases it is all the more important to remember the advantages of siamesing lines and, if necessary, reducing nozzle sizes to cut down on friction losses.

On large-area interior fires, each standard 2½-inch hand line can cover about 1,000 square feet of area.

Back-up lines. Generally speaking, if a fire is large enough to create a questionable extinguishing problem for one line, then lay a back-up line for support. If the fire is of such intensity that men could be cut off or in trouble because of burst hose lines, lay an additional hose line for support. Where fire may move up shafts, pipe recesses, or any vertical artery, lay lines to cover above to head off fire travel. If fire in a hanging ceiling space threatens to move laterally (as fires commonly do), lay lines to cover the potential extension on either side of the hanging ceiling space. If a fire involves materials of explosive nature or hazardous chemicals, lay additional support lines. Cover both men and exposures with back-up lines.

These guidelines take into account ordinary combustibles. But in cases of flammable liquid fires, explosively rapid combustion, or dense smoke accompanied by extreme heat, these guidelines will vary considerably. Here judgment of the experienced fire officer is of paramount importance. This also presupposes an operating crew that is not afraid to take a "beating" and move in on the fire.

FIGURE 6. *Fire blows out of cellar windows, trapping people on the fire escape. They must be protected by hose line.*

FIGURE 7. *People on fire escape (upper right) are afraid to come down. Fireman is moving up but trying to get away from the heat. If time permitted, a 20-foot ladder should be raised to the balcony.*

FIGURE 8. *Attacking the fire by way of the inside stairs and protecting the stairs at the same time is proper. Note that combustion products are forced ahead and out of the window, keeping the halls and stairs clear for evacuation.*

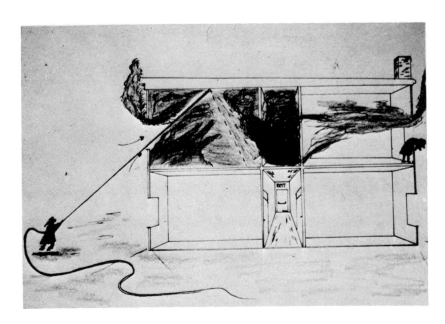

FIGURE 9. *This is the same fire shown in Figure 8. Note what happens when outside stream is used. Fire and combustion products are driven back into the building and involve other areas and the stairs.*

Advantages of inside streams

Far too many fires extend without the man in charge becoming aware of such extensions —because too many fires are fought from the outside. There are certain definite advantages to the use of inside streams as opposed to outside streams. Here are some of them:

1. The nozzleman sees where his stream is aimed and whether he is hitting the fire.

2. He shuts down as soon as the fire is darkened. Thus there is less water damage. And since he hit fire and not the smoke, the smoke is not wet and remains more buoyant, so that it lifts readily. Otherwise it is difficult to ventilate the building.

3. The nozzleman can vary the pattern of his fog stream because he sees the need of such variance.

4. The fire is being attacked where it should be—at its seat, not at just flame tongues and smoke.

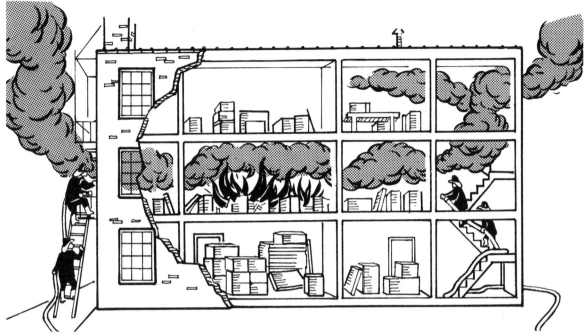

FIGURE 10. *Two lines working against each other drive combustion products toward opposing crews. Neither crew can advance and the fire continues to burn on and up through the structure. Proper technique here is to have both lines work together from one direction. This pushes fire out of the building. Have third line protect rear stairs or fire escape and a fourth protect the floor above.*

5. The nozzleman is in a position to judge the path of the fire and any extension. For example, the fire may be getting out through a rear window and into an adjoining building, or a dropped ceiling may show that fire has entered the ceiling space, indicating the need for shifting lines or for additional lines.

6. The nozzleman may come across an unconscious or trapped victim while he is operating in the building. He can cover the victim with a line until help arrives.

Exterior streams

When using exterior streams, note how much runoff there is. Most of the water you see running down stair shafts or down the street is wasted. It did not hit the fire. Here are some additional disadvantages of such exterior streams:

1. Your stream may be entering a shaftway window, with water just filling the cellar. (If your objective is to keep fire from traveling up this shaft, the stream is warranted.)

2. The stream may be just bouncing off interior partitions.

3. You may cause injury to men operating on the interior or drive them off the floor.

4. The water damage resulting from large streams may be tremendous.

5. You may add sufficient weight to the already weakened structure to cause collapse. This is particularly true if the water is retained by absorbent materials inside the building.

Extinguishing capabilities of water

Firemen sometimes forget that one 2-inch tip at 100 psi nozzle pressure throws 1,200 gpm. This is about 10,000 pounds of water entering the building every minute. How much fire inside a building can stand the impact of so much water? Isn't it obvious that if the fire does not darken down within minutes you are not hitting the fire, that the line should be shifted or shut down?

We should take a closer look at this extinguishing medium we throw around so

FIGURE 11. *This sequence of four pictures of a training fire shows why a line must be taken inside if possible. In this picture, the training fire is just starting to burn.*

FIGURE 12. *Men are being assigned incorrectly to hit the fire from the outside.*

FIGURE 13. *Note how exterior stream pushes fire back in and blows it out the windows.*

FIGURE 14. *Now second crew hits fire coming out window at left. This attack not only fans fire, driving combustion products back into house, but imperils any people inside. The line should have been taken inside to prevent the fire from spreading within the building.*

carelessly. How efficiently do we use this water? Let's take a quick look at how water does its work for us at fires. The heat combustion of wood is about 8,000 Btu's per pound. One Btu (British Thermal Unit) is the amount of heat necessary to raise the temperature of one pound of water one degree Fahrenheit. The average structural fire releases about 3,000 Btu's per square foot per minute. Consider a 10x10-foot floor area completely involved. This would be 100 square feet. Multiply this by 3,000 Btu's per square foot and you get a total heat release of 300,000 Btu's per minute.

One gallon of water when raised in temperature from 60° F. to 212° F. absorbs about 1,250 Btu's (obviously not enough to absorb the heat being generated). However, a peculiar phenomenon occurs when the water is turned to steam. Right at this moment the water absorbs more than six times as much heat in turning to steam as it did going all the way from 60° F. to 212° F. So we can see that when water is turned to steam from the heat of a fire, we use it to its maximum. The total heat absorption of one gallon of water changing to steam is 9,300 Btu's.

If we go back to our 100-square-foot floor area with its heat generation of 300,000 Btu's, we can see that if we divide the 9,300 Btu's into it, we will need only 30 gallons of completely vaporized water to extinguish the fire on this floor.

Water has one more unique feature which works to our advantage. When turned to steam, it has an expansion factor of more than 1600 to 1. So in addition to the cooling effect, we have the advantage of a blanketing effect.

It is often argued that outside streams may also be of small capacity (you commonly see this at fires). If the fire is small enough to use small streams from the outside, then it is small enough to use inside lines. The objective of exterior, large caliber streams is to contain a large spreading fire, driving it back with the cooling effect of tons of water.

Normally one would use the smallest nozzle on a hose line that would do the job properly. By the same token, don't send a boy on a man's errand. When you have a raging lumber-yard fire, don't stretch a booster line. You need large streams. This is when you should know that large nozzle tips eat up pressure because of the large flows and resultant large friction losses. This is when you should know the advantage of proper hose layouts, larger diameter lines, siamesing of hose lines, and large mains. The simple expedient of siamesing a hose line cuts your friction loss by about 75 percent.

Frequently at large fires an effort is made to surround the fire with hose lines. As a result, these lines, placed at opposite positions, are sometimes pointed toward other crews. This causes unnecessary punishment for the operating forces but may be unavoidable at large fires to protect exposures. This should never be permitted within a structure. There is no place for the heat and smoke to be driven except directly at the opposing crews. In such cases, it is far better to have two lines working abreast and advancing together to drive the fire ahead. You should, of course, have the upstairs protected by a line.

When to call for help is a problem that plagues commanding officers at fires. Suppose a commanding officer has all his companies operating at a fire. He keeps wondering whether he should call for help on the chance that the fire may begin to travel. The answer is obvious. He should already have called for help. As soon as you have committed, or know you will commit, your last unit, call for help. To wait is to take a terrible gamble. If the fire moves you will have nothing left with which to combat it. You should always have at least one reserve unit. With large fires, more than one unit should be available.

Nearly every structural fire of any consequence has six points which may require coverage: the top, the bottom, and the four sides. If these points are not checked upon and covered as the need requires, the fire may extend.

A general plan for line placement

From an over-all point of view, line placement at fires should follow this general plan: The initial hose lines are laid to cut off fire spread and supply sprinkler systems. Then additional lines are laid to surround the fire area, with

FIGURE 15. *Example of an inefficient exterior stream. Not only is stream breaking up, but there is no penetration. This stream should be shut down.*

FIGURE 16. *This street stream is accomplishing very little. It should be moved into the doorway toward the seat of the fire or shut down.*

FIGURE 17. *A stream that does not penetrate is useless. The need is for elevating platforms or* *ladder pipes to darken the fire down. Then men can move to upper floors with hand lines.*

back-up lines placed in heavily involved areas. Subsequent lines are supplied to fill in the supply to sprinkler systems or heavy stream appliances such as ladder pipes or elevating platforms. You may have to assign units as a spark and brand patrol in case this becomes a factor.

While ventilation is not properly within the scope of line placement, the point should be made that to advance a line into an involved building and hold that position, the building must be promptly and thoroughly ventilated.

When to give up the inside fight

Now let me tackle the most ticklish point in this matter of line placement: When do you back companies out and make an outside fight of it because you fear building collapse? First, we will not consider the possibility of explo-sions of weapons, gunpowder, etc. Second, we will not consider the reinforced concrete building, nor the so-called fireproof struc-ture because, barring the unusual or unfore-seen, these buildings do not collapse from fire. We will consider the combustible build-ing, the ordinary brick exterior, the wood joisted building, the building with unpro-tected metal structural members.

Factors you must consider are the occu-pancies, floor loads, absorbency of stored ma-terials, age and maintenance of the building.

A good general rule is this: When fire has substantially involved more than one floor and is out of control after 20 minutes of in-side operation, back all companies out and resort to the use of exterior streams. You may lose the building, but you may save your men. (Figures 8 through 17 will help to ex-plain some points of line placement.)

Chapter 4

Ladder company operations

THE BASIC unit of a fire department, regardless of its size, is some form of pumping engine carrying hose and tools. In rural areas without a water supply, the basic unit must incorporate its own water supply.

In addition to the engine company functions, there are other facets of fire duty which must accompany the laying of hose and application of water on the fire. These functions will vary with the size of the fire, its complexity, and the loss-of-life potential. Generally speaking, these additional functions are carried out during the operation by the original crew, by those arriving later, or by mutual-aid companies. Again, depending on the need and prevailing conditions, these functions sometimes are sadly neglected, usually because of lack of manpower in the initial response, lack of organization, or both.

For example, let us assume a fire in a multi-residence structure of three stories. A fire starts in the cellar during the early morning hours and by the time the first engine company arrives a fair amount of smoke has built up on the floors above. If only one engine responds, the men will be busy laying lines. Even where volunteers respond to the fire, the situation is less than desirable because there is no assurance as to the number of men responding or the speed of their response. The operation cannot be planned in

its entirety, but in a piecemeal manner. Look at the tasks that require immediate consideration:

1. Forcible entry.
2. Laddering.
3. Ventilation.
4. Search for people overcome.
5. Search for fire extension.

Even with two engine companies on the initial response, many of the related ladder company (also called Truck company) functions are often neglected.

Seven points of ladder company operations

There are seven cardinal points of ladder company operations. They are given not necessarily in order of importance, because each fire establishes its own priorities. The seven cardinal points are:

Point 1. Saving of life, saving those in actual peril first.

Point 2. Forcible entry where needed.

Point 3. Ventilation—higher levels first, roof outlets, scuttles, and skylights.

Point 4. Laddering the building; aerial and/or portable.

Point 5. Search of structure for those overcome or who for other reasons are unable to move. At the same time, examine for extension of fire.

Point 6. Use of auxiliary appliances present; standpipe lines if necessary, extinguishers, smothering agents, sprinkler shut down if operating needlessly.

Point 7. Overhauling—opening walls and ceilings where fire may have traveled, eliminating all means of rekindling. For a close inspection of all fire arteries, or removal of heavy volumes of water.

Before a community reaches a population of 50,000 these necessary functions of a fire department are rarely assigned to a specific unit. Such units are called ladder companies. Even when a city has a ladder company assigned (including a powered aerial), the performance at fires is generally substandard because the ladder truck responds with only one or two men, and they are not specifically trained in ladder company operations.

In larger municipalities, with a properly staffed and trained ladder company crew responding routinely with pumping units, fire operation becomes more professional.

Again, this in no way impunes the small community, the rural department, or the city without funds to staff the equipment. But although the fault is not always that of the fire department, one must admit that it exists.

Ladder company functions

Regardless who does them, or when they are done, ladder company operations must be carried out. In contrast to engine or pumper companies, ladder companies do not operate as a team. That is, their assignments carry them to different parts of the building and at times are carried out simultaneously. Therefore, if a ladder company operated as a team and did everything together, it would seriously delay vital operations at the crucial stages of the fire.

A well-trained ladder company often insures the success or failure of the operation at a fire. It is a part of their function to determine life hazards, and the possibility that the fire might extend in the rear or to adjacent buildings by way of shafts, cellars, or cocklofts.

A ladder company on its toes will know the rear of a fire building is at times more important than the front. People in the rear may be trapped or may have jumped, fire

may be extending by way of auto exposure, by burning into the other buildings, or in other ways. At night, rescue and venting at the rear is more difficult because vision is limited. In slum areas, windows are often heavily barred. Stream operation is hampered because it is difficult to gain access to some rear areas. You may have to bring in lines and ladders through adjoining yards, courts, or by going through from the front to the rear and out the rear windows.

In a well-organized ladder company, men are told their functions and what tools to carry at the roll call. This insures that key points will be covered as soon as the company arrives. If manpower is available, there are some jobs which can be handled more safely with two men. Let us look at these assignments and the equipment carried.

Roof ventilation is generally handled by the driver and one other man who may have raised the aerial to the roof. They should carry an axe and a six-foot pike pole. After venting the roof, they should go down the front or rear fire escape, venting by windows and moving in on the floor above the fire to search for people overcome, vertical fire extension, or the presence of shafts that could allow fire to spread.

Laddering. Portable ladders should be raised if and where needed.

Forcible entry should be handled by two men carrying forcible-entry tools and one pike pole. If the ladder company was first due, they should carry a water-based extinguisher as well. This crew forces entrance for the engine company and opens ceilings and sidewalls to expose hidden fire. They may have to force entrance to the floor above, as well, for examination. All hands ventilate by way of windows as they proceed.

Obviously, in today's undermanned companies, no one ladder company could perform all the necessary tasks at a serious fire, particularly where people may be trapped. In such cases, priorities are determined by the number of men available and the importance of prevailing conditions. It may be possible for the first ladder company to handle only roof ventilation and forcible entry. Incoming units would have to fill in for the other jobs, this to be determined by the officer in command.

While trained ladder companies know what to do, engine company performance, when pressed into ladder company functions, sometimes is inefficient. Engine companies should be taught how and what to do under these circumstances.

Building search. All buildings involved in fire or directly exposed should be searched. This is an important ladder company function. Children sometimes play in abandoned or vacant buildings. Watchmen are sometimes overlooked, as are derelicts who may be sleeping off the effects of too much drink. When men are told to search the premises, they must be instructed to report back to the officer whether they were able to complete the assignment. If, because of heat and smoke, they could not search the floor for people or for the presence of a shaft, they should so report. The officer can then send in a fresh team or place lines to cover what may turn out to be a serious exposure.

An example may help clarify this point: A fire has seriously involved a building separated from a bank building by what appeared from the street to be a solid wall. As chief in charge, I sent a lieutenant to examine the bank structure to be sure there were no openings in the brick wall. He reported back that there were none. Because I knew from experience that shafts do sometimes exist at the rear of such buildings, I sent a second observer to check this vital feature. He made a more diligent search and reported back that there were two windows facing on just such a suspected shaft and that fire could enter the bank through them. Lines were immediately laid into the bank and the fire was confined to the original building.

Lines would have been laid to the bank building both into the exposed floor and the roof regardless, but this would have been done by second alarm units because there was immediate need of lines in other areas. If the wall had been solid, we would have had sufficient time to cover the bank. However, the presence of windows changed the strategy instantly.

The first lieutenant was careless. In searching part of the bank floor, he had taken a beating from smoke and heat, so he took a chance that there would be no openings at the rear. Had he reported back that he could not complete the search properly, I would immediately have assigned another team.

Officers should keep with them a list of their men. If one does not report back in a reasonable time, a search must be made for him.

Search procedures. There are definite techniques to use in searching a building, particularly in residential structures. Look for unconscious victims at the point of egress from a room or area. As you progress into the room or area and visibility is nil, stay alongside the wall until you come to a bed. Look on and under the bed, feel with your pike pole, your hands, or your legs for a victim. Look in closets and toilets. When you come to a window, open it and get a breath of air, then proceed with your search, feeling for hot spots on floors and walls, and always looking for possible fire extension points. Don't panic if you get mixed up in your search. Staying along the wall eventually will bring you to the door through which you entered or a door to another area which may be a point of refuge. Make occasional forays from your side wall position to see whether anyone is lying on the floor.

If you get lost and come across a hose line, drop down and crawl along the hose. It will bring you eventually to the nozzle team and the safety of numbers. Or if you go the other way it will lead you to the fresh air outside. If you feel trapped, reach the nearest window, stick your head out, and yell for help. If you are not heard, throw your coat or helmet to the street. Someone may see it fall, know a man is trapped, and start the search for you.

If you feel you are losing consciousness, turn your flashlight on—you should never be without a good one—and set it on the floor with the light pointing toward the ceiling. The beam may make it easier to find you.

It is often desirable to learn the floor layout before moving in on the fire floor. This can be done by entering the floor below and noting the layout. Armed with this informa-

FIGURE 18. *This ladderman almost lost his life when fire enveloped the aerial ladder. It shows the vulnerability of a man on a ladder when flame erupts from a building. The turntable operator must remain alert to bring the ladder out or swing it away if such emergency arises.*

FIGURE 19. *Balcony-type fire escape has no stairway to lower landing. It may have access route to an adjoining apartment via the window. But if this apartment is also on fire people will be trapped.*

tion, you can proceed into the fire floor. Experienced men are cautious in smoke-filled areas where visibility is zero. They shuffle one foot ahead of the other or push a pike pole ahead to see if the floor is intact. When entering through a window, probe with a foot or pike pole, or drop the nozzle down a bit to see if the floor is intact.

When to ladder a building

While high-rise fires are covered in a separate chapter, the subject of ladder company operations at such fires will be discussed in this chapter, too. We will also discuss some basic techniques which sometimes are not well understood.

In our business, we like to package all problems in neat little bundles that won't come undone. But because we deal in the unexpected and unusual, in stress situations, where snap judgment is often called upon, a standard operational technique for all cases is impossible. Also, too often we do things simply because they have always been done that way. For example, traditionally in larger departments, ladder companies always laddered the fire building if they were assigned first due or first to arrive.

There was good reason for this because it presupposed that if people were trapped and in danger, the ladder company would quickly ladder the building and get them down. But like so many procedures with merit, the original thinking became moss-bound through habit, tradition, and nonsense.

Ladder companies still ladder buildings if they are first to arrive. In most cases it is completely automatic—a robotlike reaction. There may be no fire at all or just an odor of smoke, but the ladder is raised. To show how ridiculous this can get, I have seen a 20-foot ladder raised to a high-rise building without a semblance of fire anywhere.

Some people say the custom dates back to the old volunteer days when this was the customary way of showing what building was on fire. Other people say it shows a crackerjack fire department. Still others say it is good practice—even though unnecessary. Some departments have been commended because they raised the aerial at every multi-storied building whether or not it was necessary. The reasoning behind this is that it is good public relations, that the public will feel the department is on the ball, that it is a good drill, anyway. I disagree completely.

Raising the aerial. If you wish to drill with the aerial, do so by all means—but at a drill where all safety precautions are observed, where you can take the time to teach, to climb, to try evolutions. *You don't drill at fires.* If you need to do so, you are very late and very lax.

An aerial ladder truck costs more than $50,000. This apparatus is expensive, cumbersome, and carries some risk—particularly under stress situations at fires. Men on aerials may be needlessly and dangerously exposed. Figure 18 will give an idea of the risk potential.

Please realize, too, that raising and placing your aerial ladder routinely when it is not needed may prove costly for several reasons. Here are a few:

1. You may decide during the operation that it is needed at another point. There will be a serious delay in lowering and moving the ladder.

2. It may unnecessarily block the street for other apparatus.

3. If the ladder is raised to the roof and needed for a lower floor later, there is a delay in lowering, particularly if men were sent to the roof who would have to return by way of the aerial.

Portable ladders. In general, the same reasons prevail with portable ladders, but to a somewhat lesser degree. Raising, carrying, and placing ladders takes manpower. In these days of critical manpower shortages, isn't it foolish to have men raise and place ladders you don't need?

Raising portable ladders as indicated by need is a vital function of a ladder company. While this is academic, in too many cases engine companies forget that they, too, carry portable ladders.

Here are several ways the portable ladder can be used to decided advantage at a fire:

1. Where there is a balcony-type fire escape (no stairs to lower landing), people would be trapped because they cannot get to the ground or the roof. True, the balcony type of fire escape generally provides access to an adjoining apartment via the window, but this is little comfort if the other apartment also is on fire. (See Figure 19.)

2. To bridge narrow alleyways.

3. To use as a stairs in case fire burned away the first or upper floor stairs.

4. To ventilate windows by pulling the tip out and allowing the ladder to fall against the glass.

5. To advance lines to upper floors because the regular stairs are being used to evacuate people.

6. Where the stairs are inadequate to get all the people down fast enough.

7. To get down shafts, excavations, etc.

8. To get to the roof of the adjoining building.

9. To raise against the fire escape so people can use it to get down, in addition to the fire escape stairway.

10. For forcible entry of store doors. Place the heels of the ladder above and below the lock; then space four to six men on each side of the ladder and push against the locked door. This can only be used against inward opening doors.

11. To bridge a larger opening for the use of a cellar nozzle.

12. To push open partitions behind store show windows to ventilate the store proper.

FIGURE 20. *Fireman on the third floor (arrow) could be in trouble if the smoke builds up heavily in the stair shaft.*

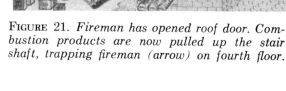

FIGURE 21. *Fireman has opened roof door. Combustion products are now pulled up the stair shaft, trapping fireman (arrow) on fourth floor.*

How to get to the roof

Sooner or later the question comes up about getting men to the roof to ventilate. Some argue that it is quicker to get to the roof by the aerial ladder. Usually this is true—if the ladder is in position! But if the building is one of a row of buildings of equal height, then it is quicker and safer to go up the inside stairway of the adjoining building to get to the roof. Again, when the aerial is raised to the roof it is lost for rescue purposes or to advance lines to lower windows. Note I say that men should use the inside stairway of the *adjoining building*. This not only gives them a safe route to the roof; it also is a good line of retreat for leaving the roof.

What if there is no adjoining building of equal height? Is it not then feasible to get to the roof of the fire building by its own inside stairway? This is often done, and men usually get away with it. But it can be extremely dangerous, for several reasons:

1. On your way to the roof the smoke buildup can trap you quickly. You may get into serious trouble—even be overcome. (See Figure 20.) If this appears likely, get out of the stair shaft into an apartment and head for the front windows. Get your head out the window for some air and call for help if you need it.

2. Should you make it to the top, you may have difficulty opening the door to the roof. In heavy smoke, vision would be limited and again you could be in serious trouble.

3. It is possible that line operations have not yet succeeded in reaching the fire below. If the fire should start to run the stair shaft, you will be trapped. Only an inexperienced man would chance this.

4. As you are trying to force the roof door open from the stair shaft side, another man is sent by the aerial to the roof to open up. He forces the door from the roof side. Thus fire from below now is pulled up the shaft instantly and traps you right in its path. (See Figure 21.)

5. Don't do it this way!

When to use the aerial to get to the roof.
There are situations where the aerial is the best way to get to the roof; don't hesitate to use it in such cases. Some reasons follow:

1. There is no adjoining building of the same height.

2. The stairs are burned away or weakened.

3. The stairs are being used to evacuate people.

4. To advance hose lines to the roof and if the inside stairway has two or more lines going up that way.

5. To get hose lines in on the upper floors. Be careful of getting men above the fire unless lines are controlling it from below.

6. The stair shaft is untenable because of smoke and heat.

The situation cited in No. 5 occurred at a fire where I was in charge. The fire was showing on the second and third floors at the rear of a frame tenement. An engine company was ordered to move up the rear fire escape and completely extinguish the fire on the second floor; then to move back out on the fire escape to the third floor to repeat the operation. Water damage was not a factor because the building was not occupied and was due for demolition.

A few minutes later I again checked the rear. This is what I saw: the engine company was on its way up to the third floor landing but fire was showing beneath them coming from the second floor. They had carelessly disobeyed the order to complete extinguishment of the lower floor before moving up. They now were in a precarious position because from their positions they could not attack the fire coming out of the second floor windows. In order to do so they would have to move back down against the fire to reach the second floor fire-escape landing.

Fortunately, a back-up line had been ordered to cover this company for just such a contingency and it was now ready to move up. Otherwise the first company would have been seriously burned. The officer in this case should have known better but he was excited and careless.

If you are the driver of an aerial truck that has been used to send men to the roof or upper floors, make sure your men are down before moving the ladder.

FIGURE 22. *Stream from ladder pipe is ineffective. It is hitting only flame tongues and smoke. The ground stream is missing window completely.*

Using the aerial ladder in rescue

Before leaving the matter of aerials to reach upper floors, let me touch briefly on its use as a rescue medium. When needed for such rescue the aerial is truly a lifesaver. But if it is possible to get people down the stairway or to the roof, and from there to an adjoining building and down the stairway, it is wrong to use the aerial ladder. Its use for rescue is difficult and dangerous.

Here are some reasons why a stairway rescue is preferable:

1. With a fire-resistant structure, it is generally only necessary to move people to the floor below or to an adjoining area.

2. Stairs have banisters, are lighted at night, and are wider than ladders.

3. People on ladders are exposed to falling objects.

4. There is less danger of falls.

5. Old or sick people can be helped down a stairway; they have to be carried down ladders.

6. One adult can guide a dozen children down a stairway—not so on ladders.

7. Many people will resist getting out of a window onto a high ladder.

8. If you are carrying an unconscious person down a stairway and you become tired, you can stop and rest, or stop to shift your grip. This would be dangerous on a ladder.

9. One stairway serves all floors at one time, but you need a different height of ladder for each floor.

10. Many more people can be taken down a stairway at one time. Compare the evacuation of a school by ladders with the usual fire drill evacuation by way of a stairway.

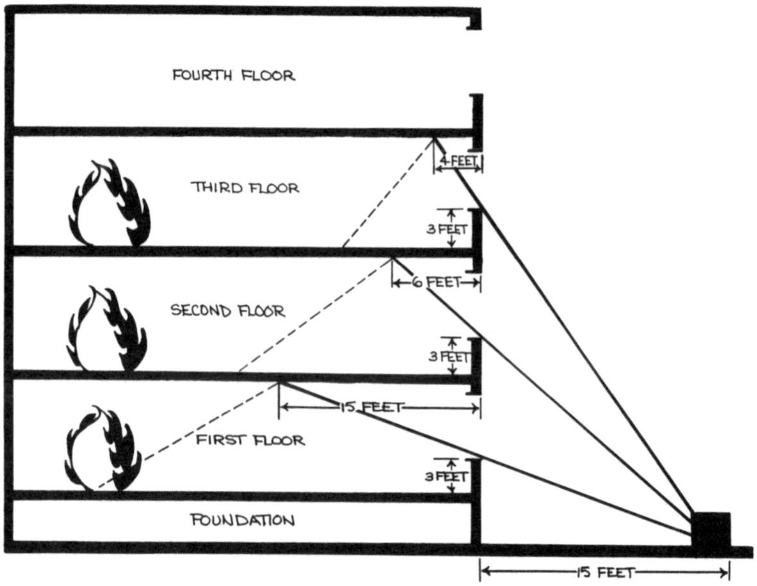

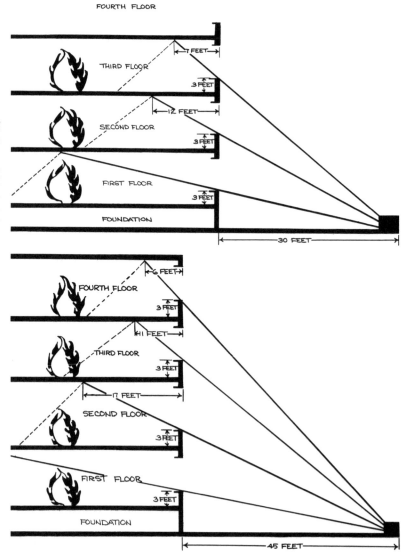

FIGURE 23. *How floor level affects penetration of stream from street-level exterior appliance 15 feet from building. The stream reaches the fire on the first floor, but on second and third floors does not reach the seat of the fire. (For consistency, all hose streams are shown going through bottom of window. On some floors they will be more effective if raised.)*

FIGURE 24. *Moving street-level appliance further from the building changes penetration. With appliance 30 feet from the building the stream applied to the same fire as shown in Figure 23 will be effective on the first and second floors but poor on the third floor.*

FIGURE 25. *If the stream appliance is moved to 45 feet from the building the stream will be effective on the first and second floors, but less effective on the third and fourth floors.*

This is why it is so important to advance hose lines into the interior of a fire building; to try to hold the stairs from becoming involved. No aerial ladder or elevating platform will get people out of a building as quickly or safely as a usable stairway.

Other uses for aerial ladders

There are, of course, several other uses for an aerial ladder. We all know of its use with a ladder pipe. It does excellent work in many such cases. However, when used as a water tower without a man at the pipe, its efficiency is open to question. The stream often is not visible or is poorly visible from below. It is difficult to see whether the stream is entering the window at the proper angle to assure the desired penetration. Generally speaking, it is more efficient to have a man at the tip operating the ladder pipe. He can observe from close proximity, and if he is temporarily blinded by smoke, he can listen for the stream striking a wall if it is not getting through the window. He can shift the stream as needed and call for shut-down if he feels it is warranted. Vital water supplies may be saved and there is less danger of overloading weakened structures by pouring in additional needless tons of weight.

This is not to say that even with an operator at the ladder pipe efficiency is assured. There are numerous instances where the results have been less than desirable. This may be because the operator's vision is obscured by smoke, or he may be on his way down because his position is becoming untenable. Frequently, exterior streams may look efficient; they may appear to be hitting straight at the fire. However, in too many cases the stream is hitting flame tongues and not achieving concrete results. (See Figure 22.)

Should you open boarded-up windows with an aerial? This point is controversial. I have used the tip of an aerial to open boarded-up windows. I refer particularly to those closed with light-gauge metal or thin plywood sheathing. This procedure is simple. Place the tip of the powered aerial in the center of the boarding and apply a little power. The window will push in. Retract the ladder, swing

it to the next window, and repeat. You will open the front of a building faster than you had ever thought possible. Figures 23-26 show some additional limitations of exterior, street-level streams.

Placing the aerial ladder tip

Here are some suggestions on placing the aerial ladder tip for various positions:

1. At roofs, place the ladder five rungs above the roof level. Otherwise it will be difficult for men to get back onto the ladder from the roof (try it both ways at the next drill). Paint your ladder tips with reflective paint. They will be easier to spot from the roof at night.

2. At fire escape balconies, place the ladder one rung above the fire escape railing at the opposite side to the fire-escape stairs.

3. At windows: (a) For rescue purposes, place the ladder just below the sill, to the right of center. (b) For hose line operation, place the ladder one or two rungs above the sill, squarely in the center of the window. (c) For line advancement into the window, place the ladder level with the window sill.

Many firemen have been burned because they were careless when advancing a line through a window. There is a proper procedure for this. Assume you have darkened the fire down from the ladder. Now the order is given to shut down and advance through the window onto the fire floor. Here is the way to do it: while you hold the nozzle in ready position, the second man behind you moves to your left, climbs in onto the floor through the window. As soon as he is in the ready position you hand him the nozzle, then climb in. In this way someone has the nozzle ready at all times should the fire flare up. Otherwise one of you could be badly burned. This happened to a fireman at a training fire. Fortunately, using the above technique, the nozzleman was ready and instantly darkened the fire down again. No one was hurt.

If you respond to a fire in a multiple dwelling or a hotel and you *are sure* the fire is, or can be, contained to its point of origin and will not endanger the sleeping occupants, work quietly and do not disturb them. This

FIGURE 26. *Stream at left is useless. Stream at right is little better. Both should be shut down and lines moved in to top floor by inside stairs or ladders. Fighting fires in this way almost assures the total loss of the building.*

is preferable to having a panicky horde of people running down the stairs, tripping over hoselines, getting in your way, throwing things out windows, and dragging trunks and suitcases behind them, blocking the stairs.

When working under stress, it is easy to concentrate on the obvious. That is to say, you ladder the front of the building—force entrance, ventilate, etc. But you often forget the rear. People here may be at the windows shouting for help but they are ignored because they are not seen or heard. The same may be true of inner courts. To repeat, you may have to bring your extension ladders into rear yards or inner courts by going through apartments and out rear windows.

What about the use of aerial ladders at high-rise fires? Obviously it is impossible to build ladders high enough to reach all structures. The answer to high-rise buildings is not ladders, but proper building codes—enclosed stairs, fire-resistant construction, sprinklers, etc. Unfortunately, there are conditions where the so-called fireproof high-rise

is a death trap. I refer particularly to the so-called garden apartments where you can't get your equipment to the rear because of chained fences, hedges, or trees. If the occupant is on the 20th floor and is trapped in his apartment by fire between himself and the apartment door, he dies. You must try and get to the fire apartment with a hose line quickly enough to extinguish the fire and save the trapped victim. But going up in the elevator, working with rolled-ups off a standpipe, forcing a well-made door may take more time than you expect.

It may be possible to go to the floor above and drop down off a rope to take him out the window to be lowered to the street or pulled up again to the upper floor. This also has the advantage of allowing you to see the interior room layout above the fire, which is generally the same as below. It is also possible to scale the building (if not too high) from the top of an aerial ladder with a scaling ladder to get the person down.

In hotel fires, much precious time is lost by truckmen having to force doors to guest rooms. Use public address systems and loud hailers to shout instructions to people at windows. Tell them to close their doors but leave them unlocked.

Take all your tools with you when you report for an assignment or if you are going up for examination. If there is a possibility of bad smoke conditions, take your masks along. Consider the delay in having to go back to the elevator, down 20 floors, then a half block to the truck for the masks—and then back up again. This is easily a 10-minute delay and inexcusable. In the interim, a person may be trapped in a smoke charged hall bedroom for 10 minutes because some fireman came poorly equipped and couldn't reach the room.

Many times, ladder company men in their ventilation, search, or opening up procedures find a hidden fire. They may have to use the house standpipe line, rather than waiting for the engine company to bring their hose lines up. This makes sense.

For further information on this, see the chapters on standpipe and sprinkler operations, Chapters 11 and 12.

Chapter 5

Evaluating the fire problem—sizeup

PROPER SIZEUP of a complicated fire problem is necessary before intelligent assignments of men and machines may be made. Preferably, the operational techniques and key items will have been planned out well in advance and thoroughly rehearsed.

It is unreasonable to expect any man to operate efficiently if he arrives at the scene of a large fire without any advance planning or familiarity with the structure. Since most fires are quite different in scope, type, and complexity, they require different operational methods. Simply having a prearranged key or sizeup guide is insufficient. One must have broad, detailed knowledge as to how to use this key, to be able to change the strategy for varying conditions.

The sizeup therefore should really begin with prefire planning. This requires a detailed inspection, not only of the physical plant but of the surrounding areas as well. This will give you valuable insight as to the type of construction, location of the stairs and exits, whether the building is sprinklered or has standpipes, the type of occupancy (hazardous, explosive, chemicals), fire walls and fire doors, exposures both internal and external, water supplies, etc.

Some departments put all this information, plus a sketch, on a card system and carry it on the apparatus. In this way vital information is available on the scene should it be needed.

This information may now be correlated with the sizeup made at the fire. It will help determine the severity of the problem and guide you in your actions. It may simply be the use of a large main a block away as a primary water supply rather than the four-inch main on the same street as the fire, because you intend to use heavy streams. Trying to get much water from a four-inch main could be a serious error allowing the fire to roar out of control. Another factor may be the dispatching of a man to insure closure of the fire doors separating the two wings of a warehouse. Without knowing the location of such fire doors (or even of their existence) fire in one section of a warehouse could involve adjoining sections. Such fire doors, while supposedly operated by fusable links, frequently are rendered inoperative by blocking them open or by storage of stock against the door.

Before explaining the use of the key sizeup items, this point should be realized. There can be a different value judgment of the same items depending on who makes them and at what time during the fire they are made. The initial sizeup, though necessarily sketchy, is usually made by the first-in officer. Since he has to place his company most advantageously and then operate with them, he has little time to seriously evaluate the entire picture. In some cases he may even place an additional company if one arrived almost simultaneously with him. But usually he does not gain an over-all viewpoint of the fire situation.

In such cases, there is no correlated, organized attack.

Therefore, when the Chief arrives he must make the needed changes based on his total evaluation of the fire situation. In addition, the fire conditions may have changed between the chief's arrival and time the first in companies went to work. What may have been correct initially now is incorrect and requires changing. There is a fine line between the constructive changing of strategy and "Monday Morning Quarterbacking." Avoid sharp criticism of officers for what may turn out to be less than efficient company placement but rather use the fire postmortem technique to suggest different approaches. Where the first in officers are energetic, willing, and hard-working, be careful about hampering their initiative in future operations by being over critical.

General sizeup

We are now ready to begin our fireground sizeup, bearing in mind that the present discussion will be general and will not apply to a specific fire. What follows is a listing of items which the commanding officer may have to apply to his specific fire. Later in the book there will be more detailed descriptions of more specific fire problems.

Life safety

In making a sizeup, there are several factors to consider just in the saving of life. The time of day and day of the week can have a bearing here. A theatre fire presents no life hazard at 4 A.M. but has a serious potential when occupied by an audience. A factory on fire at 3 P.M. on a weekday would be fully occupied, but 3 P.M. Sunday would find the factory empty. Here are other lifesaving considerations:

1. Are people trapped in the building?
2. Are the people above the fire?
3. How many are there?
4. Are the exits cut off by fire or combustion products?
5. How can you best remove or protect the

people? Should you remove them by ladder*, by elevating platform, by bridging ladders across narrow courts, drop down from above by rope, protect them by getting hose line between them and the threatened means of egress, or should you use life nets (a last resort)**.

6. Can hose streams be advanced to safeguard threatened exits?

7. Are people endangered in adjoining buildings? Should they be evacuated?

8. Are spectators endangered? If so when should you call the police department to establish fire lines?

9. Are there hazards to the operating forces—will additional breathing equipment be needed, will medical help be required?

Time of fire

The time of the fire affects the life hazard considerably. Here are some other important considerations in which the time of the incident is a factor:

1. Visibility if at night. There is a need for good lighting and a greater possibility of injury.

2. Traffic congestion. This may impede response of apparatus at busy hours. Plan to use alternate routes during rush hours.

3. Season. Certain seasons may mean unusually heavy crowds in department stores, causing a greater life hazard. Heavy stocks of merchandise will create extra fire loading —you may need extra help.

4. Companies may be out on fire inspections. If this causes a delay in response, the fire may get away from you.

---

*When placing ladders against buildings, be aware of this possible danger: You may be placing the ladder to a third floor window to remove a person seriously threatened by fire. There is a panicky occupant on the fourth floor, but he is not as seriously threatened. He sees the ladder rest at the third floor window and in his panic thinks the ladder is short and he will die. He may jump for the ladder. He could fall to his death, taking the fireman climbing the ladder with him. The rule here, when practical, is to take the people by ladder from the highest windows first. The hotel raise, where the ladder is held flat against the wall by pushing in on the tormentors, may be considered when many people are showing at windows on different floors (This refers only to portable ladders).

**If you are going to use a life net, do not carry it in the open position held chest high as if it were ready for use. People trapped above may jump for the net before you are in position and ready. Open the net but carry it in a vertical position until you get under the window where you will use it. Then turn it to catching position. Be careful here, too. More than one person may jump at one time from different floors. Try to advise who should jump first and hope they will listen. Never put the net down in the full opened position and leave it. Someone trapped above may jump for it without thinking. He might land on the pavement below.

5. Buildings may be closed because of time of day. This indicates forcible entry and delays which could require greater alarms.

Height of fire building

Buildings beyond the reach of portable ladders and streams constitute difficult extinguishing problems whereas low buildings, particularly one-or two-story structures, offer easy access to roofs for examination, ventilation, and cellar nozzle use. Search for and rescue of trapped people is simpler in lower structures. Stream penetration is comparatively effective from street positions into one- or two-story buildings, whereas above the second floor such penetration becomes questionable. Although fire operations are simpler, they form a serious exposure hazard to higher buildings alongside.

Higher buildings may have standpipes and sprinklers. Stairways may be enclosed and there may be elevators.

Area of fire building

Large open areas expose the entire floor to the action and effects of the fire, with nothing to hold back its progress. All the combustibles on the floor are in the path of the flames. Firemen cannot approach to the fire area behind the protection of partitions, fire doors, or other physical barriers. Therefore they take a great deal of punishment trying to advance. Such fires generate great heat and the draft effect is often heightened, helping to fan the fire to greater intensity. Heavy calibre streams frequently are required. Where the area is so large that firemen cannot advance and where exterior streams are ineffective, the fire will continue and destroy the structure. In such cases, it would be wise to anticipate heavy involvement and possible collapse. Get help in early.

On the other hand, small area fires can be readily controlled by moving in with hand lines. Even if exterior stream appliances have to be used, it would be for short time—only until the inside lines can move in.

Construction of fire building

The type of building construction is probably the major controlling factor at any fire. Fire-proof* construction will confine the fire to one floor or area, and there will be little other than contents to add fuel to the fire. The main structural members are either of reinforced concrete or protected steel. The floors and roofs are reinforced concrete. The stairways are generally enclosed so that one floor does not expose others. Doors are fire-resistant and self-closing. Where there are shafts, they are enclosed in fire-resistant materials. Such structures rarely collapse in a fire. This is not to say disastrous fires cannot occur in fireproof buildings. They can and often have. Even though the walls and floors will not collapse, enough combustible contents or combustible construction inside the building could burn with sufficient intensity to gut the interior.

Combustible construction, on the other hand, not only fails to confine the fire but literally adds fuel for its extension. There is probably poor or no fire-stopping, providing many concealed spaces for fire to travel both horizontally and vertically. If the building is frame it will generate great heat and a mass of sparks and brands. Conflagrations have resulted from such conditions.

Structural steel. There may be unprotected steel structural members. If these steel beams are highly heated by the fire and then struck by a hose stream, structural failure can result. The hose stream will cause unequal cooling, and bowing or twisting can occur. Where the structural member is cast iron, the danger is even greater. Steel gives way gradually. Cast iron will fail suddenly with little or no warning. While cast iron has great compression strength, it has little tensile strength. This is why it can be used for columns but never for beams or girders.

Why do metal structural members fail under fire conditions? How does unequal cooling occur?

Most building materials have different coefficient of expansion; that is, they expand different amounts under the same heat conditions. Heat a metal beam made of two different metals strapped or laminated together

---

*Where the term fireproof is used in this text, it is not used in the literal sense. Nothing is really fireproof. Everything will fail if the heat is high enough and for sufficiently long periods of time.

and the beam will bend, because one metal expands more than the other. The same thing can happen with a metal member of homogeneous material. If such a structural member were heated evenly in a furnace, the expansion would be similar throughout the beam. But in a fire this is not the case. Fire usually attacks the underside of exposed metal members, causing unequal heating and unequal expansion. The effect is similar to heating a beam of dissimilar metals. The member will warp and bow.

Even if the metal support member were to undergo uniform heating and expansion, the effect of a fire stream striking and cooling only the exposed faces would be to cause uneven cooling and bowing.

In addition to the bowing and twisting characteristics of unprotected structural steel, it has other undesirable characteristics under fire attack. Structural steel actually gains in strength until about 400° F., but rapidly begins to lose strength above that temperature. At 1100° F. it has lost about 75 percent of its weight-carrying ability and is sure to collapse at about 1400° F. If the floors are heavily loaded and the fire has been unusually severe, collapse may occur earlier.

There is one more factor to consider, namely expansion. This begins to take place at comparatively low temperatures. At temperatures above 1000° F. there may be sufficient expansion to push walls and other supporting members out of place, precipitating early structural collapse.

Masonry construction. There is a common misconception that all masonry (natural stone, artificial stone, concrete, etc.) are strongly fire-resistant. This is a dangerous oversimplification.

There are five types of building stones: limestone, marble, granite, sandstone, and cast stone (artificially made). All of these masonry materials will crack and fail under prolonged heat. They should not be used in construction where severe exposure from fires may result.

Limestone is subject to greater damage from heat than the other four. At about 800° F. limestone decomposes into lime. It crumbles and flakes at high temperatures

and is subject to expansion and contraction stresses.

Granite, under intense heat, may explode into flying fragments or it may break down into a fine dust. Like limestone, it is subject to expansion or contraction stresses.

The behavior of marble under heat is quite similar to that of limestone — except that marble breaks down even more quickly.

Because of its simple texture, sandstone offers better resistance to fire up to about 800° to 1,000° F. Above 1,000° F. sandstone suffers severe injury. It is also subject to expansion and contraction stresses.

From a fire viewpoint, stone cannot be depended upon to resist fire. It should not be used to insulate metal structural members. It is dangerous under fire conditions, particularly if used as decorative trim on the face of buildings. Pieces may shatter and fall. If stone trim is exposed to heat, cool it with hose steams. But if stones have already been highly heated do not strike them with hose streams.

Brick is manufactured by a careful mixing of clay, silica, and other products. The fire resistance of brick depends to some extent on the craftsmanship of the mason, the type of bond, the mortar mix, and the ability to absorb water. The uniform texture of brick prevents rapid temperature changes between the exposed and interior faces. Because bricks are small units, they can absorb the stress of higher temperatures. And the ability to absorb moisture limits the temperature rise to some extent. Generally, brick is a substantial fire stop except for defects in construction such as unprotected openings.

Concrete requires water for its strength. Fire calcines concrete. The heat of a severe fire may drive enough moisture from the concrete to cause it to lose 60 percent of its strength. Concrete, like most masonry materials, expands and contracts under high heat. Under these stresses, chips and pieces may fly off the structure. For fire resistance, concrete should be reinforced with steel rods or mesh. (See Table I for a comparison of brick and concrete.)

Concrete and cinder blocks have the same faults as concrete and other masonry units.

TABLE I

COMPARISON OF BRICK VERSUS CONCRETE UNDER FIRE CONDITIONS

Brick	Concrete
1. Small units — joints absorb expansion — no damage	1. Single large mass — expansion at severe fire — may crack
2. Temperature in excess of 2,000° to manufacture	2. Calcines at 600°F
3. Tensile strength is as strong as weakest point	3. Stronger than brick particularly when reinforced
4. Has high insulating value	4. Has high insulating value
5. Spalls under high temperature	5. Spalls under high temperature and also calcines
6. Not as strong as concrete when unsupported	6. Stronger than brick
7. Absorbs water readily, which increases insulating value	7. Absorbs water readily, which increases insulating value

Their resistance to fire is poor. Essentially they are a cheap form of concrete in the shape of building blocks.

Gypsum is a hydrous calcium sulphate that is usually found in the form of plaster boards and plaster of Paris. At fires, the heat drives out the moisture. An advantage of gypsum is its comparatively light weight. Its low heat conductivity makes it suitable for protecting metal structural members against heat. It has no expansion or contraction stresses.

Terra cotta is available in three types. Porous terra cotta is made by mixing pure clay with sawdust. It is then molded into forms and burned. The burning causes combustion of the sawdust, leaving the material in a porous state. Porous terra cotta resists fire better than other types, but it is not as strong. Its principal use is for fire-retarding columns, beams, and girders. It can be used for nonload-bearing partitions.

Semiporous terra cotta is made by mixing clay with clean calcined fire clay, coarsely ground, with a percentage of ground bituminous coal. This mixture is placed in forms and burned. The burning consumes the coal, leaving the material in a slightly porous state. Thus the semiporous terra cotta is stronger than the porous type and offers more resistance to fire than hard-burned type.

Hard-burned terra cotta is made of natural clay without additional materials. During manufacture it is subjected to high pressures, giving the material a dense structure and great strength under crushing loads. However, it is brittle and will fail under shock. Hard-burned terra cotta conducts heat more readily than the other two.

The fire resistance of any type of terra cotta depends on these factors: (1) the nature of the clay, (2) the method of burning in manufacture, (3) the arrangement and thickness of the shell and cellular construction, (4) adequate weight-heavy webs, and (5) how well the cement or mortar has been laid.

The two weaknesses of terra cotta construction are its light weight and the size of the units. The large-size units used make it liable to destruction by expansion and contraction.

It is often easier to gain access to a fire building through a terra cotta partition than through a well-constructed door. Terra cotta arches are easily broken out for ventilation. Be careful—broken pieces are often sharp.

Older buildings

Building construction is probably the major determination in firefighting strategy. Certainly there is an urgency in fireground operations required by older structures. They are often built predominantly with combustible materials such as wood joists, wood flooring, and wood lath in wall partitions. This kind of construction usually is accompanied by concealed spaces which allow fire to travel readily because of the absence of fire stops. It is obvious such a building will become seriously involved in a short time.

The unprotected vertical openings were predominant features in the old sweatshop factories — open wooden stairs, open ornamental metal grillwork around the elevator shaft, and air and light shafts. Thousands of these structures are still in use today in most large cities.

These unprotected vertical arteries allow a fire to race upward, exposing all floors above. Sometimes this fire travel is not noticed by the operating forces. Where such unprotected vertical openings exist, they create conditions conducive to rapid fire spread, calling for line placement to head the fire off and protect people who might be cut off from the exits.

The same faults prevail in the older, cheaper type hotels. But in these structures there often is an additional hazard. It is common to find linen and mattress storage rooms on each, or alternate, floors in flimsy frame closets.

Occupancy of the fire building

Knowing the occupancy — who and what is in the building — helps determine the severity of the life hazard and allows you to better predict the rapidity of fire spread.

The life hazard is greatest where the occupants are aged or infirm, handicapped, held in legal restraint, or where large numbers of people would normally be asleep at the time of the fire. Some examples of this type of occupancy are: nursing homes, homes for the aged, hospitals, asylums, jails, dance halls, and cabarets.

Fires in such places require an immediate call for extra help, particularly ladder equipment. Medical aid is vital in case of the aged and sick. Keep in mind that evacuation of such premises is a severe problem which requires a great deal of specialized help. For example, extra police would be required to remove the occupants from a jail or mental institution.

If the decision is made to evacuate an old age home, hospital, or nursing home in winter, how will you remove the occupants, and where will you take them? You should plan in advance for such a possibility.

In a commercial establishment the material used or stored may be volatile, flammable, or highly toxic. Because of extra flammability, conditions may be so severe that they preclude reaching the fire. If the occupancy is such that grinding operations are carried on, a dust explosion hazard could be a possibility. On the other hand, while fire conditions may be relatively simple to handle, the toxic qualities may be so severe that men would be seriously endangered. This would call for self-contained breathing equipment. In some cases toxic material may be absorbed through the skin. Here, waterproof clothing would be required. Companies that normally respond in areas with such construction should be aware of these hazards and equipped to handle them.

Prior knowledge of the occupancy is desirable information to have on the pre-fire plan. But if this information is not available, the officer often can gain some idea of the occupancy by simply noting the names of the occupants. Business firms frequently have their names on ornamental brass plates on the front of the building. If this is not the case, you may find the name in the hall or lobby. A company name often carries a helpful description of the occupancy. For example, "Jones & Co., Manufacturers of Fine Furniture," would give you an indication of what to expect. Furniture manufacturing will certainly mean large amounts of wood, sawdust (dust explosion possible), flammable wood finishes, solvents, and glues. If the firm makes upholstered furniture, expect heavy smoke conditions and a slower burning fire.

If the name plate said, "Jones & Co., Bed

Springs," you would be much less concerned about rapid fire involvement because of building contents. Yet you should be alert for the possibility of flammable paints used in painting the springs. You also could expect heavy floor loads because of machinery and steel stock.

Whatever the occupancy, these clues can help prepare you for corrective action such as a call for additional help, withdrawal of inside forces, the use of heavy streams, or breathing apparatus.

Location and extent of fire in the building

No sound plan for fire control can be developed until you know where the fire is and its extent.

A cellar fire will produce heavy smoke and create severe problems in locating it. And it will inflict severe punishment on the fire forces. The fire can spread upward by way of shafts, open stairs, or partitions. A cellar fire may render elevators and stairs unusable, making escape from the building difficult and creating a real problem for the fire department in trying to advance lines if fire extension to upper floors is evident.

Fire in a combustible stairway indicates a vertical fire which can move upward rapidly. If not cut off or properly vented, it will mushroom into upper floors and spread laterally. It is not uncommon to find people dead on upper floors from the action of a cellar fire. They are often asphyxiated in their apartments by the mushrooming effect and show no burn marks.

Fires in upper stories may be relatively small, but because of a shortage of manpower and the need to bring hose lines up several floors, considerable delay may be expected until water hits the fire. This may allow the fire to gain great headway and extend into the hanging ceiling. It would be wise not to underestimate the potential of such high fires because of the possible delays.

Exposures

There are three kinds of exposures to consider at fires: life, internal, and external.

Life. (1) Hazard to occupants by flame spread, either in the fire building or in adjacent or adjoining buildings. (2) Hazard to occupants from dangerous fumes or gases, either in the fire building or in adjacent or adjoining building. (3) Hazard to firemen who would have to operate in precarious positions. (4) Hazard to spectators from falling walls and explosions, or both.

Internal fire exposure. This is the exposure the fire building offers to itself by way of one of the following routes: (1) Burning through floors or walls. (2) Unprotected horizontal openings such as blocked open fire doors, shafts, traveling through horizontal runs such as floor joists, cocklofts, etc. (3) Unprotected vertical openings such as stair and light shafts, pipe chases, etc. (4) Fire lapping out of window upward and into the floor above. (5) Conduction, radiation, and convection. (6) Building collapse. (7) Sparks and brands.

External exposure. This is the exposure the fire building offers to other buildings or structures by way of one of the following routes: (1) Burning through side walls. (2) Openings in party walls not properly fire-stopped. (3) Hanging ceilings. (4) Poorly fire-stopped roof cornices. (5) Burning through roof and over parapet to adjoining roof. (6) Burning through roof and into window of adjoining building. (7) Unprotected horizontal openings such as inoperative fire doors, shafts, etc. (8) Conduction, convection, and radiation. (9) Building collapse. (10) Sparks and brands. (11) Grass and brush. (12) Wood shingle roofs.

Operations at major fires must be conducted so that control is always maintained on six sides of the fire — north, south, east, west, top, and bottom. It is sometimes difficult to maintain such constant supervision, particularly when heavy smoke conditions obscure vision and positions are difficult to hold. Because of this, the chief in charge should have a competent aide assigned to him. After working together for a while they develop a team attitude. The aide, trained in the chief's strategy, needs little instruction from the chief at the fire. He does the chief's legwork, helps co-ordinate incoming units and equipment. In this way the chief can re-

FIGURE 27. *Air and light shaft at rear of apart-ment hotel is open to rear yard. This shaft is visible only from the rear or roof. Fire blowing out of fire apartments could enter windows of other apartments. With fires in such buildings, all apartments with windows opening on the shaft must be checked for fire spread. Move hose lines into threatened apartments.*

FIGURE 28. *Typical blind shaft between build-ings. It is called blind because there is no opening to such shaft from the exterior. If the adjoining building has a similar shaft with windows or win-dows opening into this shaft, fire can easily pass from one building to the next or to the floor above through the windows. For this reason it is important to check buildings beside the fire build-ing and the upper floors and move hose lines into the threatened exposures.*

FIGURE 29. *Blind shaft with wire cover. Shafts such as this often have glass covers. If there is fire below it is important to remove the cover. These shafts can be used to ventilate fire apart-ments by removing the cover. Also remember to examine apartments facing on a common shaft for fire extension.*

FIGURE 30. *Looking down into blind shaft. Note proximity of windows of two separate areas of floor space and how easily fire could involve the adjacent area as well as the floors above.*

main where he should be — in front of the fire scene.

Usually the priorities for exposure protection are the areas above, the sides, and the rear of the fire. There is no rule as to which of these will be the most serious threat. This is one reason why the commanding officer must make a quick and accurate appraisal of the fire before he can assign positions to the arriving companies. Where companies are in position before the chief's arrival. he must know what positions are being protected. If not, then it becomes his duty to see that this is done — either by reassigning companies or by calling for additional help.

The chief should not make the mistake of surveying all exposure threats personally. It could take him up to ten minutes to do this; larger fires may require even more time. This is too long for him to be absent from the frontal command position. Even with portable radios the chief should maintain his command position so that incoming units can readily reach him for positioning.

The survey of such exposure threats should be conducted by competent officers assigned by the chief. They should have specific instructions to report back, either in person or by radio, on conditions found in their assigned areas. Unfortunately, even the best portable radios seem to operate with less than reliable efficiency under heavy stream and icing conditions, so don't rely on the radio exclusively. As help arrives, the chief makes his assignments based on the information reported back to him.

In order to insure adequate supervision of all areas, junior chief officers generally are given the following positions: The first assistant chief takes the rear. The next assistant takes the interior of the structure. Then other incoming junior chief officers are assigned to cover the buildings on each side of the fire.

The chief, at his command position, should require frequent reports from the junior chiefs as to the progress/or lack of progress/ from their segments. In this way he remains aware of the entire situation and is able to make more valid judgments as to the need

for more help in any area. Incoming companies need not always report in person. Frequently they may be directed by radio to report to a particular segment of the operation. This saves considerable time.

The company officer need not direct his trucks to drive close to the command center, report in, receive orders and then move to his assigned location — possibly having to back his truck out again. Even without such radio instructions, a competent company officer will not allow his truck in too close but will report on foot for instructions. In this way he does not block roadways and doesn't risk being blocked in by apparatus arriving behind him.

The spread of fire to other buildings is affected by many factors. In severe exposure fires the original fire often becomes of secondary importance, with the exposures receiving primary attention. The force and direction of the wind will affect the placing of companies. Naturally, with a strong wind blowing fire and sparks toward a nearby building, it will be necessary to cover the threatened building with hose lines even before you attack the main fire.

Wood shingle roofs have been responsible for many major fires. An ordinary fire, well within the capability of the first units due, may rage out of control because burning shingles carried by the wind ignite other wood-shingled roofs. Because of their light weight, these burning shingles can be carried great distances by winds. But they have sufficient bulk to continue burning and ignite other wood-shingled roofs on which they fall.

Another factor increasing the fire hazard of wood shingles is their tendency to curl and crack from weathering and age. This helps to trap burning flying brands and makes them more susceptible to ignition.

The weather will affect the chief's decisions in covering exposures. Sparks and brands landing on a combustible dry roof are a hazard, but if the roof is protected by several inches of snow the threat is mitigated. Buildings thoroughly soaked by recent rains have greater resistance to ignition by sparks and radiated heat.

Natural breaks offer considerable aid in

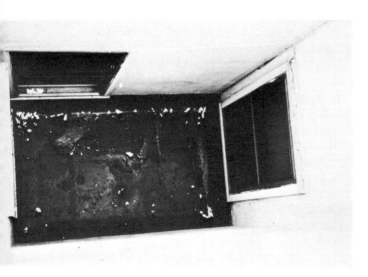

FIGURE 31. *Another type of blind shaft arrangement as seen from above.*

FIGURE 34. *A fire from an apartment in this building could get into this shaft and involve roof of building next to it. In such cases place a hose line on the exposed roof and use water to drive back fire from apartment. This is another example of a dangerous exposure condition which is not visible from the street.*

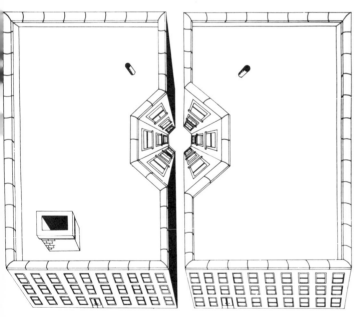

FIGURE 32. *Helicopter view of multi-story blind shaft. A large body of fire entering this shaft will roar up many floors exposing every window on every floor. (For purposes of illustration these buildings are shown separated. Actually there is no space between the buildings at front or rear.)*

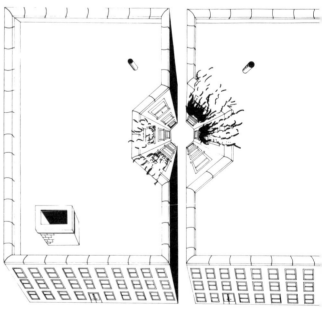

FIGURE 33. *This is the same building shown in Figure 32. Fire easily travels up the shaft and into windows above fire floor.*

fighting a fire. I refer to wide streets, arterial highways, railroad tracks, empty lots, parks, and streams.

While is is true the floors below the fires are generally least exposed, do not neglect examining them periodically. Burning embers can drop down through shafts, open stairways, hoistways, pipe recesses, and holes in burned floors.

Fire officers frequently are fooled by exposed buildings which adjoin or are closely adjacent to the fire building. One might assume there is no need for concern about the adjoining building because there is a separate, solid brick wall protecting it. Unfortunately this may be a serious error. A more careful survey may reveal three conditions which could cause serious involvement of this adjoining or closely adjacent building:

1. There may be wooden porches at the rear which will begin to burn if the fire blows out the rear windows of the building.

2. There may be windows in the adjoining brick wall at the back which are not visible because of heavy smoke.

3. There may be a blind shaft between the structures which is not visible from the front or rear. This can be observed only by examination from the roof or by going into the adjoining building.

The fact that there is a parapet wall is no assurance such a shaft does not exist. The shaft may be open to the rear. In such case, visual examination of the rear would disclose the potential, unless smoke were so heavy you could not see. Of course, there is always the chance of fire going through the roof and involving adjoining roofs by either sparks, radiated heat, or direct fire contact. (See Figures 27-34.)

Structural features which aid firefighting

The commanding officer at a large operation must take into consideration every advantage offered by structural features that will help him in his battle to keep fire from spreading. He should be cognizant of built-in protective features which will stand him in good stead. Some of these features are:

1. Unpierced masonry walls which offer excellent fire stops.

2. Fire doors and shutters of metal, or those with approved metal coverings.

3. Roof parapets (parapet wall).

4. Fire-resistant enclosed stairs.

5. Sprinklers and standpipes.

6. Interior alarm systems.

Masonry walls. The substantially constructed unpierced wall not only holds fire and smoke back to help confine the fire, but it aids in breaking the draft effect created by large open areas. However, it is wrong to assume that no attention need be paid to the protected side of such fire walls. Walls can shift, a minor explosion could dislodge masonry units, or the push-pull effect of a collapsing roof member could create openings. Therefore, periodic checks must be made of the protected side of such walls. And as soon as a unit can be spared, a protective hose line should be placed to guard against such a possibility.

Fire doors and shutters are useless unless they are closed. Some are designed to close automatically, but the old-type swinging shutter had to be closed manually at the close of each work day. In too many instances this was either neglected or forgotten during a daytime fire. People rushing from a burning building rarely stop to close fire shutters.

Somewhat the same limitation exists with wired-glass windows. They must be closed to function protectively against fire. And fusible links (on either fire shutters or windows) are not the complete answer. Sparks and brands can fly through open windows and ignite combustible contents long before enough heat has accumulated to cause the fusible link to operate. This is one reason the seasoned fire officer always sends a man or two to close these shutters or windows, even though protective devices are provided. He wants to know they are closed. The men can also make a quick examination of the floor to be sure no fire already has entered.

Wired glass does offer some advantages. You can see through it to note whether there is fire involvement on the floor. While the glass eventually will crack, it stays in place up to about 1,600° F. If you need to ventilate through a wired-glass window or skylight and such glass has been heated by fire, direct a stream at it and it will fall apart.

Roof parapets (parapet wall) are that part of the dividing wall between buildings which is carried on through and above the roof. It is usually about two or three feet higher than the surrounding roof. Roof parapets indicate a dividing wall between the building which does not end at the ceiling level to create an open hanging ceiling. The parapet wall also helps confine the fire should it break through the roof and expose the adjoining roof structure. Precautionary measures still indicate checking adjoining ceiling spaces for fire spread via defective party walls and covering adjoining roofs with hose lines as soon as men can be spared.

Fire-resistant enclosed stairs serve a triple function in fires. The first is their primary function — to get the people out safely. They do this by providing an enclosed refuge, cut off from the fire floor by self-closing doors, leading safely to the outside. Second, they serve to limit the spread of the fire by confining it to the floor of origin. Most fires extend by way of unprotected vertical openings such as stair shafts. Third, they allow the fire department to come to the fire floor behind a protected enclosure, free of smoke and heat.

Sprinklers and standpipes. The two built-in features of most help to firefighters are sprinkler systems and standpipe systems. Here the commanding officer should know the laws of his particular city which govern these built-in features.

Standpipe systems generally are found in tall buildings and those that cover a large area. They are also found on the stage of legitimate theatres (those with stage shows).

Sprinkler systems generally are found where it is desirable to exceed height, area, or exit provisions — usually combustible occupancies. They also are generally required where large numbers of people congregate — such as department stores.

The use of sprinklers and standpipes in firefighting operation is explained throroughly in Chapters 11 and 12.

Interior alarm systems which may be used to alert the occupants to evacuate are found in hospitals, department stores, hotels, factories, schools, old-age and nursing homes, and high hazard occupancies.

There are other features which aid the firefighter. Special hazards may have special extinguishing systems. For example, oil refineries may have built-in foam extinguishing systems and yard hydrants; large lumber yards may have yard hydrants with fixed monitor nozzle systems.

Very tall buildings sometimes have a telephone system with portable phones and jacks on each floor. These may be used to maintain communications between the chief and his operating forces in the building. In buildings with elevators, the elevators should be reserved for fire department use in emergencies.

The use of exterior streams

Just because a building is completely involved does not always mean there is equal exposure priority on all sides. We have already mentioned that fire could be extending toward an open lot, an unpierced exterior and substantial masonry wall, or an arterial highway. Here it might be necessary to halt traffic. Such cases can receive attention later.

What is the greatest exposure threat? Here is where the emphasis should be placed. Here is where you should place large diameter exterior streams. Sweep both the exposed face of the threatened structure and the fire floor. Swing the stream back from the exposure and try to get water on the fire floor as well.

Whenever possible use large streams, 500 gpm or larger. It is axiomatic: If you are going to have to resort to outside streams, they should be of large calibre to assure reach and penetration. There are some exceptions to this, however. You may be operating in inner courts, rear yards, alleys of limited width, and against lower building heights with smaller fires. In such cases, the mobility of smaller streams is desirable.

But use large streams when feasible, even if you have to combine the water of several smaller lines into one master stream. Such heavy streams have greater range and may succeed in reaching the fire. Small streams are usually evaporated by the heat before they reach the body of fire.

Frequently, firemen operating heavy streams do so without using special appliances. On dozens of occasions, I have seen four or five men wrestling the reaction of large streams. This makes no sense. It not only tires the men but, should the line get away, someone may be injured severely. We have equipment designed to do such work. Probably the best is the deck pipe, or deluge gun as it is sometimes called. Years ago these devices (called wagon pipes) were fixed to the apparatus. One had to move the apparatus to the desired location for effective use of the appliance. This is still true of today's ladder pipe and elevating platform though these appliances can move from side to side and, to some extent, up and down. The modern deluge gun can be removed from the truck and placed in any desirable location. Once it is in operation, one man can easily maneuver a large calibre stream.

It is wise to put an extra length or two of hose into the stretch near the deluge gun. Then if you wish to move it nearer the fire, it can be done easily. (Be sure to shut down before moving.) Such streams may be operated in the front, in alleys, on roofs, or at other location where the stream is needed. Whenever possible, gate your incoming lines at the deluge gun or appliance. This allows you to shut down and revert to hand-line operations and move in or out.

The effectiveness of deluge gun streams above the third floor is limited. Above this level you must rely on streams which can be elevated. Before the use of the aerial ladder pipe this could only be accomplished by hand lines taken up and used off aerial or portable ladders, hand lines operated from adjoining roofs, or water towers. Of the three, the water tower was by far the most effective. It could deliver streams with great pressures and gallonage as high as 100 feet. The other two methods are still used, though less frequently as more fire departments put aerial ladder pipes and elevating platforms into service.

Since a primary objective is to keep the fire from spreading, lines must be placed

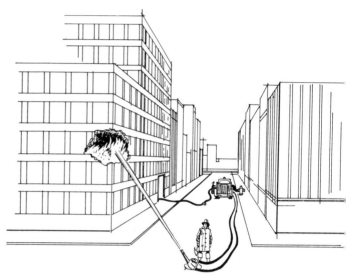

FIGURE 35. *Fire will soon involve upper floors by way of exterior windows. Use heavy exterior stream to drive fire back (as shown in this cutaway drawing) and darken it down while hand lines move up the inside stairs. One line should move to the fire floor and another to the floor above the fire. Exterior stream must be shut down as soon as companies make the floor.*

ahead of the fire, in the path of the wind. The buildings in direct line facing the wind are nearly always the most susceptible to the danger of exposure. But as with most rules, there are exceptions. If a fire has burned its way through the roof and there is a higher building nearby with windows overlooking the burning building, these windows must be protected immediately. Place hose lines in on the floor of the exposed windows. Operate these streams through exposed windows onto the fire below. This accomplishes a dual objective: it keeps the fire out of the exposed building and attacks the fire below. What this really adds up to is a priority of effort dependent on the severity of the exposure threat.

Streams frequently are used as an aerial water curtain. For example, a fog stream is commonly used to set up a spray between the fire building and the exposure. This is not advisable. Radiant heat can pass through water drops. It is better to direct the stream back and forth to alternately drench the exposed building and then hit the parent fire. If there are protective openings in the exterior walls of the threatened building, the drenching will protect these openings and prevent fire from getting in onto the floor. The use of an occasional water curtain to contain flying brands is permissible and desirable. A water curtain also may be used to break up concentrations of flammable gases or to absorb caustic vapors such as ammonia.

First-in companies will sometimes witness a heavy body of fire blowing out of upper floor windows and threatening the floor above. In this case, good practice dictates the use of an exterior heavy steam to drive back the fire, thereby not only attacking it but also preventing its extension. (See Figure 35.)

A common error in the use of exterior streams is to concentrate on one or two windows. Heavy streams should sweep the row of windows on the fire floor within reach of the stream. This is to assure adequate coverage and distribution. Avoid directing streams at windows marked "shaftway" or "elevator shaft" because the water will only fall into the cellar or lowest floor of the structure. Your objective is to get penetration on the fire floor. Water falling down shaftways will only be wasted and create considerable unnecessary damage.

There may be fire situations where it is proper to direct your exterior streams into such shaftways. If you suspect a lower fire is extending up by way of such shafts, you may need to keep a stream operating into the opening to prevent fire that has entered this shaft on a lower level from sweeping up to involve upper floors.

When possible — provided the building is structurally sound — exposure conditions are nearly always better checked by bringing hand lines to the fire floor and floors above. Interior lines never are larger than 2½-inch. Frequently, where manpower is limited, 1½-inch lines are used. The advantage is mobility, allowing the department to cover vertical exposures by directing streams into various vertical means of fire communication. Where necessary, open walls and ceilings to disclose hidden fire travel. Remember, it is not uncommon for fire brands to drop down vertical shafts and start fires below. Be sure to check this out thoroughly.

Men often get so engrossed in laying protective hose lines they forget the simplest means of protecting exposures — closing a blocked fire door, windows, or shutters. This may be, and often is, the most effective way to prevent fire from involving adjacent areas or buildings. This is particularly true of exposed windows directly above an adjoining fire structure. Getting these openings closed may give you enough time to put protective lines into play before the fire breaks the glass to involve the floor. Feel walls of adjacent exposed areas. If they are warm, move combustible stock away from the exposed wall to a safer location. Ventilate the floor by opening windows on the side away from the exposed wall and check on conditions throughout the course of the fire.

Miscellaneous sizeup considerations

Water supply is of paramount importance. No fire department is better than its water supply. Any defects or poor conditions should be noted when you make your sizeup. Consider the following items at the pre-planning stage:

1. Diameter of mains and flow pressure.
2. Are mains well cross-connected in a grid pattern to preclude dead end mains?
3. Hydrant spacing.
4. High-pressure or low-pressure supply.
5. Is a high-pressure loop available (or river and fire boats)?
6. Use of standpipe tanks and pumps of adjoining buildings in emergency.
7. Tank trucks of sanitation department for grass fires, bonfires, and flying brands at large fires.
8. Booster pumps and tanks on apparatus.
9. Private plant water systems.
10. Prompt call to the department of water supply to improve low pressures, to divert water, and to operate control valves to insure supply.
11. Hydrants frozen or covered by snow.

Weather conditions. The weather is an important consideration in sizeup. Temperature, atmospheric conditions, wind velocity and direction can exert a powerful influence on firefighting operations. A strong wind, for example, can fan the fire and scatter sparks and flaming brands for hundreds of feet. Wind also breaks up fire streams. This adversely affects penetration of a stream and increases exposure problems to the leeward.

Freezing weather indicates the possibility of frozen hydrants and hoselines. Ice will coat roofs, fire escapes, and ladders. This makes outside operations hazardous and slow. Men heavily clothed move more slowly and are less efficient, particularly when exposed too long to severe weather. Hose lines may freeze.

Snow, sleet, and icy conditions make driving hazardous and tends to slow response time, allowing the fire to gain headway.

Heavy rains and fog can impede vision and retard effective ventilation.

Hot weather enervates men. Windows will be open in buildings that are not air-conditioned. This allows fires to gain easy penetration.

Apparatus on hand. Based on previously developed information in the foregoing items, the commanding officer can now determine whether he can handle the situation with the available equipment. His decision will be based principally on three considerations: (1) the size and intensity of the fire, (2) the exposure problems, and (3) the life hazard.

Communications. If the operation proves to be a large one, a command post with a communications center will be needed. Additional portable radios will be needed to maintain communication between the chief and his forces.

Salvage. Salvage should be started as soon as fire is under control and men can be spared for the task.

Time of fire. In addition to the factors mentioned earlier in this chapter under the time of the fire, now the chief officer must consider these factors:

1. Where are his other companies? Are they in quarters or out on inspections? How long will it take to get them to the fire?

2. Heavy smoke conditions at the time people are coming home from work — traffic blocking incoming units, train traffic badly exposed by smoke and heat — should he stop train traffic?

3. Should the chief officer recall the off-duty platoons? If the change of shifts is only a short time away, it may be wise to do this now while both shifts are in quarters and instantly available.

Life. The chief in charge must consider these possibilities: His forces may take a great deal of punishment at the fire. Men may be hurt, they may be exhausted. Should he bring the off-duty platoon in to relieve the exhausted men? Should he send the exhausted men back to quarters? How can they best be transported?

Size and type of fire. The fire may occur in a suburban area where the companies do light fire duty, such as controlling grass and brush fires. The firemen, possibly having had little experience with large fires such as a furniture warehouse, may not push on in or hold their positions, as would more experienced crews. Should the chief get help in now or take a chance?

Sprinkler system. Should the sprinkler system be shut down yet? Is it safe to do so? Can it be restored to service so as not to leave the building more vulnerable to a second fire than before?

Water supply. Should the chief officer call the water department to boost pressures? (Sometimes this causes mains to break.) Would it be feasible to bring in several large pumpers to set up relay operations from a distant pond or river?

Special considerations. There are many conditions affecting your firefighting operations which cannot be adequately catalogued. Here are some of them:

1. The potential for explosion and or collapse.

2. The need to contact someone with special knowledge of hazardous processes or storages at a particular fire.

3. Allaying panic conditions.

4. Need for extra masks.

5. Elevated structures which will interfere with stream operations or placing of ladders or elevating platforms.

6. Provisions to safeguard firemen working under dangerous conditions.

7. Need for special extinguishing agents where water is not adaptable.

8. Unusual street conditions which might impede approach of apparatus.

9. Overloading of old fire escapes.

Common fireground errors

There are several errors commanding officers make most often on the fireground. Since they are so common, it is worth pointing them out:

1. The usual major mistake is underestimating the fire potential.

2. The chief vacates his frontal command post to go into the fire building to survey the situation personally while units are still arriving. He loses sight of the whole picture, frequently staying to supervise one or two interior hose lines. As a result, incoming units assign themselves.

3. Failure to supply sprinklers early.

4. Failure to head off the fire initially; instead the commanding officer waits until the fire shows up in an adjacent area, then he frantically tries to get lines into position to combat the new threat.

5. Failure to use self-contained breathing equipment.

6. Failure to realize exhausted men will need relief.

7. Failure to call mutual aid soon enough.

Mutual aid

No chapter on fire problem evaluation would be complete without a realistic appraisal of the situation as it exists. It is not enough to say help should be called, then assume such help is available promptly and has the required proficiency.

For the most part, the large metropolitan departments have well-staffed and well-trained firemen. First and subsequent alarms quickly bring in additional companies that are trained to act as units. Because of the frequency of fires, these men develop an expertise that shows up in adequate results.

But most of the country is protected by volunteer organizations. These departments, as well as the small paid and the combination small paid/volunteer departments, often are undermanned. To supplement their manpower, they band together in mutual-aid pacts. Some mutual-aid organizations are models of efficiency — others are not. They function well in small fire situations, but the more complex the fire problem the greater the possibility for breakdown in efficiency.

Let us examine a large operation in a small municipality — one where mutual aid is urgently required. Too often, experience reveals that the commanding officer at a major fire did not realize its potential. The result: failure to call for adequate help before it was too late. The chief or commanding officer had not prepared himself for large-scale operations, and when the situation arose he was unable to cope with it. At the fire scene you will see frantic scurrying about, confusion, conflicting orders, yelling and counter yelling, no leadership, and very little direction.

If there is no advance planning for the large emergency, the help called from a neighboring community may be less than desirable because the neighboring community won't know what is needed. In their enthusiasm to help out a neighbor, they may spontaneously rush in personnel, food, clothing, and medical supplies. While the intent is praiseworthy, the result is unorganized and wasteful. And the stricken community may not need most of the assistance sent.

But mutual-aid plans if well made are a vital necessity to the small community. Most communities start out with small volunteer departments. As a city grows and industry comes in, fire hazards increase, usually without a compensating increase in the fire department. It becomes progressively more difficult to attract and keep volunteers. Therefore, the need for some paid men becomes apparent. But it would be fiscal suicide for the average small municipality to maintain a paid department large enough to protect itself adequately. The obvious answer is an agreement between neighboring communities to assist each other when necessary.

A good mutual-aid plan can provide help in the form of manpower, pumping equipment, ladder equipment, or special equipment such as elevating platforms, tankers, rescue trucks, light rigs, and self-contained breathing equipment.

How does mutual aid work?

Mutual aid in its simplest form is a verbal agreement between fire chiefs of adjoining communities to help each other if called. The town officials are apprised of the agreement and sanction it.

In a more complicated form, it can be an automatic response of manpower and equipment dispatched where needed by a central dispatching unit from among the communities joined in the agreement.

In one Midwestern area, spreading to a radius of about 40 miles, there are three general systems of mutual aid. A look at these plans will show their advantages and defects. We will call the plans Group A, B, and C.

Mutual Aid Group A. This plan encompasses about 40 towns and private fire brigades in a loosely arranged gentlemen's agreement. There are certain regulations and bylaws, but in general the plan relies upon the kind of arrangement where I say, "Jim if I need you, will you come out? I will do the same for you."

The shortcomings of this arrangement are obvious:

1. There is no specified order of calling.
2. Responses may be from a great distance.
3. It lends itself to a friendship kind of response, rather than one based on need — not a businesslike approach.
4. There is no automatic response or move-up.
5. Surrounding communities may not even know of the call for help because it is not mandatory for them to be on the same radio frequency. There is no mutual receipt of all alarms.

The organizational structure is far too cumbersome for an efficient, close-knit co-operative operation.

Mutual Aid Group B. This group is made up of about 14 towns which broke away from Mutual Aid Group A because of its unwieldy size and informality. Here are some advantages of this system:

1. There are written bylaws and responsibility is tied down to some extent.
2. Responses are definite and prescribed.

There is a running card clearly showing who goes where.

3. It is a legal contract entered into by the co-operating municipalities.

4. There is a cross exchange of all equipment furnished each fire chief.

5. All municipalities are on a common radio network.

6. Meetings are held monthly to discuss and iron out problems.

7. There are mutual-aid drills.

8. There are infrequent training schools.

Here are the shortcomings of this arrangement:

1. Insufficient fires. This means there is not enough experience in using the plan to make it a smooth, efficient operation.

2. It takes some of the communities a long time (particularly the all-volunteer groups) to assemble enough men for an adequate response and still have enough manpower left to cover their own village.

3. Even when paid departments call in their off-shifts, the resulting additional responses are less than satisfactory. First, the response is slow — it may take the off-shift people an hour to report. They are not always readily reached and they have to respond by private car under traffic conditions, among other difficulties.

4. Men report in singly. Therefore there is no team operation.

5. Some of the chiefs insist on varying the response from that of the prearranged printed response charts.

6. Some of the chiefs have concluded verbal arrangements with other communities outside the formal organization. They may respond to help such towns. Should another town in the organization have a fire requiring help from this chief, he may not be able to supply it if he already has sent equipment to a town not included in the legal agreement.

7. It is difficult to get some of the chiefs to agree to assigned responses for large-scale operations. In fact, some refuse to plan further than a second alarm. It is up to the individual chief to specify whom and what he wants in the initial planning of the response chart.

FIGURE 36. *A sample running card. First alarm response calls Engine Companies 1, 4, and 7; Ladder companies 2 and 5; searchlight truck 1; and the chief of the 3rd Battalion to the fire. Engine 8 would cover Engine 1 quarters, Ladder 7 would cover Ladder 2 quarters. For second alarm, all units listed on line 2 would respond, line 3, third alarm and so on. Master alarms could mean mutual aid companies. Special apparatus could mean equipment such as public utilities. The makeup of the card should be tailored to the department's needs.*

RUNNING CARD

BOX NUMBER 120   LOCATION   SMITH & JONES STREETS

	ENGINE CO.	HOOK AND LADDER CO.	SPECIAL UNITS	CHIEF	CHANGE CO.
1.	1 - 4 - 7	2 - 5	LIGHT TRUCK 1	3rd Batt.	E 8 to E 1 L 7 to L 2
2.					
3.					
4.					
5.					
MASTER ALARMS					
SPECIAL APPARATUS					

ASSIGNMENT CARD

OPERATING UNITS	WHERE ASSIGNED
ENGINE COMPANIES	
LADDER COMPANIES	
RESCUE COMPANIES	
SEARCHLIGHT UNITS	
GAS COMPANY	
ELECTRIC COMPANY	
MISCELLANEOUS UNITS	

FIGURE 37. *This is a sample assignment card to be kept at the command post at a large scale operation. It is filled out as specific assignments are given.*

Mutual Aid Group C. This arrangement covers about a half-dozen municipalities. It is the most progressive, and therefore the most effective, for these reasons:

1. The departments work together on an assigned automatic response to certain boxes.

2. This has a distinct advantage in that they respond more frequently and are used to working together.

3. Their pre-fire planning is more effective.

4. In essence, the rest of the practices are quite similar to the Mutual Aid Groups A and B.

Mutual aid problems. Here are some of the problems you generally run into with a mutual-aid program.

1. Many participating municipalities have agreements with other departments not included in the original legal document.

2. Some mutual-aid plans are too complicated. For example, there are cumbersome details where one mutual-aid company will respond if the fire is in one specified part of the city, and another department will respond should the fire take place in a different part of town. It is difficult for departments that at best respond infrequently to remember complicated arrangements and respond without error.

3. There is a serious question of who assumes command. Volunteer chiefs are reluctant to take command if an incoming mutual-aid company is in charge of paid men and officers.

4. Failure to set up command posts is a common error.

5. In too many cases, chief officers are not available to take charge.

6. The plans fail to provide guides for outside companies coming into unfamiliar territory.

7. There is a multiplicity of orders — too many bosses countermanding orders.

8. There is a lack of communication between operating units and between operating units and command posts.

9. Chief officers may not be sufficiently trained to handle many companies and large fires.

10. Another complicating factor is the difference in threads and the need for adapters.

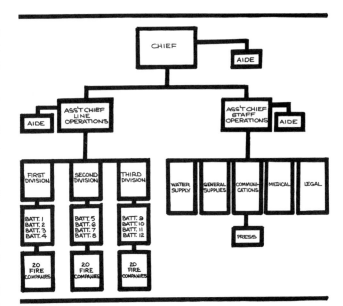

FIGURE 38. *Sample fireground organization chart. Note that there are only three persons reporting to the chief. This prevents time-consuming contacts with too many people. Line operations (fire duty) are under the control of the assistant chief. For large scale operations sector commands are designated to cover all four sides (See Figure 39). Staff functions are under jurisdiction of an operations officer. The fire chief, assistant fire chief and operations officer all have their own staff assistants.*

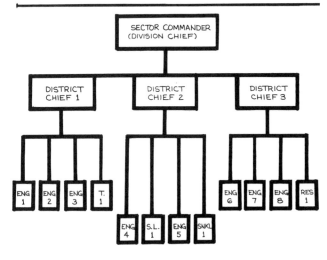

FIGURE 39. *A sector command organization chart. Individual units and junior chiefs comprise the sector.*

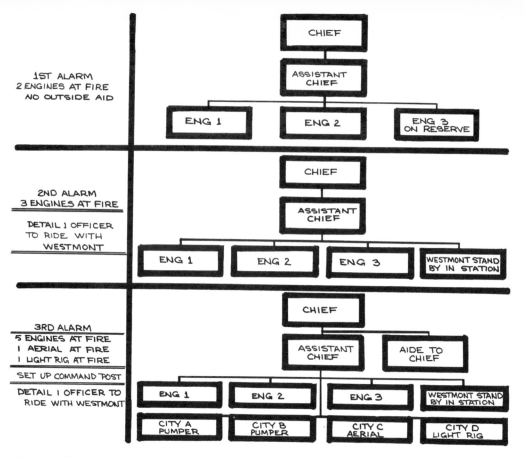

FIGURE 40. *A fireground organization plan up to a 3rd alarm for a small city. This plan provides not only for specific responses but related details as well. For example, there is provision for a fire officer to ride with a change company from out of town. It also gives a running summary of the numbers of units operating.*

FIGURE 41. *Organization for 4th alarm. This is a normal progression of response for a 4th alarm for the same city as shown in Figure 40. Empty box under chief is for any special need of a particular emergency.*

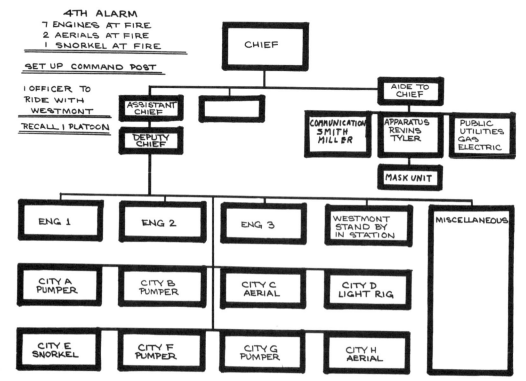

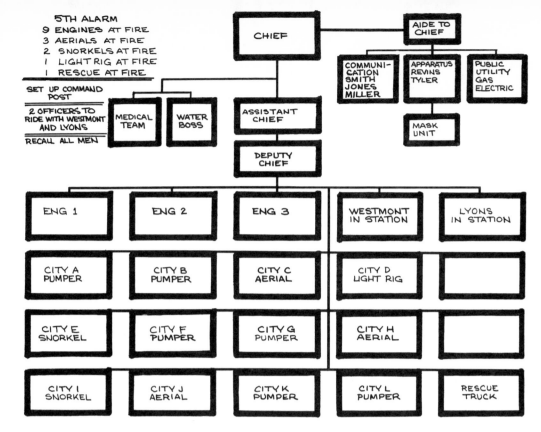

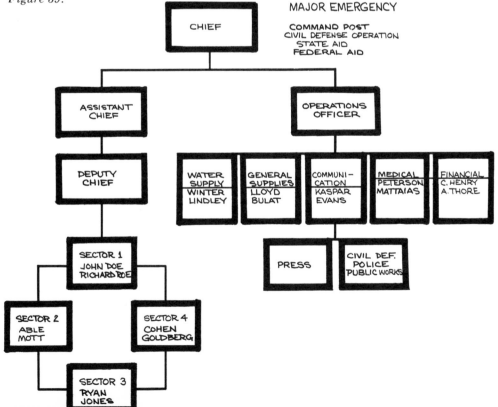

FIGURE 42. *Continuation of same plan, going to 5th alarm. This plan would be improved by taking the medical team and water boss from its present position and placing it under the jurisdiction of the chief's aide (who should be of at least the rank of assistant chief). The plan is also weak in junior supervisory personnel (battalion or district chiefs) for the number of firefighting units shown reporting directly to the deputy chief. He would be unable to supervise this number of units properly.*

FIGURE 43. *This is a fireground organization plan for the same city as in Figures 40 to 42, but for a massive operation requiring 25 or more pieces of mutual aid equipment and over 200 men. The sector commands are organized in similar manner to those in Figure 39.*

51

Crucial lines may be negated because men under pressure forget to bring adapters with them.

11. Some fire departments are eager beavers and respond without being called or in incorrect order of response. They clutter the already crowded streets with their equipment and tie up the air waves with their own communications.

Prepare for large scale operation

We have discussed mutual aid on a modest level — an operation that would bring in units from a distance of about 15 miles. What if the operation is of massive proportions — a conflagration or a disastrous plane crash in the heart of a large community? We will certainly have to reach out further for help. We may get help from across the state line. The operation may revert to a Civil Defense operation. Here are some of the problems to anticipate in such a major operation:

1. Insufficient planning in depth for such major scale movements of men and materials. (a) You may have to sleep 200 men. (b) Are there sanitary facilities for the men? (c) Where do they eat, change clothes, etc.? (d) Has medical aid for injured been anticipated?

2. Insufficient knowledge of emergency sources of water supply, should normal sources prove inadequate. (a) Are long hose layouts from rivers feasible? (b) Are there private pools, standpipe or sprinkler tanks which can furnish some water supply? (c) Has thought been given to milk tankers, other tankers, trucks, for carrying water? (d) In case of caved-in streets with the resulting main breaks, have plans been made for drafting water from the hole filling with water? Do you have storm sewers from which you can draft?

3. No provisions for servicing of trucks, gasoline, oil, spare parts, repairs.

4. No co-ordination of departments that have never even seen each other, much less worked together

5. Mass-scale communications generally are unsatisfactory — radios may not be on compatible wave length. Even when they are, excited personnel tend to clutter air waves

so as to render them comparatively inefficient.

6. Poor traffic control or none — unrestrained crowds, people rush to the scene in their cars. There will be a need for local police, sheriff's police, and Civil Defense personnel.

7. No provisions for fire protection coverage in towns left vulnerable by massive assistance moving to the stricken area.

8. No guides for incoming units.

9. Looting.

I think we can all agree this is quite a problem. The man in charge of such operations has enormous responsibilities, and must prepare himself for them.

The fireground is not the place to correct errors in strategy. Obviously, plans must be made in advance for large-scale operations. Lay out a course to follow. Perhaps it can follow this type of general outline:

1. Select a planning committee.

2. Discuss mutual-aid problems.

3. Catalog available manpower and equipment.

4. Card index this information and distribute it to participating units.

5. Preplan emergency actions.

6. Try them out in large-scale drills.

7. Where faults show, correct them on the master plan.

8. After corrections are made, try them again.

9. Record the results of these exercises. Study the results, try to determine where they may still be improved.

Here are some points the wise chief will consider in planning for a possible large-scale operation:

There must be a unified command, with only one commanding officer.

A command post should be established. It may be a chief's car or squad unit, but it should be clearly designated by special lighting, flags, or other suitable markings.

Where the operation is of sufficient scope and magnitude, subordinate command posts should be established. All incoming units should be checked in and out at the main or subordinate command post where they will

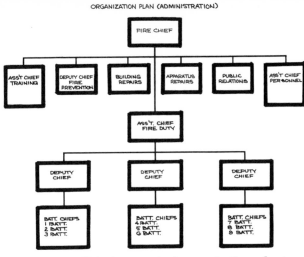

receive their assignments. Keep records of these assignments.

Establish a communications unit at the main command post to correlate all radio messages, relay requests for help, maintain contact with operating forces, and transmit routine and special instructions. It is possible to cross-communicate with other units even if on different frequencies. Try to have additional help (if on a different wave length) assign one piece of equipment to the command post — perhaps one of their police squad cars. This additional unit is to remain at the field communications unit to transmit and receive radio communications.

In the large metropolitan centers, additional functions would appear on the assignment plan. These would be assigned to an operations officer who would be in charge of all staff functions and act as a liaison officer between the chief and the area fire commander.

An officer would be assigned the responsibility of the water supply system. He would advise of actual or anticipated weakness in water supplies. He also would co-operate with the water department for on-the-spot decisions regarding water supplies.

The communications officer would be in charge of all communications and could call for assistance in maintaining and repairing communications equipment on-the-spot.

The supply officer is a key person and should know where to get special equipment within or outside the department, food, shelter, clothing, and any other needed supplies.

A medical officer would handle first aid, summon additional help and ambulances, and set up a field hospital if necessary.

The legal officer (finance officer) would provide the legal answers to problems in the hiring of special help such as blasters, riggers, and earth-moving equipment. He could advise the chief of legal obstacles during unusual operations such as blowing up houses or moving people out forcibly.

The prudent fire official prepares himself with as many aids as he can. Certainly he should have instantly available a running card which shows what he can expect under normal conditions. For the really major pos-

FIGURE 44. *This is a typical organization chart for fire department administration. Note the faulty arrangement with six ranking officers reporting directly to the chief including the assistant chief for fire duty. This span of control is too broad. It may indicate a chief reluctant to let go of some of his authority.*

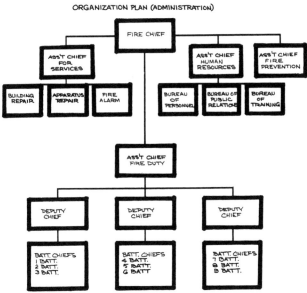

FIGURE 45. *In this administrative chart only four ranking officers report to the chief. It is a more workable plan than that in Figure 44. It makes little difference what titles are used for an organization chart. The function is the important distinction. Related functions are better grouped under one head.*

sibilities, he should have prepared and tested in dry runs an organizational chart for fire-ground operations which show the line and staff functions. There should be a sufficient number of blank forms on which can be recorded the assignment of units and the sectors to which they are assigned. (See Figures 36 to 45.)

Chapter 6

Ventilation

VENTILATION IS a planned procedure designed to rid a building on fire (or in danger of taking fire) of heat, gases, and smoke that have accumulated through predetermined channels.

Effective ventilation can accomplish three desirable objectives:

1. Save lives. Ventilation will draw fire, heat, and smoke away from trapped people.

2. Reduce the extension of fire through lateral spread or the mushrooming effect.

3. Make it possible for firefighting forces to move in. Firefighters can reach the seat of the fire more quickly and with the least physical punishment.

There are additional beneficial side effects: There will be less water damage, out of service company time will be lessened, there will be less chance of firemen being overcome, and there will be less likelihood of back drafts or smoke explosions.

Why ventilate?

One of the major reasons fires get out of control is the lack of proper and adequate ventilation. It is difficult for inexperienced men to realize the amount of noxious, choking, blinding smoke one bedroom fire can produce. It can fill the entire floor of a dwelling and produce serious smoke involvement of the floor above as well. It follows logically then that a furniture store or similar occupancy will produce much more smoke when a fire involves several pieces of upholstered furniture or mattresses.

Firemen arriving at relatively insignificant fires are often driven out by the hot smoke and resort to using outside streams through a window or two. What this does is drive the combustion products back, spreading them throughout the interior of the building. If the firemen cannot extinguish the fire from the outside position (and generally they cannot) they may worsen the conditions. There is a natural reluctance to break windows, and this is proper. Where it is possible to open windows without breaking them, do so by all means. But if the fire will spread because windows are not broken and you can't get in with the hose line, then it makes sense to break windows to get the heat and smoke out.

It is axiomatic: If you want to move in on a smoky fire, you must ventilate or you will be driven out. Yes, you can and should use masks to hold difficult positions. But most jobs will be readily controlled by good, fast ventilation and a crew determined to move in. The second crew or other incoming units should get into their masks in case they prove to be needed.

Many of you have trained by burning down old buildings that were slated for demolition. Did you ever wonder why you had so much trouble getting a good fire started even though you used all the proper materials — old furniture, cardboard cartons? In fact, most of the time you used accelerants such as kerosene. (I hope never gasoline!) Why could your neighbor (without trying) have a fire in his bedroom, in the middle of the night, that nearly drove your entire crew out of the house before you finally extinguished it?

The reason is simply adequate ventilation. Take some upholstered furniture, chairs, and a dresser. Put them in the back yard in an open lot. Ignite them and wait until there is a roaring fire — now put out the fire with a booster line. You can do it with no trouble. Put the same furniture into an occupied home with doors and windows closed. You will have a great deal of trouble putting out this fire.

The reason is that closed doors and windows will not allow the combustion products to escape to the outer air. The heat is absorbed by the walls and furnishings. Gradually the entire room and its contents build up to a high temperature. Hot smoke and gases permeate closets, concealed spaces, and the floors above. The firemen have to advance to the seat of the fire under very difficult conditions. Even if they are protected by masks, the heat may be extremely punishing. They cannot see where they are operating.

Without masks men can be overcome by the hot smoke and gases. Their failure to move in, locate, and extinguish the fire could cause trapped people to lose their lives. Structural and contents damage will be great

Since fire operations under these interior conditions will be inefficient and at times impossible, it is obvious we should attempt to re-create the conditions of the fire we made in the open lot where we had no difficulty with smoke and heat. The only way to do this is by carefully planned ventilation. Once this is done, men can move in, get water on the fire, search for trapped people, and examine for fire travel.

We should understand why smoke behaves as it does. Hot air, gas, and smoke will rise in burning buildings. The reason is this: When air is heated it begins to expand; it wants to occupy a greater space.

If this air were confined in a vessel, the pressure within the vessel would increase. If the air in an open structure is heated by the fire, it expands and the same amount of air will occupy more space. The heated air is thus lighter than surrounding air masses,

and it rises. The hotter the air and smoke the more rapidly it will rise. A balloon filled with hot air (or lighter-than-air gases) rises and floats in the air because it weighs less than the air it displaces.

In a fire situation the heated smoke and gases of combustion rise to the top floor and bank there because they cannot get out. A minute amount of pressure is created in the top story by the heated combustion products pushing against the roof and walls. This pushing forces the heated gases into rooms, closets, partitions, pipe chases, and other spaces. It moves through cracks, ducts, poorly fitting covers to pipe chases, around poorly fitting doors, open transoms, and vent shafts. This is called mushrooming in fire department jargon. When the smoke and heated gases cannot move up and out, they move laterally, filling the entire floor. Then when this floor is filled, the heated gases and smoke spread downward to the next lower floor. This mushrooming effect can fill an entire building with the lethal products of combustion.

In order for a company to advance under these conditions, the structure must be ventilated at the top — and quickly. A company trying to make an interior stairway of a smoke-filled building will notice great relief as soon as the roof above the stairway is opened.

Normally the large departments assign this work to ladder companies because ladder companies carry the ladders and tools necessary for the work and the men are specially trained for it.

Every building has its own ventilation problems. What may be the correct ventilation technique in one building may not be proper for another. In one case it may be quite proper to ventilate the roof, yet in another building that would cause unnecessary damage. Roof ventilation is proper in multiple dwellings, which require the most ventilation because of the severe life hazard. However, in one- or two-family dwellings, roof ventilation is rarely required. Window ventilation is usually adequate in these buildings. By cutting the roof in a one- or two-story home you may cause the fire in the side walls to spread into the attic.

Ventilate at the top of constructions that offer a natural flow for the upward movement of smoke and gas. Such natural vertical arteries as stairways, shafts, elevator shafts, dumbwaiter shafts, light shafts, vent shafts, and pipe chases should be ventilated at the top. This draws the products of combustion through the roof and prevents mushrooming.

But there are cases when venting at the top of these vertical arteries is not effective. When heavier-than-air vapors or gases are present, ventilation at the roof is not effective, and must be carried out at lower points. Such gases are chlorine, hydrogen sulfide, and ether. Keep in mind that a large percentage of gases are heavier than air.

Ventilation precautions

Ventilation can be an effective firefighting procedure, but there are several precautions to keep in mind — not only for the effectiveness of ventilation, but for the safety of the firefighters:

1. Have charged hose lines ready. Never ventilate a fire that may intensify because of the ventilation until charged lines are in position. Hose lines should cover all extension points — both horizontal and vertical. Be particularly careful in public assembly areas where panic may result from smoke seepage into such areas. There are two exceptions to this. One is when life is in danger. The other is where there is a bulkhead door at the roof level, or a skylight or scuttle cover at the roof over the stairs in a multistory dwelling. In this case, opening at the roof level will pull the smoke and hot gases up and out, drawing them away from the upper apartments.

2. Never ventilate so that your path of escape may be cut off. (See Figures 46 to 50.)

3. If men can get to the roof by using adjoining buildings of the same height, use this means rather than ladders.

4. Caution men against working close to the edge of roofs without parapets. Remember an earlier admonition. Teach the men to walk in smoke with a shuffle — putting one foot forward while retaining the balance of their weight on the other foot. If the forward foot feels no firm footing or an empty

FIGURE 46. *The part of the wall coming straight down from the skylight is an ideal place for examination of the hanging ceiling space. It is also an excellent place for sweeping the space with a hose stream if fire did get in. It is simple to break away the lath and plaster partition. In this fire plaster fell exposing the wood lath. Burned lath shows that there had been extension of fire to the hanging ceiling.*

space, the man can easily stop his forward movement. Another way to do this is to push a long tool ahead — such as a pike pole, axe, or forcible entry bar.

5. Be careful to check the roof supports to be sure they will not fall under the weight of firemen.

6. Plan an escape route from the roof.

7. Don't cut holes in the path of travel. However, if this has been done, be sure to caution the men in the area, or place a door over the hole.

8. When cutting for ventilation be sure to cut all boards through before ripping them up. If you do not, smoke may drive you off the floor before you can finish the job. Remember, natural openings which are in the proper location are preferable to cutting — such openings as skylights or scuttle holes.

9. Where you do cut, make the openings large enough to do the job. One large hole is preferable to several smaller ones. (Two holes each 2x2 feet have half the area of one hole 4x4 feet.) Not only is it more efficient, but there is less likelihood of men fall-

FIGURE 47. *Improper venting technique. This fireman opened windows on his way up, working away from his point of retreat. He may find himself unable to get down if fire, fanned by draft of opened windows, extends beneath him.*

ing into them. It is also easier to patch one large hole than several small holes.

10. When you open a roof, make sure the room ceiling is also opened. You can push ceilings down with pike poles or ladders.

11. Do not break doors, windows, or skylights if they can be opened without damaging them.

12. Always work with your back to the wind. This will keep you on the windward side of openings and help to avoid the toxic effects of escaping gases.

13. Use breathing masks where needed.

14. A hose stream directed into a natural opening (door, window, or skylight), or one cut by firemen, can seal off such opening and prevent the desired smoke removal.

15. Provide good lighting at night or at smoky fires.

16. When your assignment is completed, notify the chief in charge of your segment of the operation. He may be waiting to move companies into the building when ventilation is completed.

Where to ventilate

Roofs. Send two men, if you can spare the second man, to remove covers from all vertical arteries such as skylights, scuttle covers, open roof bulkhead doors, and windows.

Some skylights (in older homes) may have an ornamental glass below, level with the top floor ceiling. If so, remove or break this glass to vent the stair shaft and top floor. Where conditions are severe, cut one large hole directly over the hot spots or enlarge the opening made by the skylight or scuttle cover. Always remember to push down the ceiling after cutting a roof to ventilate the floor below the roof. Keep the wind at your back to blow the smoke and heat away from you.

Removing a skylight or scuttle cover to vent a cockloft (hanging ceiling) will be ineffective unless you break out the part of the side wall which closes off the cockloft from the stair shaft. This technique is excellent for examining the cockloft for fire involvement and for stream penetration. (See Figure 46.)

Skylights should always be removed in preference to breaking the glass. Pry the flashing loose on all sides where it is nailed to the roof. Lift the skylight off completely. Turn it upside down after removal so that it will be obvious to other men that it has been removed and the opening is nearby (to avoid accidents under smoky conditions).

Another way to do this is to pry away the flashing on three sides. Then using the remaining side like a hinge, tip the entire skylight over onto the roof. Men sometimes try to remove the individual glass panes by prying open the metal dividing strips which hold the glass in place. Usually this method is too time consuming and not practical. If neither method works, break the glass. But first warn any men below who may be cut by the falling glass.

Floors above the fire. It is vital to keep control of the floor above the fire. Therefore you must ventilate it thoroughly or you will be driven off. Open windows at top and bottom on the leeward side first. Make sure to open or remove screens, storm sash, drapes, and blinds. Be careful working on fire escapes. Open the window furthest from your line of escape first or you may trap yourself. (See Figures 47 to 51.)

If you are going to cut the floor to ventilate the area below, cut it under on open window so that the smoke vents directly to the outer air. Instead of making one large square hole, it may be feasible to cut only one or two boards and make an opening the entire length of the room. This is the quickest and safest thing to do.

If the building has hot-air registers, remove the grill and push down the hot air duct. This will have an effect similar to that of cutting the floor. It is fast and causes less damage. But remember, in severe smoke conditions the ventilation area will be too small to do the job.

If you can't get into the fire floor, try using a scaling ladder from below or a pike pole from the floor above. Another method is to use ladders. Raise a ladder to the window and hold it away from the window. Then let it fall against the window to break the glass. Exterior heavy streams also can be used to break windows.

Cellars. Few fires cause more trouble than seriously involved cellar fires. This is because they are so difficult to ventilate. Usually a combination of the following methods will achieve some success:

I. Shafts leading to the cellar should be opened at the top.

2. Open deadlights in the streets, yards, or courts. Deadlights are thick, heavy pieces of glass set flush with and into the sidewalk. They start at the building line and project out for about three to four feet from the building. Their only purpose is to allow some light to illuminate the cellar area below. They are difficult to break. You must use the pike point of an axe, or some other sharp pointed tool.

3. Open at hoistway doors in the street.

4. If the cellar has windows, they should be opened. Cellar windows often are recessed in enclosures which are covered with an iron grating at the street level. The bars can be spread so that a pike pole may be used to break the glass. By breaking the concrete at the corners, the grating can be removed entirely.

5. Open the door covering exterior stairways to the cellar.

6. Open up through the front and rear of the floor above the cellar. Cut flooring near the windows. To retain possession of the street floor in serious fires, break out these windows entirely.

Because of the lack of sufficient oxygen, cellar fires are slow burning and smoky. The products of combustion are not as hot. Consequently, they lack buoyancy and tend to lie low. This is the reason cellar fires are so difficult to ventilate, making them stubborn to control.

Exposed buildings. Ventilate exposed buildings on all sides away from the fire area.

High-rise buildings. Fire does not commonly travel beyond the floor of origin in high-rise buildings which have enclosed stairways with fire-resistant self-closing doors. Confine ventilation in such buildings to windows or by using mechanical methods. You can imagine the consequences if you were to ventilate into these enclosed stair shafts and occupants were attempting to leave the building through these stairways. The same is true of an enclosed elevator shaft. This is a mistake because fire, heat, and smoke drawn into these shafts would render them unsafe for occupants as well as firemen. It can also cause serious damage to cables, machinery, and the elevator car.

If at all possible, men should move onto the fire floor for extinguishment — even though they may suffer considerable punishment. Wear masks if necessary.

Open stair shafts can cause a serious problem: the exposure of all floors above the fire floor. In such a situation it is necessary to open skylights, roof, or bulkhead doors. But with extremely high buildings it is doubtful whether roof ventilation will do the job. As the products of combustion rise, the heat is gradually absorbed by the walls, floors, and furnishings. This heat loss reduces the buoyancy of the gases and stratification may occur. Stratification is when the smoke will not move higher or drop down, but simply settles to act as a cover for the gases below. This forms a barrier which retards the beneficial results of roof ventilation.

It is difficult to predict at what level stratification will occur, but it depends on these factors: the size of the fire, the amount of heat and smoke, the height and size of the shaft, the amount of roof ventilation, the

FIGURE 48. *These firemen are in grave danger. Fire is blowing out of top floor windows and roof. Note roof cornice beginning to fall. These are commonly light gauge sheet metal nailed to roof. If roof boards burn through, the entire cornice will fall endangering men below.*

FIGURE 49. *Showers of burning debris fall as cornice falls. Some protection is afforded by upper fire escape balcony which breaks the falling debris and partially shields the exposed men. These men should move in on the floor, at least until the debris stops falling.*

length of time the fire has burned, and the heat absorption characteristics of the shaft and other materials exposed to the traveling combustion products.

When stratification occurs, it is wise to ventilate by windows, doors, and with mechanical methods, in addition to roof ventilation.

Pier fires. Because of dense smoke build-up the danger of the fire spreading so rapidly that it may trap men, pier fires are extremely difficult — and dangerous — to ventilate. Ventilation will be effective if the roof can be opened, as well as the large cargo doors. But be careful of roof positions on piers. It is dangerous for men to attempt to ventilate pier roofs when the building is fairly well involved. In such cases it is better to use the powerful streams from fireboats to break skylights and force in the siding or break the cargo doors.

If you send men to the roof or they work in other precarious positions at pier fires, they should carry life belts and ropes as a means of escape.

Land companies may move along the stringpiece of the pier and open the huge cargo doors. If possible, open doors on both sides of the pier to create cross ventilation. A word of caution: men should work from the farthest point toward the shoreline. They should open the furthest door first, working toward land, or they may be cut off.

Pier fires can develop enormous amounts of smoke. Be sure to anticipate rapid involvement of the pier when fresh air is introduced by ventilation.

Ship fires. With ship fires ventilation is a highly specialized operation. The ship's construction and its ventilating system are of paramount importance. You must check with the ship's officers. There is no other type of

FIGURE 50. *Here you can see a faint outline of men still on fire escape as flaming debris and brands continue to fall.*

fire in which it is more important to check with the officials in charge — and be guided by their advice. It may be necessary to shut down the normal ventilation system. If ventilation is to be attempted you are generally limited to the following procedures:

1. Remove the hatch covers from the involved cargo holds.

2. Trim the ventilators; that is, turn the ventilating funnels away from the wind. Otherwise the wind may not only prevent the smoke from leaving, it might intensify the fire below by increasing the draft.

3. Some older ships have skylights over their engine rooms which could be used to vent such area in case of fire.

4. Use large smoke ejectors.

5. Cut holes in the decks and sides of the ship to ventilate heat and smoke — also for stream penetration. If early strategy dictates the use of smothering agents, then ventila-

tion must not be attempted in the areas of total flooding with inert gases.

Mechanical ventilation

When you encounter a fire with smoke of low-heat intensity, natural ventilation is not effective. In some fires natural ventilation is insufficient to do the job quickly enough. In such cases you must rely on mechanical aids. There are two types of forced, or mechanical ventilation: (1) The use of water sprays with good velocity (fog streams), and (2) fans.

When to use mechanical ventilation. There are several factors to consider in determining whether to use mechanical means of ventilation. Consider the following:

1. Type of structure. The structure may not be suitable for natural ventilation for one of these reasons: (a) The lack of exterior or overhead openings, or other means of ventilation. (b) The lack of shafts or other vertical arteries. (c) Lateral ventilation may not be possible or practical using the normal methods. (d) Because of the building's construction, it may be hazardous to open walls or roof.

2. Exposures. When natural ventilation would expose adjoining structures. If venting were handled in the normal way, it might involve a nearby structure such as a hospital.

3. In cellars, subways, tunnels, or ships.

4. Life hazard. Where, because of life hazard, normal ventilation would be inadequate.

5. Where there is a dangerous accumulation of toxic gases or fumes, even though there may be no fire — in tunnels, wells, or subways, for example.

6. In windowless buildings. The so-called windowless buildings normally rely on mechanical means to circulate air from the heating or air-conditioning systems. During a fire this system may be shut down automatically or fail. In that case there would be no other way of moving the heat, smoke, and gases other than the fire department's mechanical ventilating methods.

Fog streams for ventilation. For practical reasons, fog streams are not often used for

FIGURE 51. *If these firemen had vented as they went up, they might have been caught in the holocaust on the floor above. They are working properly, venting as they work their way back to safety.*

ventilation in the fire service. They require manpower and water which are better used for other purposes in the emergency stages of a fire.

Once the fire is completely controlled the picture changes. Fog streams are efficient movers of air and smoke. For maximum effect the fog stream should be directed from inside the room — a few feet from the window opening through which the smoke is to be discharged. Try for a fog pattern which will cover as much of the window opening as possible. The closer you move up to the window with the nozzle, the less smoke you will move because as you move close, more of the fog pattern will move outside the window.

Regardless of fog nozzle positioning, the water as it leaves the window opening will create sufficient air currents to pull the smoke outward. But there are problems to anticipate. Ask yourself these questions:

1. Will water runoff damage the exterior areas?

2. Will there be a serious ice buildup in cold weather?

3. Will the water runoff (with nozzle inside the room) do damage?

4. Can you spare the manpower needed to man the nozzle?

Fans for ventilation. Fans in use range from the common 16-inch-square unit to giant size ones. Most are powered by electricity, some by gasoline motors. Some of the large departments have motorized vehicles designed to power huge suction fans.

Fans have been used not only to exhaust smoke but to force air into a structure. The latter method is particularly effective in below-grade areas such as tunnels or shafts. They provide an air supply which otherwise would be deficient in oxygen. In such use particular care must be taken so the air intake for the fan is not near any source of contaminated air, such as an engine exhaust. You may force a dilute mixture of poisonous carbon monoxide into the critical areas.

Whenever you use powered fans to create air movement (and this is the purpose of ventilation) whether to pull smoke out or force air in, remember that you may intensify the fire, pull poisonous gases into adjacent areas, or cause a backdraft or smoke explosion. At times two or more fans are used to create a push-pull effect. This may reverse the normal ventilation pattern in which smoke is leaving the structure, though slowly, through the roof openings. The smoke may be pulled back down into the building and drive the firemen out or precipitate the dreaded back draft or smoke explosion.

Smoke explosion caused by improper ventilation. Smoke explosion or back draft is essentially the instant burning of an explosive mixture of heated air, smoke, and gases which flashes back through openings around the fire area such as doors and windows.

As with fire, the three ingredients needed for smoke explosion are heat, oxygen, and a combustible gas or dust. Some fires progress through three stages. The first is the so-called incipient smoldering stage which becomes a small free-burning fire. In the second stage, as the fire grows it spreads, generating great amounts of heat and rapidly moving air currents. These currents carry the heated smoke and gases throughout the building. The heat breaks windows, allowing a continuous supply of fresh air to feed the fire. As with any free-burning fire, there is no chance of smoke explosion yet.

The third stage is reached if the fire continues to burn without venting itself to the outer air as it did in Stage 2. Now the fire slows because it has used up most of the free oxygen in the surrounding atmosphere. But the destructive heat begins to transfer itself to the contents, walls, floors, and ceilings. It distills off gases from all carbonaceous materials — gases which are readily combustible. These are added to the free carbon monoxide resulting from the incomplete combustion. All that is missing now is available oxygen.

The oxygen necessary for the formation of an explosive mixture is supplied in several ways. It may be introduced into the area through windows or doors, when they are opened in the course of firefighting operations. The fire also may burn through to the outer air after a long period of smoldering. When a fresh supply of oxygen is admitted into the fire area, it mixes with the flammable gases present.

The source of ignition may be from a spark or static electricity but it usually comes from the heat of the fire. Remember, in the third stage the heat was absorbed by the surrounding structure and its contents. There also will be deep-seated glowing embers. Ignition may result from either of these, or from a combination of the two. There are cases on record where conditions were such that the flammable gases coming from holes cut in the roof for ventilation burned with a torch-like flame above the roof without scorching the roof beams below. This was because two of the three necessary factors needed for combustion were present and the third, oxygen, was added as the escaping hot gases mixed with air above the roof openings. (See Figures 52 and 53.)

Most common combustible gases at fires have a wide explosive range. Natural gas explosive range is from 5 percent to 13.5 percent (by volume in air), hydrogen is from 4

FIGURE 52. *Hot gases ignited far above the fire building. This is because these gases were too "rich" to ignite below. They needed oxygen. As the gases rose there was a mixing with the oxygen and when the proper mixture was reached, ignition occurred. No flame was needed because the gases were at or above their ignition temperature.*

FIGURE 53. *Note the ball of flame at the left and in front of the elevating platform basket. This is the same phenomenon as in Figure 52. Ignition occurred harmlessly above the building in open air. This is because the roof was opened and the hot gases could get out via the roof opening. Had the roof been closed and the entrance forced at lower levels there may have been a reversal of flow of gases and the ignition would have been in the building.*

63

FIGURE 54. *Smoke appears to be drawing back into the opening at lower left (probably a loading platform). This indicates a reversal of the heated gases. The scene may be set for a back draft.*

percent to 74 percent, and carbon monoxide is from 12.5 to 74 percent. A sampling of gases at fires shows sufficiently wide variation between the lower and upper explosive ranges to indicate the ready explosive potential.

The natural movement of heated gas is upward. But suppose the gas cannot get out at the top of a structure. It will mushroom on the upper floors. Remember these are heated, combustible gases. While this is occurring, fresh air is coming in along the floor toward the fire. The heated gases have begun to circulate. If they do so with enough movement to mix with the fresh air, there may be an explosion.

The reason such explosions are called back drafts is because the heated gases reverse their upward motion when they cannot get out. The incoming fresh air causes a reversal of the flow and this is the back-draft feature. This reversal of flow is what gives the familiar effect of smoke drawing backward toward the fire when a window or door is opened on the same level as the fire, just before a back draft occurs. It is the one brief warning we get that an explosion is about to take place.

When this happens one must instinctively and quickly take steps to avoid the blast — even if only to drop to the floor to allow the flaming gases to pass over you. (See Figure 54.) This is why it is so important to open at the top first to allow these heated combustible gases to escape — out and up — away from the interior of the building.

The greatest danger of back drafts accurs in fires in tightly closed places. While cellar fires and storage warehouses constitute the most probable danger areas, back drafts may occur in any structure if the conditions are right. Assume a hypothetical fire. A fire in a storage warehouse has gone from the First Stage to the Third Stage. It has distilled off the gases from the structure and contents. Heat has been absorbed as explained previously. The area is filled with hot, combustible gases beginning to swell around in convection currents.

Incoming units force entrance at the street level. Some smoke pours out at the top of the doorway; cool fresh air enters at floor level and begins to mix with the heated combustion products. This counter current of air sweeps toward the fire carrying unburnt combustible gases with it. When the mixture reaches the edge of the glowing embers, there will be an explosion and the entire area will burst into flame.

The proper procedure is to open up directly over the fire. This allows the hot gases to move upward through the opening and away from the fire. The counter current of air flowing downward toward the fire serves only to brighten the flames but will not cause a back draft. The opening acts as an inlet for air and an outlet for hot smoke and gases.

Summary on ventilation

In a review of ventilation principles and procedures there are some obvious positive general benefits:

1. There is less chance of firemen being overcome by toxic smoke and gases.

2. Damage from smoke, fire, and water is lessened.

3. There is less danger of a smoke explosion

4. Search and rescue procedures are facilitated.

5. Out-of-service time for companies is reduced.

To sum up this most important phase of firefighting activities, the following operational techniques and precautions should be observed:

1. Never ventilate at a location where it will endanger people by cutting off their escape route or subject them to heavy combustion products.

2. Never ventilate where it would spread fire unless a charged line is ready to combat such spread.

3. Be particularly careful that window ventilation does not allow fire to lap out and into the floor above.

4. To avoid smoke and heat blowing into your face after opening a roof, work with the wind at your back.

5. One large hole cut in a roof or floor is preferable to several smaller openings.

6. Avoid cutting floors or roofs if open-

ing windows, skylights, or doors will suffice.

7. Be careful that cutting operations do not endanger structural stability. Fire may have already weakened ceiling and floor joists.

8. Don't cut roofs in one- or two-story dwellings. This is rarely necessary and may serve to pull fire into the sidewalls and on up to the attic.

9. Remember that ventilation creates a draft effect and may pull fire either vertically or horizontally.

10. Don't ventilate through the fire curtain in a proscenium wall in a theatre. You may involve the auditorium area in heat and smoke.

11. Don't ventilate through fire doors.

12. Don't open up for ventilation below firemen or people on fire escapes.

13. Delay opening up a building at street level until the roof has been opened if the building is tightly closed, or if the fire has been burning for some time. In such a situation there is a possibility of a back draft. Opening the roof will allow most of the dangerous gases to escape and help prevent a smoke explosion.

14. If there is a possibility of heavier-than-air gases being present, create a cross-vent at floors and open above the fire.

15. With cocklofts, open over hot spots or at the highest point.

16. Remove skylights or ornamental glass at the top to ventilate.

17. With store show windows, break the upper light windows to ventilate because these windows are smaller and of lightweight glass, while the lower ones are usually thick plate glass. The upper windows will usually ventilate the store over the showcase. Break the plate glass window in extreme conditions and open the rear sash of the show window. You need have no qualms about breaking heat-stained or cracked plate glass since it has no salvage value.

18. Use smoke ejectors in such cases as cellar fires, manholes, transformer vaults, and sewers. Reverse the ejector if there is a deficiency of oxygen to pump fresh air into the area.

General Fire Problems

Chapter 7

Fires in concealed spaces

CONCEALED fires are a problem because they travel out of sight and out of effective reach of the fire department. In many cases the occupant of the building is unaware it is burning until the fire bursts out into sight. It is difficult to decide where the fire originates, where it is traveling, and the extent of the involvement. Inexperienced or poorly trained personnel are unable to determine where the hidden fire is. They fear undue criticism should they open a wall or ceiling and find that no fire has involved the area. As a result they fail to open suspected hidden spaces, and this often results in the fire's going beyond control.

If you are honest with yourself, you'll admit that these fires at times will scare the pants off you — but don't panic. Give yourself time to think. Here are some basics you should remember: Smoke pushing out of upper floors is no guarantee that fire has extended to them. Another is that, as a rule, smoke from an upper-floor fire will not fill the lower floors. When a building is heavily charged with smoke from bottom to top, the chances are you have a cellar fire.

It is particularly important where wood lath has been used for a plaster base to open any suspicious places. Wood lath is highly susceptible to ignition by sparks, and once ignited it will continue to burn because the wood is soft with a rough splintery surface, exposing hundreds of little wooden slivers for easy ignition.

What are concealed spaces?

The concealed spaces you will encounter in firefighting can be listed under the following categories:

1. Attics (not occupied as living or working quarters).
2. Cocklofts (hanging ceiling space).
3. Chimneys.
4. Ductwork.
5. Pipe chases, shafts.
6. Partitions.
7. Framed out spaces.
8. Nonfire-stopped floor joists.

Where do concealed fires start?

Fires may originate in concealed spaces from a number of sources. Here are some causes:

1. Electric shorts or overheated wiring (See Figure 55).
2. Long-time charring of wood in too close contact with chimneys, steam pipes, or other heat-producing surfaces (See Figure 56).

Fires may originate outside and penetrate inside these concealed spaces by:

1. Burning through walls into partitions. (See Figure 57).
2. Burning through ceilings into hanging ceiling space above stores (See Figure 58).
3. Burning through floors into horizontal run of floor joists (See Figure 59).
4. A stair fire burning into the soffit (underside) of the stairs above and "running"

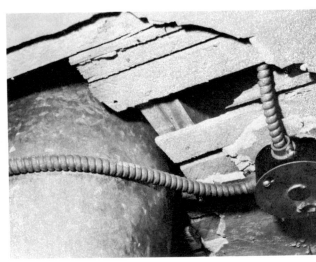

FIGURE 55. *Fire can extend into concealed spaces from an electric short circuit. Picture at left is an example of an electric box shorting out inside a wood lath partition. (For illustrative purposes lath and plaster wall is not shown on nearest side.)*

Picture at right is another example. Exposed wood lath and space around duct would allow fire to race upstairs. Fire may burn inside wall for a considerable length of time before it breaks out.

the underside of these stairs (See Figure 60).

5. Dumbwaiter shaft fires where fire and sparks enter side walls of shaft and hanging ceilings by openings around BX cables or conduits. These shafts are commonly used by repairmen to run electric cables and piping to apartments on different floors.

6. Heating, ventilation, and air-conditioning ducts which may carry fire, sparks, and heated gases (See Figures 61 to 63).

7. Heat conduction along pipes (See Figures 64 to 67).

8. Fire and sparks getting into openings around pipe risers, electric fixtures, holes in ceiling, etc. (See Figure 68).

9. Sparks and brands moving into attics by way of louvered openings (See Figure 69).

10. Grass and brush fires involving wooden siding and getting into side walls.

Detecting concealed fires

There are four techniques for detecting concealed fires: touch, sight, smell, and hearing. Remember, it is always good practice to have a charged line ready before opening up a concealed space.

Touch. Feel the suspected area with your bare hand, and if the wall is uncomfortably warm open it. Remember that a plaster wall can be quite hot to the touch and still not have fire behind it. Experience is the guide here, but if in doubt put a small hole in the suspected area.

Sight. Look for seepage of smoke from suspect areas or above them. Watch carefully for sparks dropping and trace these areas. See if there are burned spots on wallpaper or blistered paint on walls. On roofs look for melting tar, dry or steaming spots on wet surfaces, melted snow patches where the rest of the roof is still covered with snow.

Smell. Smoke from a live fire will have a different smell than trapped or "dead" smoke. This means that seepage of smoke from a suspected area will not always indicate fire. The smoke may have seeped up from a fire below and been slow to dissipate via cracks, crevices, etc. Here again, you will need experience. Try to observe this difference at fires. Again, when in doubt open up.

Hearing. Listen carefully for sounds of crackling, hissing, and a popping noise.

If a wall or ceiling has been opened and no fire is revealed, the fireman should not

FIGURE 56. *Defective chimney can ignite wood 2x4, even though only charring occurred for a long* *period of time. (Wall is shown without lath and plaster covering on near side.)*

FIGURE 57. *Fires can start in concealed spaces because of carelessness while burning paint from wooden siding with a torch. Fire can run horizontally or vertically in voids behind the wall for a* *considerable length of time before being detected. When reporting to a fire of this type, officers should check all concealed spaces carefully to be sure fire is not traveling in these spaces.*

FIGURE 58. *Cutaway drawing shows how fire in one store can move through hanging ceiling space (arrow) and spread laterally into other stores — often unknown to firemen.*

FIGURE 59. *Fire burning through floors from either above or below can run floor joists (see arrows) till it meets partitions. Then it can extend vertically.*

FIGURE 60. *Fire in closet can move into stair soffit (underside of stairs) and run this space.*

FIGURE 61. *In a cellar fire, the main heating duct carried enough heat to branch duct to cause ignition in the partition.*

FIGURE 62. *Fire in the partition (see Figure 61) then traveled in the space around the duct to involve the floor above.*

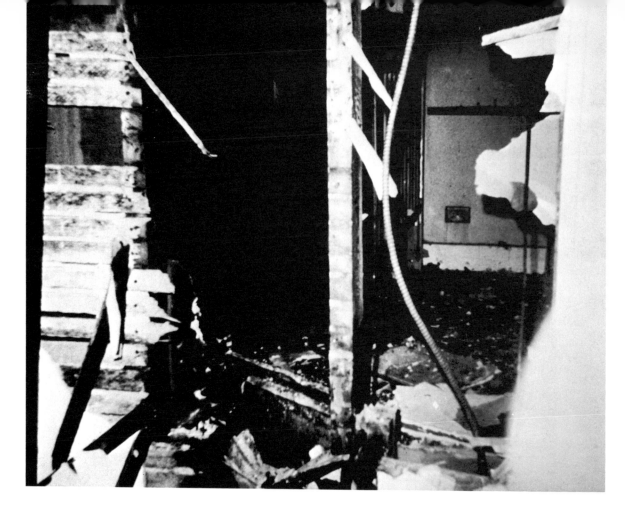

FIGURE 63 (Above). *Heat rising from a wall register through metal ducts ignited a baby crib eight feet away from the hot air register.*

FIGURE 64 (Right). *Short circuit inside an electric conduit can heat the metal enough to cause ignition of combustible surfaces inside a wall.*

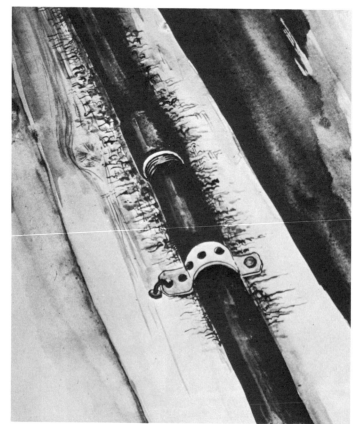

be censured, inhibiting his action at a future fire. He may be afraid to open up for fear of being penalized. It is easier to repair a small hole found to have been unnecessary than to rebuild the entire structure because it burned down.

Now let us take the nine types of concealed spaces and discuss the problems of each in detail.

Attic fires

Attics are generally unfinished and may be without flooring. Sometimes they may have a center catwalk of boards if there is no flooring. It will be easy in heavy smoke conditions to wander off this walk and fall through to the floor below — or certainly fall part-way through the ceiling. Entry to such attics will be by way of a short ladder to a scuttle cover, so it is important to bring a short ladder in with you rather than have to go back to the truck to get it.

Attics are difficult to ventilate. There usually is a louver at each gable end or if the attic is large there may be windows instead of louvers. As a rule it is not necessary to cut the roof.

Bring your line inside the building and get into the attic from the inside using a 1½-inch line with a fog nozzle. Be careful of indiscriminate use of water. It will do great damage below.

The use of a bayonet or piercing nozzle at the end of a 1½-inch line pushed through the ceiling into the attic space will do excellent work. Because the area is confined, the fog will turn to steam and permeate the attic readily and extinguish most of the fire with little water. Well-involved attic fires have been extinguished by this technique with as little as 20 gallons of water.

To understand why this is possible, consider a typical attic. The average structural fire gives off about 3,000 Btu's per square foot per minute. In a frame attic the situation would be different in that the entire interior is wood and exposed to the fire. Assume the attic is not occupied or used for storage space. For example, an attic in the average two-story dwelling is about 25x40

feet. Its floor space would be 1,000 square feet. Assume the attic peak to be 8 feet above the floor. The average height would then be 4 feet. This multiplied by 1,000 square feet gives us 4,000 cubic feet of space. The average weight per square foot of lumber in the home is about three pounds. Wood gives off about 8,000 Btu's per pound when completely consumed. Let us calculate the number of square feet of total attic surface. The floor has 1,000 square feet. Now we have two sides (the roof boards from the floor to the roof peak). With the peak 8 feet high this gives us two sides each about 15x40 feet. The 15-foot figure is computed by squaring half of the base (attic floor) of 25 feet; squaring the height; adding the sum of the squares and extracting the square root of this sum to give us the hypotenuse. We are seeking the hypotenuse of a right-angle triangle. Now we can compute the number of square feet of burning surface. It would be 12.5x40 + 15x40x2 (both sides). This equals 2,200 square feet. Each square foot weighs 3 pounds. Each pound totally consumed liberates 8,000 Btu's for a total of 6,600 pounds x 8,000 Btu's, or 52,800,000 Btu's. The 52,-800,000 Btu's would be liberated only if the attic were completely destroyed, and that would probably take one hour.

In practice this is most likely what would occur, however: It is fair to assume that a good fire department could extinguish this fire, or get it under control, in 10 minutes. This means the fire should be confined to the interior of the attic. This automatically cuts in half the total number of square feet of combustible surface attacked by the fire. Now we have 26,400,000 Btu's. However, we said we could control it in 10 minutes. This means only one-sixth of the Btu's would be liberated (it would take one hour to consume the entire attic). Therefore we take one-sixth of the 26,400,000. Thus 4,400,000 Btu's are liberated in the 10-minute free burn period.

One gallon of water completely vaporized absorbs nearly 10,000 Btu's. Divide this 10,-000 into the 4,400,000 and we find we need 440 gallons of water to handle this fire (about 2 minutes from the standard 2½-inch hose

FIGURE 65. *Electric heating wire wrapped around pipe (to keep water pipe from freezing in un-heated kitchen) caused ignition of wood surfaces which were in contact with the part of the pipe inside the wall.*

FIGURE 66. *The fire which was started by the electric heating wire extended inside wall to floor above. The wall under the sink on the floor above the origin of the fire has been opened to show how the fire traveled.*

line). Yet we have another advantage going if we handle this fire properly. Water turned to steam expands about 1,600 times. Each gallon of water expands into about 220 cubic feet of steam. Divide 220 into the 4,000 cubic feet of attic space and we get about 18 gallons of water needed to inert the attic space. This is possible using a piercing nozzle. Of course it will be necessary to get into the attic after control is established to overhaul and mop up.

Where conditions are abnormally severe, it may be necessary to take a line of 1½-inch hose and operate momentarily through the louver or window into the attic and cool it down. As soon as this has accomplished its objective, shut down the line to restore the natural path of ventilation through the window. Then move the inside line into the attic.

If the roof has to be cut, make one large hole high on the roof as near to the ridge beam as possible. Don't forget to cover the roof to keep out the weather until the roof can be repaired. It would make little sense to do an efficient extinguishing job and let the elements ruin the house through a large unprotected hole in the roof.

One last word on this type of fire. It is fairly common practice in some areas when fire is coming through the roof to take the first line there. This is improper procedure. If fire has vented itself in this way it constitutes the most helpful single occurrence outside of final extinguishment. You would be able to penetrate the attic from the inside with less difficulty. Using a line from the roof is worse than useless. You would seal off the opening and stop the fire from coming out. It would then spread laterally throughout the attic and might even drive the men off the top floor. You can't extinguish a fire inside the attic from a roof position. The superficial extension to the shingles and roof structure can be controlled by a dash or two of water from below until it is time for the complete mopup. (See Figure 70.)

Cockloft or hanging ceiling fires

Cockloft is a term commonly used in fire department language to denote a blind space at the top of the structure in flat or truss-roofed buildings. This space exists between the finished ceiling you can see on the top floor and the underside of the roof sheathing.

FIGURE 67. *The fire (in Figure 66) then moved on up a diagonal channel into the attic.*

The depth of the cockloft may range from 12 inches to six feet or more.

Imagine one long building with only exterior walls and a roof. Now subdivide this building with walls to make separate buildings within the outer walls. These dividing walls are carried up only to the top-floor ceiling level, effectively separating the buildings from each other except for the roof space, which is open over the entire structure. If fire from below can enter this hanging ceiling (as it commonly does), it can spread out over the entire roof space, feeding on combustible wood joists, sheathing, and wood lath of the top-floor ceiling.

In effect, the fire can involve the entire row of buildings rapidly, presenting a unique problem to a fire department. Now they have to operate not only in the fire building but in the adjacent building as well. This means stretching additional hose lines to top floors of adjoining buildings rapidly enough to head off the moving fire. (See Figure 71.)

Don't panic if smoke is coming from several cornices in a row of buildings. This is not necessarily an indication that all roof

spaces are involved in fire; but it is a good indication that there may be no fire stop — or ineffective ones—between adjoining cornices, and such a condition must be investigated promptly.

While, generally speaking, cocklofts in hanging ceilings refer to the spaces between the top-floor ceiling and roof boards, the same problems created by such blind spaces can and do exist in other parts of structures.

Supermarkets generally feature trussed roof construction, frequently with roof spaces as deep as eight feet that may be used for dead storage of combustible materials.

Frequently old stores with high ceilings are remodeled by dropping the new ceiling below the old one, leaving a space between. In fact, in very old structures you may find two and three ceiling spaces above the finished ceiling you now see in the store! This type of alteration once caused the total destruction of a huge department store because the fire extended through the hanging ceiling spaces. The fire department properly pulled the ceiling to expose the fire travel, and hose lines extinguished the visible fire. What the fire department did not know was that there were two more concealed ceilings above this space. Fire entered the upper spaces, ran and extended via sidewalls, engulfing the entire structure before the fire department could expose the rest of the hidden fire.

When you suspect a fire has entered or is theatening to enter such concealed spaces, operational technique is to send a ladder company to the roof for examination and ventilation. The officer should advise the chief of his findings so proper line placement may be made to head off the fire. Where a cockloft fire is threatening to spread laterally, a large hole cut in the roof over the fire area will tend to draw up and centralize the fire.

Cellar nozzles used over the fire area by way of the hole in the roof have proven effective in many such conditions. For speed of operation, it is generally faster to expose a cockloft fire by pulling the ceiling below — provided charged lines are at hand. For this reason part of the ladder company is always dispatched with the engine company in such

FIGURE 68 (Right). *This drawing illustrates how sparks can get into the floors above a fire through openings around pipe risers.*

FIGURE 69 (Below). *Sparks from nearby trash burner can enter the attic through louvers or it can enter cellars through open windows. Sparks caught in cracks of clapboard siding can ignite it also.*

FIGURE 70. *Example of incorrect attack on attic fire. This line will have no effect on the fire within* —*except to prevent the fire from venting itself, creating a more difficult condition.*

cases. They can also force entrance for the engine company, should this be needed.

It is important to check adjoining buildings and to this extent: additional companies should be dispatched to buildings on each side of the fire and where necessary should open ceilings to determine whether fire has passed the party wall. Here again, engine companies should be in position with charged lines.

The use of the piercing nozzle for the cockloft fire has not found popular acceptance; yet it is the fastest way of getting water, in its most efficient form, into this concealed area with the least possible damage. It provides initial control of a fire that otherwise threatens to race faster than companies can open and apply water in the conventional manner. (See Figure 72.)

Officers of companies operating on roofs over cockloft fires should be aware that the roof may give way under them. If the roof begins to feel spongy or sags, firemen should back off. A safe route of retreat should always be available, either by an adjoining building, an aerial ladder, or an elevating platform. Men operating on roofs should carry life belts and ropes — and if at night should make sure of good lighting. One way of operating on a potentially dangerous roof is to have men work with ropes around them which are secured to the basket of the elevating platform. Another way is to lay a long portable ladder along the area where the men are operating. This bridges the weakened area, and, if the roof begins to give way the men can step onto the ladder for safety.

Chimney fires

There are two general types of chimneys: (1) inside — wholly contained within the building, and (2) outside — only one wall of the chimney is joined to the structure. Obviously, where a chimney is wholly contained within the structure there are four sides to be considered as possible exposure problems, as opposed to one side for the outside chimney.

Many firemen regard a chimney fire light-

FIGURE 71. *Fire in the clothing store at right builds up a smoke condition showing around the roof cornice. If operations are concentrated in this store, even if the roof or cornice is subsequently opened, it may be too late. Fire could have extended to the hanging ceiling space (cut-* *away area) over the adjoining stores. The officer in charge must always suspect this condition and check for such lateral involvement. Open the roof over the hot spot and check the stores on each side by opening a small hole in the ceiling. Always have charged lines ready in case fire shows.*

ly. This can be a serious mistake. It is true that most chimney fires are easy to handle or burn themselves out. But this is where chimneys have been built correctly, with mortar joints between the masonry units packed tightly and flue linings well cemented in place for the entire height of the chimney. There should be no combustible framing against the chimney wall.

When a chimney has been allowed to soot up it can catch fire. Large pieces of soot or sparks from the chimney fire fly out and settle on combustible roofs with the risk of starting additional fires. This is one reason you should always examine the roof area in a chimney fire.

Be careful about placing ladders against the part of the chimney above the roof. The chimney may not be capable of supporting the weight of a ladder and men. This part of

the chimney is unsupported and the mortar in it may have deteriorated.

The simplest way of handling a chimney fire is to let it burn itself out. This is readily done in most private dwellings, but first make sure you kill the fire in the stove, fireplace, or boiler. Examine the attic where the chimney passes through, and check the walls in contact with the course of the chimney for possible extension.

When the chimney is heavily sooted, it may be necessary to repeatedly lower and raise a chain fastened to the end of a rope to dislodge the burning soot. If this does not put the fire out, try discharging the contents of a dry powder extinguisher up the chimney from below. If this also fails, use a small amount of water from a fog nozzle into the chimney from below. The water should vaporize from the heat of the fire. The steam

80

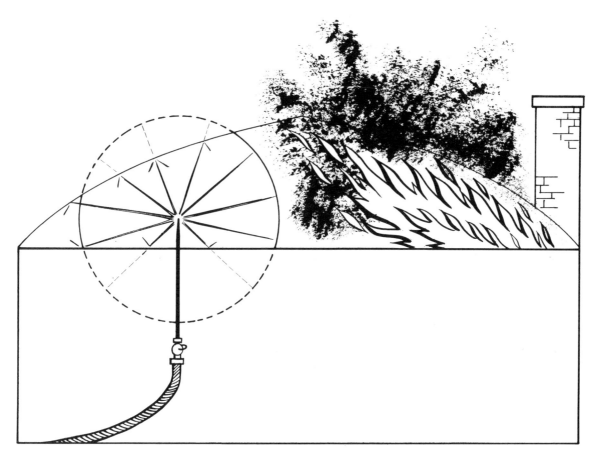

FIGURE 72. *Depending on the depth of the store, a piercing nozzle may achieve control in the roof area. Insert it in three or four places for 30 to 40 seconds at each location.*

carried up will extinguish the fire. If the steam does not carry high enough, the fog nozzle should be used at the top of the chimney. Again, use little water and only fog. Otherwise there is danger of cracking the chimney and doing water damage.

If the building is old or in the nature of an apartment house, carefully check all the walls along the course of the chimney. If there are cracks in the chimney, sparks and fire may have spread to sidewalls, under floors between joists, or to the cockloft. It is possible for very old chimneys in poor condition to allow fire to extend in several places. If these suspected spots are not opened, a serious fire can develop. (See Figure 73.)

Never use chemicals for removing or burning out soot from boilers or chimneys. Most of them are powerful oxidizing agents and develop dangerously hot fires inside the chimney; they also have been known to cause explosions. Salt is of questionable value as an extinguishing agent in chimney fires, though it is commonly used for such purposes.

Ductwork

Ductwork fires fall into three general groups: (1) grease ducts in restaurants; (2) heating, cooling, and ventilating ducts; and (3) transmission ducts (for removal of waste products by blower system to selected collection points).

Grease ducts in restaurants. These are usually short runs of duct, although sometimes they are extensive. They accumulate a heavy interior coating of grease which, if it catches fire, burns rapidly with a hot flame. The danger here is that the duct as it passes through ceilings or walls may be in contact with com-

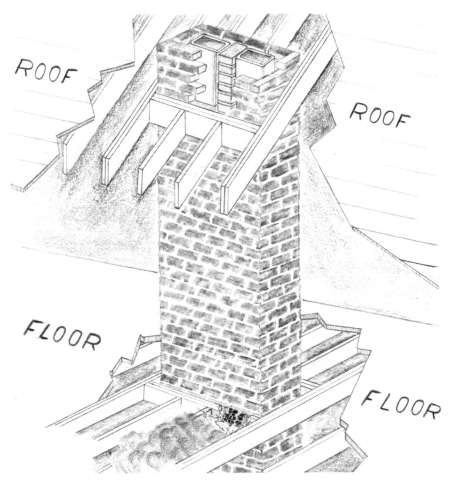

FIGURE 73. *A defective chimney can ignite wood framing and cause fire to spread to concealed spaces. Suspected spaces should be opened.*

bustible materials such as wood framing. Should the fire continue to burn, it may melt parts of the ductwork and release sparks, fire, and smoke into these concealed spaces.

Where the duct is well involved in fire and cannot be readily followed in its course through these hidden spaces, the officer in charge has quite a problem on his hands. He may have to open up a good deal of the walls and ceiling to insure that there is no fire outside the duct.

In operating at a fire of this kind, first shut down the blower which tends to speed up the fire. Try discharging the contents of a dry chemical extinguisher up the duct. If there is not sufficient draft in the duct to carry the powder all the way up, start the blower fan again (but for a short time only) to try and pull the powder through.

Another technique is to try small amounts of water from below — again using the same method of starting the fan for a very short period. Be careful in using water if there is a fryer on the counter below. This may contain boiling cooking oil. You can be seriously burned from the splattering oil. If some water sinks into the oil it turns immediately to steam. The oil slops over onto the gas burner below, starting another fire. If the water fog from below is not effective, try it from the point where the duct clears the building — at the roof or side wall.

While the extinguishing operations are going on it is advisable to have additional crews following the duct network and opening up where necessary. The men doing the opening should carry extinguishers with them to put out minor extensions of fire. It is not always practical to continually call for a line wherever openings are made, particularly if it

82

FIGURE 74. *Insulation has burned off a large air conditioning duct in the hanging ceiling space of* *a large store. Insulating materials on the outside or inside of ducts are sometimes combustible.*

covers an extensive area. The hose lines could not move fast enough and a small fire not promptly extinguished could extend by the time the hose line was brought up.

Heating, cooling, and ventilating ducts. These ducts run from the very simple system of short runs to the very extensive systems found in large multi-story or high-rise buildings. The least hazardous of these are the unit systems where the entire operating equipment is located in one room or supplies air to a single floor or area. The most hazardous are those where ducts branch off from a central station to supply many areas and floors.

A complicating factor in some systems is the employment of insulating materials inside or outside the ducts for insulation of noise or cold and heat. The insulation sometimes is combustible. (See Figure 74.)

Some additional problems to watch out for are these:

1. The fresh air intake may be located on an outside wall where it can pull in fire, sparks, and smoke from an outside source and circulate throughout the building.

2. The filters are often made of combustible materials and coated with a film of oil to trap dust and lint. Even where the filter is not combustible, the trapped dust, plus the lint and oil, provides combustible material for a fire.

Of course the major problems are associated with the hidden labyrinth of the ducts themselves. They circulate and discharge air by way of one duct network, then draw the air back by another set of ducts. Actually they are horizontal and vertical flues.

Here is a brief list of the firefighting problems uniquely associated with ducts:

1. The drafts created by the fans push

FIGURE 75 (Right). *Unused ventilating duct begins in classroom on street floor of large high school.*

FIGURE 76 (Below). *Duct runs side walls all the way to the attic where it joins large main duct in the huge frame attic. Ducts from other rooms (at rear) also lead into the large duct.*

FIGURE 77 (Below, right). *The large duct empties into the large combustible attic. Good practice dictates that all connecting ducts be tied together and continue on through the roof. As it is here, any fire, heat, or smoke entering the ductwork would be transmitted throughout the school. It would be an extremely difficult job for any fire department to trace the reason for such smoke distribution unless they were aware of this defect.*

air throughout the building. Any fire in the duct is intensified greatly.

2. Sometimes combustible linings are used in ducts for insulation or sound deadening.

3. Even though no actual fire may be circulated, smoke may be distributed and cause panic conditions.

4. There may be no automatic dampers or shutters which could cut off the involved areas, preventing the retransmission of smoke and heat.

5. The protection of fire doors is negated because the ducts go through from one fire area to another.

6. Even if the blowers are shut down, the ducts will still circulate the products of combustion to some extent.

7. Machinery rooms may be located on the roof or in the cellar. Lack of knowledge as to their location will cause delay in shutting down the system.

To give an idea of the extent of the duct problem, consider an old school building I inspected many years ago. It was a five-story building more than 50 years old, housing more than 1,500 students. The ventilating system, although no longer in use, was still in existence. Follow the network from the classrooms on the lowest floor (see Figure 75). This duct runs between the side walls, all the way up to the huge combustible attic where it turns at right angles to join the main duct (see Figure 76). Note the other branch ducts coming from other areas to join the main duct. The large (5x4-foot) main duct simply empties into the attic (see Figure 77).

If a fire starts in any room below, sparks, smoke, and heat could enter the branch duct, sweep up into the main duct, and spread throughout the school through the duct network. This main duct in the attic should have led on out through the roof. Then the problem would not have been as serious. This condition existed in a city with a paid fire department of more than 200 men. The school had been inspected regularly, but none had discovered this serious hazard.

Here is a summary of general operating techniques to keep in mind where ductwork is involved:

1. Shut the system down.

2. Ventilate.

3. Check all areas served by the duct network.

4. Large ducts may have clean-out openings through which it might be possible to examine interiors of ducts for fire spread.

5. If smoke is being drawn into the ducts by fire from the outside near the duct intake, seal off this intake with covers.

6. If fire is in the duct, use dry powder extinguishers.

7. If dry powder extinguishers fail to check the fire, use a fog nozzle sparingly.

8. Try to cut off fire spread by operating dampers if there are any.

9. Open up ceilings and side walls if necessary.

10. Check the roof.

11. Where the run of duct is not too long or high, discharging the contents of several large, dry powder extinguishers into the duct and starting the blower for a few minutes may pull the powder through the burning area and extinguish it.

Forced warm air duct systems in homes. Don't treat fires in homes with warm air systems lightly. Incipient fires or sparks may be pulled into the return ducts and recirculated via the distribution ducts to all parts of the house.

This is a particular hazard in older homes where the return ducts run wild. The term "run wild" means that an opening has been cut into the partition for an air intake grill. The 2x4 plate at the bottom of the partition (if one exists at all) was cut out to continue the flue effect. A metal connection is made here to the central return plenum. Now we have a continuous passage from the rooms to the heating plant via the inside of a *wood lath and plaster partition*. Visualize the sparks and fire being sucked into this return duct. Remember, too, that the air is being pulled by a powerful fan. (See Figures 78-79.)

Another common practice among heating engineers is to nail sheet metal to the underside of a pair of floor joists, converting this space into a return plenum. (See Figure 80.)

FIGURE 78. *This is an innocent looking wall grill on an air return duct (see Figure 79).*

FIGURE 79. *Remove the grill and wood lath is revealed. This is a return duct run wild — through a wood lath and plaster partition.*

Filters are not positive protection against circulation of the sparks and flame. While filters are not generally combustible, they do accumulate layers of grease, lint, and dust which form a mat over the filter. This mat under forced draft is combustible.

The same buildup takes place in the return duct system over the years. The heating plants often are run without the filters in place. As a result, the matted layer can build up to more than one inch in thickness.

The rise in temperature from the fire may not cause the thermostat to shut down the system, since the fire may be in a different room or floor and the temperature rise won't reach the thermostat. Even if it did, the thermostat would only shut down the burner. The blower would keep operating — in fact it is designed to operate independently of the burner to circulate the remaining heated air. It would continue to operate as long as heated air kept coming into the duct network. There is a high-limit control, but this might not be a sufficient safeguard. Such controls sometimes fail to operate. Even if the high limit control did function, the smoke

FIGURE 80. *A metal covering is nailed onto floor joists to form a return plenum. Here, metal has been pried away to reveal a thick matting of com-* *bustible dust and lint. Fire in the room above would be pulled into the side walls and the plenum by the blower in a hot air heating plant.*

FIGURE 81. *People may die even though no fire touches them. This cutaway drawing shows how deadly gases can rise through ducts to overcome* *people on floors above even though they are separated from the fire by fire-resistive construction. Always check thoroughly when ducts are involved.*

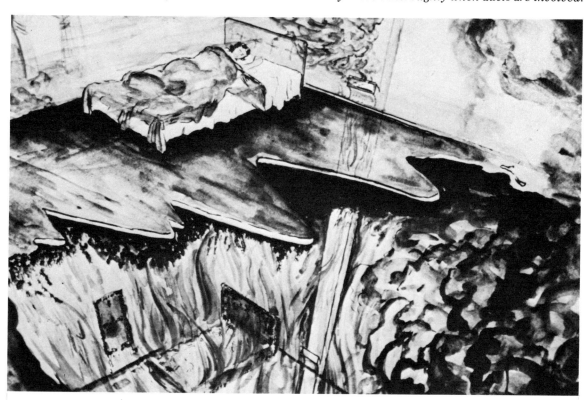

FIGURE 82. *This roof hopper is used as a collecting point for grinding and buffing operations. Material is recirculated to storage drums below for reuse later. If fire enters the hopper it may be necessary to remove the contents.*

FIGURE 83 (Below). *Use this cleanout door if it is necessary to remove contents. If fire enters hopper, don't use straight stream into contents. You may cause a dust explosion. Use fog streams under low pressure as contents are slowly emptied and wet down. Check ducts to see that no fire was carried down to collection points below.*

88

and carbon monoxide would still be circulated long before that happened. (See Figure 81.)

To show what can happen, this account of a fire on January 7, 1969, in Casablanca will serve as an example. The fire was in a fire-resistant children's home. Baby clothes were hung on a clothesline in the basement within eight inches of a metal duct connecting the oil-fired heating plant to the chimney. Air currents induced by the nearby air intake fan caused the clothes to be drawn against the hot duct. They ignited. The fire spread to the remainder of the laundry and entered the furnace air intake duct. The filters burned away rapidly. Burning clothing now readily entered the duct network and bits of burning cloth spewed out of the hot-air distribution ducts on the second floor. The ducts themselves began to burn (they were made of plastic composed of 90 percent flax and 10 percent urea-formaldehyde plastic binder).

The oil burner stopped feeding oil to the furnace because the thermostat was satisfied, but the fan continued to operate. It was designed to do so as long as the air temperature in the furnace stayed above 104° F.

Eighty-three older children on the second floor escaped down the single open staircase. There was no duct register opening into this stairway. Six babies were carried down but 13 remained in their cribs because the heat and smoke on the second floor prevented the employees from returning to the dormitory.

The fire department controlled the fire in 12 minutes, yet six babies died and several were badly burned.

This fire emphasizes the duct hazard. It shows that there can be a severe loss of life in a relatively small fire. At a recent fire in a two-story dwelling, heat rising through metal ducts was sufficient to ignite a baby crib eight feet away from the hot air register. Here then is a case where fire in a cellar created heat sufficient to move through a duct, which in itself had no fire, and ignite combustibles on upper floors. (See Figure 63.)

This is another reason why it is so important to check all areas of a building to make sure no fire has extended. Be particularly careful where ducts extend to parts of buildings cut off by fire walls. It is necessary to make complete examinations of such suspect areas because, while the fire will not as a rule pass through a fire door that has operated properly, sparks, heat, and smoke can get through by way of the connecting ducts.

The duct system in the average private house violates nearly every cardinal rule of good fire safety. It provides hidden passages for fire to travel throughout the structure regardless of the type of building materials used in construction. So if there are unexplained wisps of smoke, don't assume they will dissipate. Check them out thoroughly. Don't be in too much of a hurry to get back to quarters. Examine not only the central heating plant; also check each wall register for smoke, sparks, and heat.

If you are ever called upon to make recommendations with regard to forced or gravity air systems, consider these:

1. Filters and oil must be noncombustible.

2. Systems should have interlocks so arranged that they cannot be operated without the filter in place. This may help keep ducts cleaner.

3. Provide automatic dampers for each run of duct to individual rooms designed to shut off all circulation in the event of fire or smoke entering the ducts.

4. Provide smoke and heat detection instruments to: (a) shut blower in case of fire and smoke, and (b) activate the interior alarm.

5. Outlaw ducts "run wild." All ducts, both supply and return, should be made of tight-fitting, substantially constructed metalwork.

Transmission ducts. These are employed to remove waste products such as sawdust or grinding dust, and collect them in a hopper where they are stored until they can be removed or reused. Hoppers are often on the roof. There is not too much of a problem with these ducts, but a small fire around the machine can allow fire and sparks to enter the duct and be carried through it to the hopper. If firemen are not aware of this possibility, they extinguish the fire around the machine and ignore the fire which may be in the roof hopper.

FIGURE 84. *In this building being demolished a typical pipe chase (arrow) running from the basement to top floor is revealed. Fire and heat can easily travel these pipe chases — even in well-constructed buildings.*

Here again it is necessary to follow the course of the duct up to, and including, the collection point in or on the building. If the fire is in the hopper it may be necessary to clean out the contents while slowly wetting them down. (See Figure 82-83.)

Caution should be exercised in every occupancy where there is a combustible dust. Scattering the dust by careless overhauling or hose streams may cause a dust explosion.

Dust explosion. The phenomenon of a dust explosion is not well understood. No one would expect a piece of wood to explode. Yet this same wood ground into the form of dust can be violently explosive. This is true of any combustible material in a dust or powdered form. This, perhaps, is easier to understand if you look at an explosion as an extremely rapid combustion with liberation of enormous pressures. A piece of lumber one foot square by two inches thick will simply burn because only the surfaces are exposed to and mix with oxygen. But in a dust form every tiny dust particle can mix with oxygen and ignite, creating an explosively rapid combustion. These factors must be present to have a dust explosion:

1. A combustible dust.

2. A spark, flame, or temperature high enough to ignite the dust.

3. The dust must be properly mixed in the surrounding atmosphere.

4. There must not be too much humidity in the air.

The following factors also enter into the explosion equation. If the dust particle size is decreased it will:

1. Increase the explosion hazard.

2. Lower the ignition temperature needed to ignite the dust.

3. Increase the severity of the explosion.

Dust explosions cause flame propagation of more than 6,000 feet per second. Generally there are two explosions. The first is usually minor and serves to dislodge all dust from the area, sending it up in clouds which mix more completely with the atmosphere. This larger concentration of the dust is the setup for the secondary and more destructive explosion.

This is why you must operate with care in occupancies where you expect such combustible dusts to be present. Do not disturb the piles of combustible dust. Ventilate carefully. Open doors and windows to reduce the possibility of explosion and to reduce the pressure. Do not ventilate toward an exposed area such as a hospital, theatre, or other potential fire hazard. Use fog streams rather than straight streams to extinguish fire. Thoroughly soak suspected bins of smoldering dust before removing the material for overhaul.

Pipe chases and shafts

As with most concealed spaces, the technique consists of examining and opening suspicious areas. Usually such examination will not be difficult. The important point is to recognize that a problem can exist, that fire can extend into such arteries and move up very rapidly beyond sight and ready reach. To be sure, this requires some knowledge of building construction in order to be aware that such construction defects exist and where to look for them.

Sometimes, however, such pipe chases can pose a serious problem. These will be the ones found in the taller structures and, paradoxically, in the more fire-resistant buildings which have few hollow spaces between floors and walls. As a result the heat, gas, electricity, water and waste pipes require an invisible space. The vertical shaft, called a pipe chase, is the answer.

Somewhere in the structure one or more vertical shafts are built. These lifelines of the building run from the lowest subcellar to the highest floor — continuous from cellar to top floor. Except for the car, they resemble a miniature elevator shaft. If there were nothing to burn in these shafts the problem would be minimal. But often the steam pipes are covered with insulation. And in a "fireproof" building, who can object if the insulation is combustible? After all, what is there to burn? (See Figure 84.)

Pipe chases generally have openings at each floor level for service and repair purposes. The covers for these openings are often a thick piece of plywood or, at times,

FIGURE 85 (Above). *Large duct in hanging ceiling space goes through hole in fire stop.*

FIGURE 86 (Right). *Close-up of Figure 85 reveals space around duct. Fire can easily move through this opening.*

simply a louvered grill. If it was convenient for the architect or builder, they sometimes open into stair shafts. There is no standard location for these access panels. I have seen them in individual guest rooms, closets, washrooms. If pipe chases were vented at the roof with a large vent area, the problem would be greatly minimized. Usually they are not vented through the roof, and if they are the size of the vent is inadequate for ventilating a fire.

If a fire does get into such a pipe chase, the combustible gases build up at the top. The pressure buildup forces heat, sparks, and smoke out at every floor opening. It isn't long before the corridors and guest rooms become untenable. This, in part, was the problem contributing to the heavy loss of life in a Jacksonville, Fla., hotel in 1963.

Should you encounter such a fire, no matter how slight, treat it with respect. Get a man or two to the roof and see if you can enlarge the vent over the pipe shaft. Get your water as quickly as possible and drive a stream up the pipe chase. Don't worry about the fire below the floor you are on; the water will drop down the shaft and extinguish it. Check each floor thoroughly along the entire course of the pipe chase.

Probably the highest such fire occurred in the Empire State Building of New York City in 1962. The fire started on the 20th floor and extended up a pipe shaft to the 68th floor and communicated from the pipe shaft to two offices on the 65th and 66th floors.

The problems presented by this fire were enormous. The fire was difficult to find. Smoke and heat permeated the building and stream operation was hit-or-miss. It was necessary to force entrance into the various offices where fire had communicated or was suspected. The automatic elevators could not be controlled by the fire department. Anyone could press the elevator button and take control away. The handie-talkie radios were erratic in performance. The building switchboard could not handle all the phone calls. Even the standpipe phone was inadequate. Fortunately, the Empire State Building is remarkably fire-resistant and stable. (It resisted the impact of an airplane at the 78th and 79th floor levels in 1945.) The issue was never really in doubt, but imagine what could have happened had this building not been well-constructed. The possibilities are sobering.

Partition fires

Partition fires are becoming less of a problem with the advent of noncombustible walls — plaster bases such as rock lath and the use of large gypsum wall boards for interior finishes. In addition, new building codes require safer construction. Where combustible framing is used, proper fire-stopping methods are employed.

But there still are untold numbers of buildings where wood lath exists. Another cause of fire spread in partitions are the openings made by plumbers and electricians to run piping and cables. Whether or not proper fire stopping has been provided, this can present a problem. Fire stopping may be negated by the many holes cut by the various building tradesmen in their initial installation or later remodeling. (See Figures 85-89.)

The fact that a section or sections of a partition are warm — even if it is burning hot when you hold your hand against it — does not always indicate a fire there. Heat may be present from a fire below, passing into the partition through small openings. Although the heat may be high enough to cause the combustible material to burn, lack of oxygen in the confined area may have prevented fire from starting. It would be prudent, however, to have such a suspected partition opened up. Make sure a charged hose line is present before you open the wall.

It is true that needless damage is sometimes done by opening a wall when it isn't necessary. But if an experienced fireman is doubtful of the need to open the wall, it is no longer wise to be concerned solely about the damage. The risk is too great. Don't take a chance. Open it. In too many instances inexperienced firemen hesitate to put the hole in a wall or ceiling for fear of unjust criticism. The result is severe fire spread and loss of life. No seasoned fire officer should consider leaving a suspect area without being sure there is no hidden fire inside the wall.

FIGURE 87 (Above). *Wooden 2x6 is cut away where vent stack makes bend to go into attic and then on through roof. If fire enters this partition there is nothing to prevent fire from involving the attic of this large apartment building.*

FIGURE 88 (Above, right). *Looking down toward floor where the soil line passes up through floor. This opening would allow fire to run the partition.*

FIGURE 89 (Right). *Large void behind a clothes closet was used for this soil line. Fire moved up this space to the floor above.*

FIGURE 90. *This hole was opened because the blistering paint was evidence that there was fire traveling through the partition. The added oxygen resulted in the fire roaring out of the hole, soon involving the paint on the ceiling. This was a training fire in an abandoned building. Normally a partition should not be opened until a charged line is ready.*

Such a precaution is urgent because a building that might rekindle is usually more vulnerable to fire. There are several reasons for this. Some of the walls and ceilings may have been opened, exposing part of the wood lath. Protective devices such as sprinklers may have been turned off. It is difficult for people, who may have reoccupied the building, to determine the difference between fresh smoke and the odor from the original fire. They may hesitate to call the fire department again.

If the fire has taken place in or around a bathroom or kitchen, check thoroughly on the possibility of fire having entered these partitions. These rooms are vulnerable because of soil lines and vent pipes. There usually are large spaces around these soil lines and vent pipes, and they continue up through the roof. If you are careless in checking this out, a fire on the first floor could extend to the attic or hanging ceiling without your being aware of it until too late. (See Figures 87-90).

You can sometimes open a partition without visual damage. Remove the baseboard and put a small hole in the partition. If you see no fire, renail the baseboard and no repairs are necessary. If you see fire or sparks, open the wall. The next hole should be on the side wall, just below ceiling level.

Another technique to minimize structural damage is to open a partition from the side which will cause least damage. Consider an expensive panelled living room wall. The other side of the wall is a bedroom with dry

FIGURE 91 (Right). *The head of a piercing nozzle. In use the tool is shoved through the ceiling and water is applied for about 30 to 40 seconds. This particular nozzle flows about 50 gpm at 100 psi at the tip. It may be used in side walls or through the door panels in a well involved room without having to open the door. It can also be used on fires such as peat bogs and garbage dumps. First push the nozzle about a foot down then start the water. Now slowly work the pipe all the way down.*

FIGURE 92 (Below). *This type of piercing nozzle produces the fog pattern shown in this picture. It has its own shut-off valve. Piercing nozzles are easily made in a fire department shop. The combination of a standard breakaway nozzle and the piercing nozzle is an ideal tool for fighting hidden fires. If the piercing nozzle is needed there is no need to shut down to make the change. Simply remove the breakaway tip, screw on the piercing nozzle and go to work. If after control is established you wish to revert back to the conventional nozzle, unscrew the piercing nozzle and replace the regular tip.*

FIGURE 93. *Inserting a piercing nozzle into the blind space under a stairway will achieve rapid control of a fire in such spaces. It will still be necessary to open the space for overhaul.*

wall construction. Open the dry wall side which is readily patched.

Remember, a small glowing fire in wood lath can break out into rapid combustion when it gets sufficient air. Make sure your charged line is ready before you open the wall. (See Figure 90.)

The piercing nozzle is an excellent tool for this kind of fire. Just be sure the nozzle is not driven entirely through the partition, otherwise you will only be getting water into the adjoining room and doing water damage. (See Figures 91-93.)

Few fires cause more of a rekindle nightmare than the wood lath and plaster partition fire. Wood lath is made of cheap, unfinished spruce. The wood has a rough, splintery appearance. Hundreds of tiny slivers stick out, ready to catch any flying spark. From the builder's standpoint, this roughness is desirable because it holds plaster better than

a smooth surface. But this means it will also hold sparks and will glow for long periods. The only sure way to determine whether fire exists in a partition is to open it.

Where fire damage has been extensive, excessive overhauling to insure complete extinguishment is frequently resorted to. Sometimes this results in excessive structural and water damage. It also ties up the companies for long periods. It is often more prudent to let one or two men with a line of 1½-inch hose connected to the hydrant stand guard for several hours or overnight.

Many chief officers frown on the use of such watch lines. They feel it is a reflection on their own ability to determine whether the fire is completely out. To be sure that the fire is out and there will be no rekindle, they resort to excessive opening up and washdown. It is true this will insure an early return of all personnel and apparatus to quarters and a watch line will not be required. But the amount of additional structural and water damage required leaves the wisdom of such operations open to question.

Framed-out spaces

Often a building contractor or carpenter, in order to eliminate odd angles of wall or to conceal old piping, wiring, cracked interior walls, or to close off unused closets or fireplaces, will frame out around such objectionable features to make a smooth, straight, finished wall. These are vulnerable concealed spaces.

Generally, framed-out spaces present the same problems as partition fires. The fire is hidden, difficult to trace, and may extend vertically and laterally to involve the entire structure. The essential difference here is that such framed-out spaces tend to be larger than the partition; they are also frequent-

ly found under wooden stairs. In this location they dangerously expose and involve the main passageway up and down the building. Use the same operating techniques as with partition fires.

Other such spaces are these: framing around windows, doors, beams, columns, and furred out walls.

Spaces around windows and doors. When a carpenter frames out around a door or window, he always allows some space between the 2x4's and the actual door or window frame so he can square the door or window in the rough opening. He wedges the finished frame to the 2x4 with tapered wooden shingles, nailing through the frame and shingles into the 2x4. The open space is closed off with decorative trim, nailed across the door or window frame. In some older buildings the 2x4 openings continue on up

FIGURE 94. *Soil line recesses were provided in this exterior brick wall (arrows). The fact that there is a solid brick wall is no guarantee it does not have concealed spaces within as this wall did.*

FIGURE 95. *There are no fire stops in the horizontal run of these floor joists. Fire entering here could cross the partition and involve adjacent rooms. Duct (upper left) can carry combustion products from one area to another negating fire stops even if they existed.*

from floor to floor (balloon construction) and if fire enters around such door or window, it can run from floor to floor. Another type of older construction has sliding doors to separate the living and dining rooms. These doors slide into a recess at the side. Often such recesses are not fire-stopped at the top.

Beams and columns. Again, to close off these structural members, the carpenter frames out around them leaving a hollow space in which fire can travel — either vertically or horizontally. The fire officer must be alert, particularly where such false framing intercepts walls, floors, or ceilings. Fire traveling in such false spaces may extend to these other areas. The rule: if in doubt, open such spaces for examination.

Furred out walls. While not a common cause of fire spread, furred out walls are

worth mentioning. The inexperienced fire officer can be badly fooled. He sees a brick or other solid masonry wall on the outside and a plaster wall on the inside. The assumption: there is nothing to burn and no way for fire to communicate. Actually there is a space between the outside masonry wall and the inside finish. Such inside finishes are never applied directly to an outside masonry wall because if they were the dampness would affect the inside finish. The interior face of the masonry wall is furred out with wooden strips nailed directly to the masonry. Over these furring strips may be applied combustible insulation in the form of sugar cane compressed fibreboard. The interior wall finish is then applied. The point is this: there is generally a hollow space between the inside wall and the outside wall where fire can enter and travel.

While not commonly found, occasionally

masonry walls are furred out sufficiently to allow soil lines to run in such spaces. In some cases the brick wall may have recesses built in to carry such soil lines. (See Figure 94.)

Nonfire-stopped floor joists

Floor joists are potential flues. Fire can run between the joists, feeding on the wood lath of the ceiling and sides of the floor joists. Fire continues on until stopped by either a noncombustible structural member (such as fire-stopping) or the use of hose streams. Fire officers should be careful when they sus-pect fire may have entered such spaces by burning through floors or ceilings, or from sparks dropping in from pipe recesses.

The fire officer should be particularly care-ful when the floor joists run crosswise over partitions or across common dividing walls such as in cellars. Here the fire may travel from apartment to apartment, or from one building to another. Fire running the floor joists and crossing over combustible parti-tions may involve such partitions by dropping sparks and embers into openings. (See Fig-ure 95.)

Chapter 8

Structural collapse

BUILDINGS COLLAPSE because floors or roofs drop as a result of failure of the structural components or from explosions that cause them to fail. Many of these failures result from architectural faults which are built in at the drawing board. There are five major faults to watch out for.

Five design causes of structural collapse

Probably the worst architectural fault, and certainly the one responsible for the greatest loss of life in buildings, is the unprotected vertical opening. By this I refer to open stair shafts, elevators, light and vent shafts, pipe chases, etc. This basic fault allows a fire on the lower floor to expose all floors above. The combustion products sweep up and involve all areas of the building. Not only are people overcome, but the normal means of exit from the building are cut off.

Next in line for dubious honor is the large open floor area; the unprotected horizontal floor areas without physical barriers to fire, heat, and smoke. The entire floor area is subjected to the action of a single fire which will fill the entire floor with combustion products. There is nothing to block the path of the fire. Such areas tend to increase the draft effect, while adding combustible stock to help feed the fire. The floor soon becomes one vast sea of flame. Firemen cannot move in against such heat. They can only use hose streams through doors, halls, or windows. If the floor area is large enough, such streams cannot reach the center of the building and therefore cannot extinguish the fire. Probably the outstanding example of this was the fire in Livonia, Mich., in 1953. This was a fire in one building without dividing walls with an area 1,860 feet by 415 feet. The building was totally destroyed.

Third in line must be unprotected metal structural members. This was discussed in a previous chapter.

Fourth would be alterations in building occupancy — from a light floor load to excessive floor loads when the building is not designed for heavy floor loads. In such alterations, structural supports may be eliminated to gain greater usable floor space. Vibrational stresses from newly installed heavy machinery set up motions in the building it was never meant to take. This vibration works continually through the years to weaken the structure.

Last would be an occupancy with a fire load far greater than the building was designed for.

There are many more factors which can, and do, enter into the picture. But the five

FIGURE 96. *Fire-cut beam will help to prevent wall collapse. As the fire-cut beam (left) burns through and drops, the angle cut will allow it to release from its resting place without pulling the wall down. As the old type beam twists from its resting place it may cause the wall to collapse.*

FIGURE 97. *Sockets in wall where joists were anchored. The self-releasing feature of the fire-cut joists allowed the joists to drop during a fire, leaving the wall intact.*

faults mentioned are major. If they were corrected, buildings would not collapse at fires as readily as they now do.

How type of construction affects collapse

Of the three general construction types, the protected steel frame or reinforced concrete structure is most resistant to collapse. Then comes the heavily built, well-designed wood frame. Last is the ordinary brick exterior, wood-joisted building.

Not enough firemen realize that if one were to compare two structural members of equal strength — one of steel and one of wood — the wooden member would resist fire far better. Wooden members of sufficient mass burn slowly on the outside faces. They can resist fire for long periods. Unprotected steel has a sorry record.

Old buildings

Old buildings deteriorate. Wood joists tend to dry out and shrink. They may have only been resting on the side walls with a two-inch bearing. As they age and shrink, the two inches become only one inch. Heavy floor loads now cause some beam deflection, further narrowing the safety margin. The mortar in the side walls can, and does, deteriorate.

If any motion is set up in the side walls (vibrational stresses mentioned earlier), the powdering of the mortar may continue to the point where the walls may no longer support the floor joists. When there is insufficient bearing for the floor joists they will drop — and the building will collapse. That's why if at fires you see clean, new-looking wood at the point where a joist rests on a side wall, be very suspicious. The clean part may indicate the joist is pulling away from the side wall.

Other features contributing to collapse

The fire department often contributes toward building collapse in several ways — either during or after a fire. We pour tons of water into a structure which may have been overloaded before our operations. Baled rags, rolls of newsprint paper, or other absorbent materials readily soak up water, enormously increasing the weight of the materials. Firemen with their cutting operations may cut supporting members. Sometimes they overload fire escapes which may fall and pull side walls with them.

If a floor is packed solidly with baled rags, rolled paper, or similar materials, another factor enters the picture. These materials in baled form will begin to swell as they absorb water. They may swell enough to push out walls, causing floors to fall.

When burned through, beams which have not been fire-cut will collapse and exert a twisting action on the side walls (See Figure 96, 97.) Truss supports can burn through and in similar fashion exert a downward and outward thrust on the side walls. Finally, when a roof or floor collapses in mass, it produces a huge piston action, pushing on the area below as well as transmitting thrust against side walls.

Large exterior signs, or marquee awnings such as on theatres, can be particularly dangerous under fire conditions. They are often tied into the upper front wall which is simply an ornamental facade or stonework above the roof level. This facade is unsupported and simply rests on the lower masonry wall. The signs or awnings are tied into the unsupported wall by light steel framework or long iron rods with an adjustable turnbuckle. (See Figure 98.) If the fire attacks a steel rod, the rod may buckle and allow the sign or awning to sag. This can pull the stone facade down with the awning onto people below. This happened at a fire in a large city, killing six men.

Weather conditions have played their part in building collapse. Heavy rains have washed out or weakened foundations. Because of clogged gutter drains, roofs can hold tons of water following a heavy rain. Two inches of water on a roof 40 x 80 feet would add more than 15 tons of weight.

Location of a structure can affect its collapse potential. In an area where there are subways, heavy trucking, or construction work entailing heavy blasting, vibration can in time weaken an old building enough to cause early collapse at a fire.

Unless there is an explosion, floors and

FIGURE 98. *The diagonal iron rod is vital to the support of this heavy marquee. If the rod is weakened by the heat of fire, the canopy will sag and exert a pull on the stone facade to which it is attached. Do not allow firemen to work under these structures when you suspect such weakness.*

roofs nearly always collapse before walls. This is because the fire either burns floor and ceiling joists all the way through or weakens them so they cannot sustain the floor loads. Floor collapse is generally more serious than roof collapse because it is more damaging structurally, and because it is more likely that people will be on a floor rather than on the roof.

Roof and floor collapse have a greater potential for injury and structural damage in commercial occupancies than in residential buildings. In commercial structures, floor spans are usually larger; there are fewer dividing walls and partitions to support upper floors and roofs as fire weakens beams and joists. Consequently, when the floors or roofs sag they collapse. (See Figure 99.)

In residential buildings the floors are honeycombed with walls, separating rooms from halls, rooms from each other, and apartments from one another. If a floor or roof sags, these walls and partitions hold up the sagging members, preventing them from falling to the floor below. Not only does this prevent such total collapse of the floor or roof above, it also acts to prevent the repetition of added weight and impact on each suceeding floor below. It will prevent the huge pis-

ton effect mentioned earlier. (See Figure 100.)

This is not to say that partial or even total roof and floor collapse does not occur in residential structures. It does occur at times, but it generally is limited because of the walls.

The warning signs of collapse

There are several warning signs that will signal potential structural collapse during fire operations:

1. Heavy body of fire which has been out of control for more than 20 minutes on two or more floors.

2. Knowledge of large tanks containing flammable liquids in well-involved buildings.

3. Interior explosions, rumbling noises, or heavy puffs of smoke.

4. Creaking, groaning noises.

5. Cracks in exterior walls.

6. Walls leaking smoke or water.

7. Walls out of plumb, columns out of plumb.

8. Unsupported walls.

9. Sagging or bulging walls.

10. Spongy or soft feel as you walk on roofs.

11. Movement in any floor or roof.

FIGURE 99 (Left). *Total collapse of floors in this commercial occupancy occurred because there were so few partitions to support the floors above as floors began to give way. Note the cast iron column. It leans but did not bend. Cast iron has little tensile strength and will snap suddenly without warning. This is a major reason for collapse in older factories. Ordinary steel columns will bend and give.*

FIGURE 100 (Below). *This top floor of an apartment hotel had a serious fire. There was substantial burning of the entire floor and roof joists. Much of the roof collapsed, but note how much of the roof is still supported by the partitions.*

FIGURE 101 (Above). *This wall failure was caused when the roof collapsed and pushed out this section of wall. A previous fire in this building caused the same wall to collapse. The new break occurred where the wall had been patched. This is one reason why serious fires should be overhauled during daylight if possible. This damage was not visible under dark and smoky conditions.*

FIGURE 102 (Right). *This is the same wall shown in Figure 102. The large air conditioning unit is perched precariously on a beam supported by loose brick in the damaged wall —another reason for not overhauling this building at night.*

FIGURE 103 (Left). *Note the crack in the wall. The front wall is starting to push out. It collapsed the day after this picture was taken.*

FIGURE 104 (Below). *This picture illustrates two important points: (1) Heavy burning on top of the joists indicates that fire traveled in the hanging ceiling space. (2) Note the joists starting to pull from their resting places in the brick wall. The joists were fire-cut and therefore released safely without pulling the wall down.*

FIGURE 105 (Above). *The I-beam cut off flush with the outside wall may have originally extended into the building alongside. The building was razed and the girder was cut off. Note the T-irons on each side used to fasten the floor joists into the brick wall. If the joists fail because of fire, they either tear loose from the T-iron or topple the wall.*

FIGURE 106 (Right). *This is a typical cast iron column. These columns can be identified by the ornamental cap where it meets the girder and the plates at the bottom used to make up any height differential.*

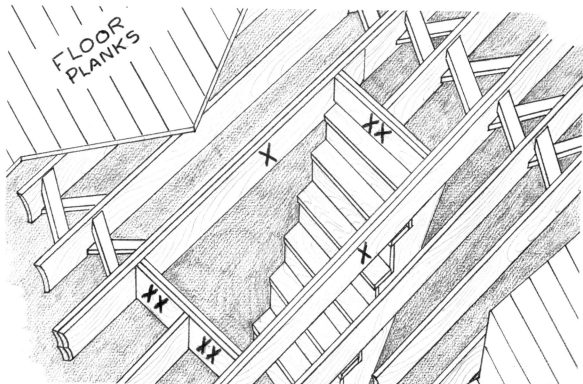

FIGURE 107. *Note the doubled floor joists (X) and the doubled header joists (XX). These structural members are doubled because they have to support not only their own floor loads but the load imposed on the joists fastened to them. The builder did this to carry the load of the missing joist which was left out to make space for the stairway. If these headers or double joists are cut (as might be done under heavy smoke conditions, darkness, or lack of know-how) there may be a collapse of this area.*

12. Ornamental stone fronts used to modernize old buildings.

13. Standpipe and sprinkler tanks.

14. Heavy signs on roofs.

15. If operating on the fire floor, watch for huge chandeliers and massive ornamental plaster ceilings. Keep your men away from the center of the floor, near the side walls. They will be safer there.

16. Limit the number of men and hose lines on the outside fire escapes. Keep the men on fire escapes close to the building to cut down on the leverage exerted by standing at the railing.

After firefighting operations

After the fire is out there still is the danger that a building could collapse. (See Figures 101-107.) Therefore your overhauling operations should take these points into consideration:

1. If any doubt exists as to the stability of the building, do not overhaul the fire during darkness. Set up watch lines if necessary.

2. Make a thorough examination during daylight hours.

3. Check with competent authorities for advice.

4. Avoid the use of jarring blows to the structure, such as cutting with axes or dropping heavy objects during the overhaul.

5. Keep a constant check on the building's stability.

6. Drain water from floors to relieve the weight.

7. Drain gravity and pressure tanks on the roof.

8. Provide a safe means of alternate retreat.

Chapter 9

Fires of major proportions

MAJOR fires (those of large size or complex in nature) fall into two general categories. They are inside or structural fires, and exterior fires such as lumber yards, extensive field fires, and flammable liquid spills which have been ignited.

Exterior major fires

In the exterior fire of large proportions, it is reasonable to expect a more intense, rapid burning which can spread rapidly because of the ready supply of oxygen, prevailing winds — and those created by the large fire itself — and flying sparks and firebrands.

Fires of this magnitude require heavy calibre streams (500 gpm or larger); small streams have limited range and cooling power. Because of these limitations, firemen cannot get close enough to the fire and in most cases the water is evaporated by the fierce heat before it can get to the flames. Because of this lack of cooling capacity, the fire grows in intensity, frequently forcing the firemen to retreat.

Suburban fire departments are used to laying 1½-inch lines. Rarely do they use 2½-inch hose. In fact, most small departments have begun to rely almost completely on the 1-inch booster line, so much so that the 1½-inch hose is becoming the "big line." They are so conditioned to the 1½-inch hose that when they do get a large fire they automatically lay several 1½-inch lines. Incoming units do the same. It is not uncommon at fairly large exterior fires to see from eight to 10 1½-inch lines being used. This can be a serious error at such fires. Generally, a far better technique is to combine several smaller lines into one master stream. Remember, there must be sufficient size and reach to get through the heat and draft effect to reach the seat of the fire. Just playing water against smoke and flame tongues will do no good.

The correct placement of heavy streams at large exterior moving fires is in the path of the wind. However, wind positions at large fires often change. It would be prudent to keep some units in reserve should such winds change and drive the fire toward a new threat in a different direction.

Interior major fires

Fires of large proportions inside buildings generally pose a more difficult problem. Such fires can range from a large warehouse to a high-rise building. They may occur in a multistory residence with people trapped. Operational techniques at inside fires will vary considerably from those at outside fires.

Fires many stories above ground at the rear of a large floor may not be visible or their severity and scope clearly defined. Such fires often will be beyond reach of ladders or the effective reach of streams. In addition to the difficulty of getting to such fires, a severe exposure condition may develop without the chief in charge becoming aware of it. Exposures often are covered by bringing in lines to the threatened windows and operating from them onto the fire. If a building has elevators and standpipes, the job will be greatly simplified. But if power should fail, the men will have to hand-stretch the hose lines up many floors, with resultant serious delays. This could allow the fire to gain great headway.

Fires inside structures, particularly those difficult to ventilate, will be smoky and hot. The fire load will vary depending on the nature of the occupancy, which sometimes is very difficult to determine because of the limited vision due to the heavy smoke. Men may have to fight fires in furniture, plastics, chemicals, corrosive liquids, flammable liquids, etc., many times with no idea of the hazards they face.

Working methods are different at inside fires. Reliance may have to be on standpipe systems. In such cases, men will move in from enclosed stairs onto the fire floor. Sprinklers may be holding the fire in check and should be supplied.

One large city has procedures on standpipe operations incorporated into its regulations which forbid the use of standpipes if the fire is below the fourth floor. This doesn't make sense. If the floor area is large or if there are many winding passageways, stretching hose lines even onto a street floor can be arduous and time-consuming, and require many lengths of hose. The standpipe should be used regardless of the floor height if it will speed application of water onto the fire.

Sprinkler systems in burning buildings should be supplied with hose lines from pumpers. Whether this should be the first or second line varies with conditions. Certainly one of the first lines should be connected to the fire department siamese connection. Where the number of opened heads warrants it and as soon as time permits, another line should be supplied to fill in the supply. Companies having 3-inch hose should use it in preference to the 2½-inch hose.

Don't forget, a 1,000 gpm pumper can supply only about 40 sprinkler heads. If more than this number have fused, you should have another pumper lay-in to augment the supply.

Frequently yard hydrants are on the same main that supplies the sprinklers. If a pumping engine is connected to such a hydrant it may starve the sprinkler supply. Where a sprinkler system is operating and shows signs of containing the fire, it is vitally important to keep it supplied. In such cases, whenever pumpers connect to yard hydrants, immediately lay-in a 3-inch line to the fire department siamese connection to prevent starving the sprinklers of water.

When structural fires burn for long periods, or in case of intense fires in shorter periods, the question of building stability exists. Where there is a doubt, back the men out and rely on heavy exterior streams. Unfortunately such exterior streams at street level become ineffective above the second floor. It therefore becomes important to use streams from elevating platforms, ladder pipes, across shafts and narrow streets from exposed buildings. Constant surveillance must be maintained so that men will not be trapped should walls fall.

If you know of unprotected metal structural members in a building, then collapse must be anticipated. Men should be backed out and apparatus should be moved back from threatened areas. Get large streams ready to cover buildings that may be exposed by such anticipated collapse. Where such collapse might occur in buildings higher than those alongside, evacuate the lower buildings —now!

Chapter 10

Buildings under construction

BUILDINGS under construction are inordinately vulnerable to fire. This is so regardless of the ultimate fire-resistant characteristics of the structure. The reasons for such vulnerability during the construction phase may be summarized as follows:

1. The presence of large amounts of wood used as scaffolding, forms, and temporary supports.

2. The storage of combustibles on various floors and surrounding the structure—roofing, straw, cardboard cartons, cabinets, flammable gas cylinders, flammable liquids such as fuel for trucks.

3. The lack of stairs between floors. Temporary wooden ladders are not only combustible, they make it difficult for firemen to move up to the fire area.

4. Lack of water supply—no hydrants.

5. Combustible tarpaulins used to shield from the wind.

6. Portable heating devices burning gas, fuel oil, or wood.

7. Large amounts of combustible rubbish.

Fire in a building under construction spreads rapidly and reaches great intensity, mainly because little effort is devoted to fire safety. There are no walls to break the wind, sparks and firebrands fly throughout the neighborhood. These fires often build up enough heat to warp steel members and burn form boards supporting concrete that has not yet cured. (See Figures 108, 109.) "Green" concrete which has not had sufficient time to harden is a collapse potential that firemen should be aware of. Concrete hardens continually for years. When freshly laid it has a greenish cast. If the forms are removed too soon (within three to five days depending on the thickness of the concrete) it may not have sufficient strength to withstand the weight of dozens of firemen and their charged hose lines. Any cutting or pounding may cause vibrational stresses which could precipitate collapse.

Should a serious fire occur on upper floors of a building under construction and there is reason to suspect the stability of the floors, fight the fire with streams from the elevating platform basket or ladder pipes until the fire is completely controlled. If possible, avoid overhauling such fires at night because of limited visibility. With daylight it will be possible to make a careful examination of the structure to see whether there is any danger of collapse. In addition, you will have the help of the building construction people and their equipment. It is safer to do it this way.

Reaching the area of the fire in a building under construction can be a most dangerous and exhausting job for firefighters. After rushing to reach the building, the men have to ladder the structure, carry hose and tools up by ladder—or perhaps 20 floors by stairs,

FIGURE 108. *Concrete form boards are designed with only enough strength to hold the concrete in place until it hardens. If fire attacks these forms they will fail rapidly, exposing firemen to the danger of tons of falling concrete and steel. This is why fires in buildings under construction should not be fought in darkness if a containing action by exterior stream is possible. Certainly they should not be overhauled till daylight and a competent structural engineer can certify as to the stability of the load-bearing form boards. (Note the propane tanks — another hazard.) In this picture, fire burned away top floor form boards. The concrete was not sufficiently set to support itself and it disintegrated. The steel reinforcing rods simply added weight to the mass but no stability.*

FIGURE 109. *Bar joists have fallen because of fire. The concrete floor above is still in place but seri- ously weakened, making this a dangerous area. The propane cylinders are another hazard.*

since no elevators are installed in buildings under construction. The hoistway used during building hours is not operative after the job is shut down for the day. It can be especially disheartening when, in spite of all possible efforts, the fire continues to burn, destroying much of the structure and equipment.

This type of fire duty is fraught with danger. Men work hurriedly in unfamiliar surroundings, on floors littered with construction materials, temporary stairs, no lighting. At times burning debris may fall on them from above.

Visualize this situation: The firemen, after hooking up to the fire department siamese at street level, charge the standpipe. They carry donuts, tools, and nozzles up 15 floors.

After reaching the floor below the fire, they find all their work was for nothing. The builder had failed to cap the standpipe at the day's finish. All the water is now pouring out of an open four-inch, useless standpipe. Now they will have to hand-pull hose up 15 floors. They have to radio instructions to shut down and disconnect the lines into the standpipe, lower ropes, and begin to hoist hose to their floor. All the while the fire continues unabated.

Laying hose to upper floors

There are several ways hose can be laid to upper floors. First, of course, the line can be hand-stretched up the temporary inside stairs. This is time-consuming and requires a great deal of manpower. If the fire is above

115

the seventh floor in a building under construction, forget this method.

The next method, and perhaps the fastest, is by use of the aerial ladder. This procedure is much the same as in ordinary fire duty where lines are run up ladders to upper floors. Make sure the line is strapped at the lower and upper parts of the aerial—when the line is in position and before water is started.

Another procedure is to have men get to the floor below the fire with all the tools and equipment needed, including a roof rope and a hose roller. Lower the rope and pull the hose up over the roller. If the fire is above the tenth floor, there may be too much weight on the hose couplings with a straight line all the way from the street to the floor below the fire. Have men space out about every tenth floor and pull one length in on that floor. Make a large loop and secure this loop to a substantial object. This will take the weight off the hose and couplings every ten floors. There will be less chance of hose damage and possible loss of water.

Perhaps the best method is to use an elevating platform as a standpipe up to its limit (about the eighth floor). From here the men can carry donuts to the floor below the fire and lower them over the hose roller by rope to the basket of the elevating platform.

For the departments without aerial ladders or elevating platforms, there is one more method. This requires a carefully planned team operation. Men go up the stairway with donuts. Every eighth floor they connect their donuts and lower the hose to where it can be pulled in and connected by the team below. You must secure with ropes at each level where the connections are to be made.

There is a hazard in buildings under construction firemen should be aware of. Carelessness in heavy stream operation may propel loose pieces of lumber, flammable gas cylinders, or scaffolding planks onto firemen below.

Conduct inspections and pre-plan

In order to keep the hazards of buildings under construction to a minimum, fire officers should inspect or cause these buildings to be inspected regularly. Factory Mutual Insurance has enumerated some excellent recommendations and check points. They are listed here for your guidance:

1. Arrange for a sufficient number of portable fire extinguishers to be distributed about the project. Antifreeze types will be necessary in cold weather.

2. Provide safe lighting equipment. Floodlights are preferable to indiscriminate use of unprotected lamps strung on temporary wiring. Properly insulate and substantially support any necessary temporary wiring; do not overload circuits or overfuse.

3. Use only flameproofed tarpaulins; secure them against damage by wind.

4. Provide safe sources of temporary heat, preferably approved heaters. Trash and scrap wood should not be burned in salamanders. Ample clearance from combustible material must be maintained, and indiscriminate relocation of heating facilities should be prohibited.

5. Contractors must provide access to buildings under construction for emergency fire department use. Roadways should be selected and maintained in passable condition convenient to the nearest hydrants. If the building has a standpipe and hose system, access to fire department connections for such standpipe should be assured. Hydrants should be kept accessible at all times. Because it is difficult for firemen to identify the standpipes to be used for fire in upper stories, signs should be placed designating the proper standpipes for floors or sections of floors which may be involved.

Plans of the building should be provided to the chief of the local fire department so he is fully advised as to the type of construction, materials used, and any special hazards which might exist.

6. Locate any necessary temporary contractor's buildings at a safe distance from the new construction to minimize exposure fire possibilities. Heating facilities for such buildings should be well-arranged. When the project calls for a detached sprinklered storage building, provide this first and use it instead of temporary sheds.

7. Use temporary enclosures and heat,

where feasible, in place of straw and hay for curing concrete. Straw or hay which must be used should be removed as soon as possible. Cutting and welding operations and the use of salamanders must be prohibited in the area until straw and hay have been entirely removed.

8. Provide watchman service as soon as combustible materials arrive at the site.

9. Require that all cutting and welding operations be strictly supervised. A permit system should be used, requiring that each proposed operation be reviewed at the start of each job or start of each shift by a designated and trained person who will issue a signed permit authorizing the work. It may be necessary to assign an area, safely located and arranged, where small jobs may be brought for welding.

10. Keep bulk storage of gasoline, fuel oil, paint, and solvents outside the buildings under construction. No more than one day's working supply should be inside at any time, and then in approved containers only.

11. Locate tar kettles outside of and as far away from buildings as possible. Provide suitable fire-extinguishing equipment nearby. Never allow tar kettles to be placed on combustible roofs.

12. Prohibit smoking in hazardous areas.

13. Remove trash daily, or more frequently if necessary, to maintain good housekeeping. Burning of this material should be restricted to locations well away from buildings. If scrap fires are permitted on the building site, see that a water hose is available. Where practical, incinerators should be used.

14. Provide temporary or "mobile" telephones which can be used to transmit fire alarms until permanent facilities are installed.

15. Instruct watchmen and supervisors in their duties and responsibilities regarding safe fire-protection practices.

16. Organize a fire brigade trained in the use of portable fire extinguishers and hose streams.

17. Exercise special care in the placement, operation, and servicing of combustion-engine-driven equipment for such powered units as mixers, compressors, elevators, and hoists. Fueling of small gasoline units should be from approved safety cans, and large units from a safely arranged drum pump. Use of gasoline engines inside buildings should be avoided. Engine exhaust piping should adequately clear all combustibles. See that engines are shut down before refueling.

18. Wherever possible, fire protective equipment, such as standpipes, hose systems, and sprinkler systems, should be completed as the building is erected, floor by floor. Water supplies should be connected and sprinkler heads installed. If automatic detection equipment is to be provided, such equipment should be installed as soon as construction conditions permit.

Chapter 11

Standpipe operations

THERE ARE two general types of standpipe systems, wet pipe and dry pipe. You must understand the difference between the two, you must know which type is in the building on fire. Your operations will vary considerably depending on whether the standpipe system is wet or dry.

In the dry pipe system, all piping is dry and reliance is totally upon a pumper pumping into the system from a hydrant or other water supply.

The wet pipe system is one charged with water to every floor hose outlet valve. The water supply may be a roof gravity or pressure tank. It may be a suction tank supply, a street main, or a combination of the foregoing. A wet system insures an instant water supply by opening the hose outlet valve. Obviously a dry system is useless to firemen if no engine is pumping into the fire department siamese connection at the street level.

There are other serious drawbacks to a dry standpipe.

The floor valve may be open on upper floors. If careful inspections of the system have not taken place, this condition may exist for years. When the engine company pumps into the dry pipe it charges the entire piping system. If, for example, there is no

hose with a shut-off nozzle on the opened upper floor valve, water will pour out. This upper valve may be on the tenth floor. You may wish to operate from the hose line on the sixth floor. If one or more valves above are opened, you may be unable to build effective pressure. In addition, thousands of gallons of water may do destructive damage on the upper floors.

If the fire is on an upper floor, it takes time for the pressure to exhaust the air and reach the nozzle. This delay can be a factor in fire spread.

There will be an air pressure buildup which could fan the fire when released at the nozzle to allow the water to flow.

If you are going to supply the outside fire department connection by pumper, make sure you are connecting to the proper siamese. Almost invariably the purpose of the siamese is stamped into the casting. It will read "Standpipe Siamese." If you still cannot determine whether you have the proper siamese, connect the hose line into the first floor hose outlet valve and supply the system in this manner. If the fire is of any consequence, lay a second line into another outside connection to insure the system of being supplied. (If there is only one outside connection,

FIGURE 110. *Two lines are laid into the outside fire department siamese connection. Other men with rolled-ups and tools go to the floor below the fire and connect to the floor outlet valve. They* *then stretch up to the floor above, pulling surplus hose to the stairs above the fire floor and folding it so it will pay out readily without kinking when they are ready to move in.*

stretch the second line into this connection.) One 4-inch riser should be able to supply three 2½-inch hose lines when fed by two 3-inch lines into the outside connection.

Often the swivel on a siamese connection will not turn easily because of age, dirt, or paint. When this happens, try one of these methods to loosen it:

1. Hit the swivel with a spanner to loosen the paint or dirt which may be binding it.

2. Twist the hose four or five turns to the left, then insert the hose into the swivel and turn the hose to the right. The hose will grab sufficient threads. When secured by a hose strap or rope, it will serve the purpose until a line can be stretched to another siamese.

3. Put a fire department siamese into the outlet (you can turn this in) and support this with a rope. Now connect your hose to this second siamese.

When possible, connect your hose lines to the discharge gates on the pumper side opposite the engineer's working side so that if high pressures are required and a hose coupling blows from the discharge gate it will not strike the engineer. It is always a wise precaution to secure the hose lines with a short rope to take some of the strain off the couplings.

If there is a break in the standpipe, close the valves on the standpipe below and above the break. If there is more than one riser, remove your hose to the serviceable riser and continue operations. Another method is to bypass the break with a hose line by connecting below the shut-off valve to a hose outlet floor valve on the standpipe, and reconnecting to a hose outlet floor valve above the upper shut-off valve.

Assume you have been ordered to take a hose line and operate from a standpipe. Here are some basic techniques you should remember:

1. Take three donut rolls of 50 foot-length hose, nozzle, spanner, forcible entry tools, masks, lights, handie talkie, phone jacks, rope, and hose roller.

2. Don't take the elevator to the fire floor. Stop at the floor below. Make your hookup to the standpipe and work up onto the fire floor. (See Figure 110.) Taking an elevator to the

fire floor is dangerous. The doors may open to a pall of heat and smoke. You may be overcome or not able to proceed to the standpipe floor outlet valve. Even worse, if the elevator operates on the electric eye principle this may happen: The doors will open, but they will not close. Elevators with an electric eye are designed so that as long as a beam is interrupted the doors will not close. This is so that as long as people are passing through the beam the doors will stay open. Heavy smoke can also interrupt an electric eye beam. That means the doors will not close and you cannot get up or down. You are trapped right there!

3. In most new buildings the standpipe floor valve is in the fire stairway. This is a poor spot to hook up. When you open the door into the fire floor, the heat and smoke enter the fire stairs which may be in use by people attempting to leave the building.

There are better methods whereby if smoke does enter the exit facilities it is dissipated by one form or another. Chicago has a novel feature in emergency fire stairs. You enter the stairway from a vestibule from the hall. Naturally the smoke from the fire floor gets into this vestibule. But inside there is a glass panel which is thermostatically controlled. Heat from the fire activates a fusible link which causes the glass panel (up high in the vestibule) to open into a huge vent shaft. The smoke and heat enter the shaft and are carried up and out by way of the roof. This keeps the vestibule comparatively free of combustion products. On the other side of the vestibule there is another door leading to the stairs. (See Figures 111, 112.)

A similar objective is achieved in a more efficient manner by the use of the Philadelphia or Smokeproof Tower. Here a person leaves the fire floor onto an open balcony. Any smoke following the person onto the balcony is dissipated into the open air. At the opposite side of the balcony there is another door leading to an enclosed stairway which goes from the roof to the street. (See Figure 113.)

4. Remove the pressure reducer (if there is one) on the end of the floor outlet valve. This is a butterfly type valve which serves to reduce the size of the outlet and the head

FIGURE 111. *Inside the vestibule there is a heat actuated device. There is also one outside the door at right. Heat triggers the device causing it to unlatch the vent window at the left (not visible) which opens into a shaft. This emergency exit system is used in Chicago's high-rises.*

FIGURE 112. *The vent window in the vestibule is shown open, leaning into shaft. Any smoke which gets into the vestibule would be pulled into the shaft. The shaft is continuous from cellar to roof and induces a powerful draft. With no smoke build-up in the vestibule, people can move through the door (at left) to the stairway and exit safely.*

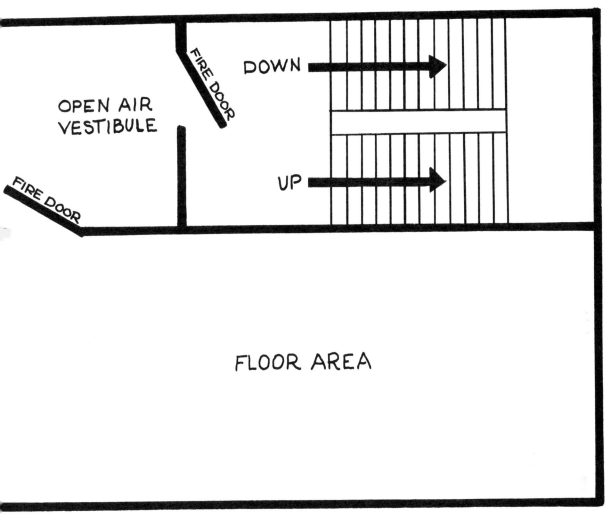

FIRE DOOR

OPEN AIR
VESTIBULE

FIRE DOOR

DOWN

UP

FLOOR AREA

FIGURE 113. *The Philadelphia, or Smokeproof Tower, allows a person to exit from a fire floor to an open air vestibule guarded by waist-high iron railings. Smoke from the fire floor will dissipate into the open air. From the open-air vestibule you may enter the stairway through another fire door and walk down to safety.*

pressure at the floor valve in tall buildings. It also reduces the water flow. It is installed to reduce the pressure so that the building personnel will be able to handle the stream reaction. Obviously, experienced firemen can handle more pressure and would be interested in the full water flow.

5. Pull the hose fully off the rack.

6. Open the valve and operate onto the fire.

If you have a roof fire or if you find it necessary to operate hose lines from the roof to protect exposures, remember, most standpipe systems have a three-way manifold on the roof for just such a purpose. The controls for this manifold will most likely be in the stair enclosure just below.

Chapter 12

Sprinkler operations

SPRINKLERS may well be described as a fireman's best friend. Statistically they have shown an efficiency rate of 96 percent or more. Failure is most often due to human error. Sprinklers failed to control the fire in the remaining 4 percent for one of these reasons: (1) water was shut off, (2) the system was improperly installed, (3) fire loading was too heavy for the system, or (4) the water supply was shut down too soon during the fire.

If the sprinkler system is operating during the fire but it is evident the fire is not being controlled, pump into the system with more pumping engines. Where the building covers a large area, two or three engines should be connected. A 750 gpm engine can supply only about 30 sprinkler heads; a 1,000 gpm engine about 40. Where there is only one fire department connection, use of siamese connections will be necessary to permit enough lines to be laid so the friction loss will not be excessive.

Connect a pumping engine into the sprinkler siamese for every fire in a sprinklered building. If an exposed building is sprinklered and the principal supply to the system is from the city mains, make sure this system has an adequate water supply by connecting an engine to the fire department connection. The draft of engines at hydrants will so reduce the pressure in the city system that the sprinkler system will not function without this additional supply at good pressure.

Many fire departments carry tools which can be used on the individual sprinkler head to stop the flow. Others close the riser or floor control valve. It is of prime importance, however, that the sprinkler systems not be cut off by control valves until there is positive assurance that the fire is out and has not spread to any other part of the building.

In some very old sections of cities you may find perforated pipe and open systems. The perforated pipe type was the earliest. It was simply piping with holes in it. The water supply was from the domestic system controlled manually by a valve.

The open sprinkler was similar except that there was some sort of distribution head over the holes in the piping. Water supply was the same as in the perforated pipe type.

Some cities called for outside fire department connections to such systems. In such cases, a pumper would lay a line into the system to provide the water supply. Where the pumper supplied the water, one had to be careful about exceeding 75 psi. The piping, being old and rusted, could rupture easily.

When responding to an alarm of fire triggered by a water flow alarm in a large sprinklered building, it is generally possible to determine the area of concern by examining the alarm panel—usually on the lowest floor. If, however, there is no such indication on the panel, you must examine the entire structure. Do not assume there is no fire because there is no visible smoke or fire. Split your companies into squads and assign various floors to each squad for search. Where doors are locked, listen at the door for sounds of water flow rather than force entrance immediately. Sometimes you may see the flow coming from under the door. This then is the area of concern.

Feel the door. If there is any sign of heat, stretch a line from the standpipe or pumper in the street before you force entrance to the floor.

While the search is going on, the pumper takes a hydrant position and lays a line into the fire department siamese. Preparations are made to start laying lines into the building in case they will be required. Don't charge the lines with water unless specifically called for. It will take only seconds to open the hydrant if water is needed. If it isn't needed, the job of disconnecting, draining hose lines, and replacing the hose on the trucks will be much more time-consuming—particularly in freezing weather.

If you have to shut down a sprinkler control valve and the location is not visible because of smoke, go to the floor below and look for the control valve location there. The valve on the floor above should be in a similar location.

If this does not work, you will need to trace the piping back to the valve. The diameter of the piping will increase in the direction of the control valve. After shutting the control valve, open the drain valve to drain the sprinkler piping and stop the water flow.

Sprinkler quiz

Because of the importance of sprinkler systems in firefighting, firemen should have a good background in their function. The following questions and answers will serve as an educational and practical quiz*:

---

*These questions and answers are updated and revised from a set of questions used by the author in a course he taught at the Mt. Vernon Firefighting School, Mt. Vernon, N. Y.

Q. The forerunners of the automatic sprinkler were the perforated pipe and open sprinkler which were controlled by a gate valve outside the room or building. What were the disadvantages of these systems that were corrected by the development of the modern automatic sprinkler system?

A. There was a great waste of water, probably poor distribution, and they were in no sense automatic. By discharging water over the entire area of the room where there was no fire, the water damage usually greatly exceeded the fire damage.

Q. Since the size of the opening in all sprinklers is about the same, what determines the amount of water discharged?

A. The water pressure.

Q. What is generally considered the minimum working or flowing pressure for the proper action of the sprinkler?

A. Seven to eight pounds per square inch. At this pressure, the sprinkler will discharge about 15 gallons per minute and cover a floor area of more than 100 square feet.

Q. Describe briefly a "wet pipe system."

A. It employs automatic sprinklers attached to a piping system containing water and connected to a water supply so that water discharges immediately from sprinklers open by fire.

Q. Describe briefly a "dry pipe system."

A. It employs automatic sprinklers attached to a piping system containing air under pressure instead of water. Release of the air by the opening of sprinklers permits the water pressure to open a valve known as a "dry pipe valve." The water then flows into the piping system and out the open sprinklers. After the dry pipe valve is tripped, the entire system functions as a regular wet system.

Q. Under what circumstances can the ordinary wet system not be used?

A. Where subject to freezing, even for short periods, an ordinary wet system cannot be used. There are several types of non-freezing sprinkler systems, but because such systems cost more and present greater maintenance difficulties than wet systems, it usually is preferable to heat sprinklered properties when feasible.

Q. Describe briefly a "pre-action system."

A. It is a system employing automatic sprinklers attached to a piping system containing air that may or may not be under pressure, with a supplemental system of heat-responsive devices installed in the same area as the sprinklers; actuation of the system of heat responsive devices, as from fire, opens a valve which permits water to flow into the piping system and to be discharged from any sprinklers that may open. Systems which contain air under slight pressure (one or two pounds) send in an alarm when the pressure drops for any reason, whether from fire or accidentally.

Q. What is a "deluge system?"

A. This is a system of open sprinklers controlled by a quick opening mechanical or hydraulic valve (deluge valve) which operates by the action of heat-sensitive devices or manually. Generally, the manual operation is an auxiliary control. The purpose of this system is to wet down a whole area at once, rather than to wait for the action of sprinkler heads of the conventional type.

Q. What is "light hazard occupancy?"

A. "Light hazard occupancy" includes buildings such as apartment houses, asylums, clubhouses, colleges, churches, dormitories, dwellings, hospitals, hotels, libraries, museums, office buildings, schools, and tenements.

Q. What is "ordinary hazard occupancy?"

A. This class includes buildings housing occupancies such as mercantile businesses, warehouses, manufacturing, and occupancies not considered "light hazard" or "extra hazard."

Q. What is "extra hazard occupancy?"

A. This class includes only those buildings or portions of buildings housing occupancies where the hazard is severe as determined by the inspection department having jurisdiction.

Q. How do these classifications of occupancy affect sprinkler standards?

A. They have provisions for spacing sprinklers, water supply, etc., the purpose being to provide protection commensurate with the hazard and to avoid unnecessary expense.

Q. At what pressure are new systems tested?

A. All new systems should be tested hydrostatically at not less than 200 psi pressure for two hours, or at 50 psi in excess of the normal pressure in an excess of 150 psi.

Q. When a new dry pipe system cannot be tested hydrostatically as described in the last question because the season of the year will not permit testing with water, how are these systems tested?

A. They should be tested for two hours with at least 50 psi air pressure. When possible, however, they should be tested hydrostatically.

Q. Why is the fire department siamese connection on the outside of sprinklered buildings a valuable auxiliary supply?

A. Because this source can furnish a considerable volume of water under heavy pressure, the fire department siamese connection on the outside of sprinklered buildings is a valuable auxiliary supply. Under certain conditions, such as a great number of sprinklers operating, the public water or tank supply may not provide an adequate or completely satisfactory water supply. Also the public water pressure may be materially reduced by hose streams from hydrants.

Q. What size should the feed pipe from fire department connections be for (a) pumpers and (b) fireboats?

A. (a) Four inch for pumpers (b) Six inch for fireboats. Each connection should be fitted with a check valve but no gate valve.

Q. When should the fire department connect to the outside siamese connection and what pressure should be maintained in the event of a fire in a sprinklered building?

A. It is of primary importance that fire departments immediately connect pumpers to the sprinkler system and maintain a pressure of 100 pounds until it has been determined that the fire has been extinguished.

Q. Why is it best to install sprinklers in an upright position?

A. To permit draining and to reduce the danger of clogging from foreign material in the piping, sprinklers are installed in an upright position.

Q. When it is necessary to install sprinklers in a pendent position, such as under false ceilings or where concealed piping is used in a dry system, what special equipment is used?

A. A special type approval pendent sprinkler is installed.

Q. Automatic sprinklers are constructed to withstand how much water pressure?

A. Automatic sprinklers are constructed to withstand 300 psi or more.

Q. What is the size of the orifice in a standard sprinkler?

A. Standard automatic sprinklers have ½-inch discharge orifices. (See Table II.)

Q. What is a "bulb-type" sprinkler?

A. This type of sprinkler, known as Quartzoid sprinklers (older models were called quartz bulb and silica bulb), consist of a bulb composed mostly of quartz nearly filled with a liquid which expands with heat, shattering the bulb and releasing the valve cap and subsequent flow of water.

Q. What is a "solder-type" sprinkler?

A. This type of sprinkler consists of a soldered link which is connected to a valve cap by various combinations of struts and levers. When subjected to the rated temperature, the special solder melts, releasing the strain imposed on the link and valve cap by the levers or struts, thus permitting the valve cap to be forced open by the water pressure.

Q. Describe briefly a "spray-type" sprinkler.

A. A "spray-type" sprinkler discharges the water in all directions below the plane of the deflector with little or no water being discharged upward to wet the ceiling. The distribution pattern is roughly a half sphere completely and uniformly filled with water spray. A circular area of about 20 feet in diameter is covered 10 feet below the deflector at minimum water pressure. At distances of more than 10 feet, the area covered is greater; it is less with lesser distances.

Q. Name the two types of spray sprinklers.

A. Upright spray sprinkler and pendent spray sprinkler.

Q. Can an upright spray sprinkler be installed in a pendent position?

A. No. An upright spray sprinkler can be installed only in the upright position. A pendent spray sprinkler can be installed only in the pendent position.

Q. Describe briefly a "regular" or "conventional" type sprinkler.

A. A "regular" or "conventional" type sprinkler distributes about 60% of the water upward against the ceiling with the balance out and downward. Water falls in large drops and irregularly covers an area of approximately 15 feet in diameter, 10 feet below the sprinkler at

TABLE II

Discharge Capacities of Automatic Sprinklers Having Orifices of Nominal ½-inch Size

Pressure at Sprinkler psi	Discharge gpm	Pressure at Sprinkler psi	Discharge gpm
10	18	35	34
15	22	50	41
20	25	75	50
25	28	100	58

minimum discharge pressure. Due to the amount of water discharged on the ceiling and its direction of fall therefrom, the greatest concentration of water occurs in an area of about 10 feet in diameter.

Q. Can "spray-type" sprinklers be identified from "regular" or "conventional" type sprinklers?

A. Yes. The deflectors on spray sprinklers are marked "SSU" to identify upright spray sprinklers and "SSP" to identify pendent spray sprinklers.

Q. Can a "regular" or "conventional" type sprinkler be used to replace a "spray-type" sprinkler?

A. No. A "spray-type" sprinkler can, however, be used to replace a "regular" or conventional type sprinkler.

Q. What is a sidewall sprinkler?

A. This is a regular standard sprinkler equipped with a special deflector to give the proper distribution of water when mounted horizontally on a side wall. Such sprinklers are installed at or near the top of walls or rooms with no sprinklers at the ceiling as ordinarily provided. They cover a distance of 15 feet with their spray.

Q. Under what circumstances would sidewall sprinklers be installed?

A. Where property owners refuse to install piping below ceilings of decorative rooms, such as parlors, lobbies, lounges, dining rooms, etc., in hotels, clubs, and similar light-hazard occupancies, sidewall sprinklers would be installed.

Q. What is a "small orifice" sprinkler and where is it used?

A. These are sprinklers with ¼-inch or ⅜-inch orifices used in small enclosures or other locations where a small discharge of water is desirable.

Q. Sprinkler heads come in different colors. What do such colors signify?

A. They indicate the various temperatures at which they will fuse and discharge water. Table III lists these temperature ratings and color codes. (See Table III.)

Q. What standard test is used to determine the operating temperatures of sprinklers?

A. The temperature ratings approximate the temperature at which the sprinklers operate when immersed in a liquid, when the temperature of the liquid is raised very slowly.

TABLE III*

Temperature Ratings, Classifications and Color Codings

Maximum Ceiling Temperature °F	Temperature Rating °F	Temperature Classification	Color Code
100	135 to 170	Ordinary	Uncolored
150	175 to 225	Intermediate	White
225	250 to 300	High	Blue
300	325 to 375	Extra High	Red
375	400 to 475	Very Extra High	Green
475	500 to 575	Ultra High	Orange

*This is Table 3651, Volume 6 of the 1970-1971 National Fire Codes.

Q. Why are the temperature ratings of sprinklers as determined by standard tests not necessarily representative of ordinary fire conditions?

A. When exposed to heat from fire, there is a time factor involved, owing to the fact that the metal parts absorb heat, and some time must elapse before the heat-sensitive element is raised to the operating temperature. Thus, the air temperature around the sprinkler usually reaches a point substantially above the normal temperature rating of the sprinkler before it operates.

Q. What abnormal conditions will tend to shorten the life or period of satisfactory service of sprinklers?

A. If the sprinklers are abused structurally or if the ceiling temperatures are carried beyond the recognized safe figures for a given rating, or if severe corrosion sets in—all these tend to reduce the period of satisfactory service of a sprinkler.

Q. What can be done to protect sprinklers against corrosion when they are installed in occupancies where this danger is present?

A. There are several approved coatings that can be applied to sprinklers as protection against corrosion. Among them are wax-coated, lead-coated, wax-and lead-coated, and lacquer and wax-coated.

Q. What protection is given to sprinklers so located as to be subject to mechanical injury?

A. By approved metal guards, available from the sprinkler companies, those sprinklers subject to mechanical injury due to location may be protected.

Q. What is meant by the term "cold flow" as it applies to sprinklers?

A. When a solder type sprinkler is subjected to long exposure to temperature sufficiently high to cause gradual weakening, as indicated by partial separation of the soldered members, this is called "cold flow." This usually is caused by overheating, sprinklers too close to steam pipes, heating ducts, etc. In some cases, a fire which opens a number of sprinklers may weaken other sprinklers in that vicinity. This is not a common occurrence.

Q. What is meant by "loaded sprinkler?"

A. A sprinkler is termed "loaded" when in certain classes of properties conditions exist that cause an accumulation of foreign material on sprinklers so that their operation may be retarded or prevented. Any accumulation of foreign material tends to retard their operation owing to the heat-insulating effect thereby provided. If the deposit is hard, it may prevent necessary movement of the parts to permit the flow of water when the solder or other heat-sensitive element is released due to heat of the fire.

Q. What should be done with loaded sprinklers?

A. The best practice is to replace them with new sprinklers rather than to attempt to clean them. However, deposits of light dust, such as may be found in woodworking shops or grain elevators, can be blown off or dusted off with a soft brush. Hard deposits, such as those due to cement dust combined with moisture, or hardened deposits of paint or varnish are very difficult to remove without damage to the sprinkler; such sprinklers should be replaced.

Q. What are the restrictions in regard to painting sprinklers as found in the NFPA Standards for Sprinkler Equipment?

A. No coating shall be applied except by the manufacturer—except if necessary to repair part of any coating broken off during installation.

Q. What is included in the Sprinkler Standards in regard to stock of extra sprinklers?

A. There should be maintained on the premises a supply of extra sprinklers (never less than six) similar as to type and temperature ratings to the sprinklers in the property. They should be kept in a cabinet where the temperature never exceeds 100° F. A special sprinkler wrench also is kept in the cabinet.

Q. What is the function of the dry pipe in a dry pipe system?

A. The dry pipe valve holds back the water in a dry pipe system until a sprinkler opens and the air escapes. The design is such that a relatively small air pressure will hold back a much greater water pressure. After the valve operates, the entire sprinkler system functions as a regular wet system.

Q. What are the two types of dry pipe valves?

A. Differential and mechanical.

Q. Describe briefly a differential dry pipe valve.

A. A differential dry pipe valve consists of two clappers of unequal size, so assembled that the larger clapper subject to air pressure holds closed the smaller clapper which shuts out the water supply. The trip point is determined by the ratio of the area of the one clapper to the other. The ordinary ratio is about six to one. With ordinary water pressures of from 50 to 100 pounds, the tripping air pressure will be about 15 pounds or less, but in order to have a margin of safety, it is customary to carry air pressures of 30 to 40 pounds. It is undesirable to carry higher air pressures than necessary, because of the time element involved in the escape of air and resultant lowering of air pressure to the trip point. (Where quick-opening devices are used, this time is reduced to a minimum.)

Q. Describe briefly a mechanical dry pipe valve.

A. In the mechanical dry pipe valve, the air and water seats may or may not be of the same area. The air clapper, under the influence of air pressure, holds the water clapper shut through a system of multiplying levers. The trip point is set mechanically by a stress screw and the amount of water pressure has little or no effect on it. These valves are designed to operate under fixed air pressure of 10 to 15 pounds less, even as low as 10 to 14 ounces per square inch. Air pressure is produced and automatically maintained by hydraulic or electric air compressor.

Q. According to the Standards, when is a quick opening device required?

A. Dry pipe valves controlling more than 500 gallons of capacity should be provided with an approved quick-opening device.

Q. According to the Standards, how large a system can be controlled by one dry pipe valve?

A. Not more than 600 sprinklers or more than 750 gallon system capacity should be controlled by one dry pipe valve.

Q. What is the maximum air pressure (in excess of the tripping pressure of the dry pipe valve) considered necessary to maintain?

A. Fifteen to 20 pounds. High air pressure in a dry pipe system is undesirable.

Q. What is the required capacity of the air compressor in a dry pipe system?

A. It must be capable of restoring normal air pressure within 30 minutes.

Q. What is the maximum allowable leak in air pressure in a dry pipe system?

A. Not more than 1½ pounds air pressure in 24 hours is the maximum allowable leak for a dry pipe system.

Q. What precautions should be taken to avoid excessive air pressure building up in a dry pipe system?

A. An approved relief valve between the compressor and controlling valve set to release at five pounds in excess of maximum air pressure for the system.

Q. How much delay is there in water reaching a sprinkler in a dry pipe system?

A. The maximum delay should not exceed two minutes, and it is much less under most conditions. If more than one

sprinkler opens, the delay is even less.

Q. What are the two general types of quick-opening devices?

A. The two general types of quick-opening devices are the accelerator and the exhauster.

Q. Describe the action of these two devices.

A. In the accelerator type, when the sprinkler opens and pressure drops one or two pounds, the diaphragm becomes unbalanced. This forces open a valve which permits the air pressure in the system to enter the intermediate chamber and the valve trips. In the exhauster type, the diaphragm causes a larger valve to open and the air in the system discharges to atmosphere through a 2-inch outlet. Air pressure in the system is thereby rapidly reduced until the tripping point of the dry pipe valve is reached.

Q. How quickly will the dry pipe valve open in a dry pipe system equipped with a quick opening device?

A. With an accelerator type, the valve should trip in 10 to 15 seconds, while with an exhauster it may take a little longer depending on the size of the system, but water will reach the open sprinkler in about the same time with either.

Q. If the quick-opening device fails to operate, will the dry pipe valve still function?

A. Yes. If the quick-opening device fails to operate, there will be a longer delay in the water reaching the open sprinkler. The system will operate the same as a small system which is not required to have a quick-opening device.

Q. What are "small dry pipe valves?"

A. Small dry pipe valves are intended to control small portions of a wet system which are subject to freezing. The sizes are mostly 2 to 3½-inches.

Q. With how many alarms should all dry pipe valves be equipped?

A. Dry pipe valves should be equipped with two approved types of both water motor and electric circuit closer (or opener) alarms with gongs properly located. A bypass should be provided so that these alarms can be properly tested by water flow.

Q. When can a nonfreezing solution be used in a system subject to freezing?

A. Nonfreezing solutions may be used for maintaining automatic sprinkler protection in minor unheated areas which otherwise would be unprotected during freezing weather, but they should not be encouraged as a substitute for approved dry pipe valves or air check valves.

Q. What nonfreezing solutions are recognized by the NFPA Sprinkler Standards?

A. Water solutions of glycerine or propylene glycol if public water is used in sprinkler system. Water solutions of diethylene glycol, ethylene glycol, propylene glycol or calcium chloride if public water is not used for the sprinkler system.

Q. What special health hazard is introduced when these nonfreezing solutions are used in a system supplied by a public water system?

A. The danger of polluting the public system. Only chemically pure glycerine is satisfactory from the standpoint of safety to health.

Q. When is it permissible to shut off and drain a portion of a wet system in cold weather?

A. Where only a few sprinklers are subject to freezing in a wet system, such sprinklers are sometimes shut off and drained in cold weather if the hazard is not great. The Sprinkler Standards provide that no more than 10 such sprinklers can be so shut off, but in practice the fire hazard is the determining factor. These shut-off valves are sometimes referred to as "cold-weather" valves, not to be confused with small dry pipe valves, which are sometimes known as cold weather valves.

Q. In what types of occupancies would a deluge system be found?

A. In various high-hazard occupancies requiring quick application of large quantities of water.

Q. Describe briefly a pressure tank dry pipe system.

A. This type of dry pipe system with a pressure tank located in the basement is designed for use in "light hazard" occupancies such as schools, small hotels, country clubs, small mercantiles, etc., under conditions where an adequate water supply is not available. It is not likely that more than five or 10 sprinklers will operate. A limited amount of water under heavy pressure should give adequate protection. The air in the sprinkler piping is under heavy pressure, usually about 100 to 110 pounds, the same pressure being maintained in the pressure tank with an equalizing orifice bypass. When the air pressure in the system is reduced due to the opening of a sprinkler, the water in the pressure tank is forced into the system due to the pressure of the air confined in the tank. An outside fire department connection should be provided if there is any form of water supply at all available. These systems are approved with a maximum pipe size of 2½-inches. The time it takes for the water to reach the sprinkler depends on the distance from the pressure tank to the open sprinkler. Generally, this distance should not exceed 300 to 400 feet, under which conditions the time delay should not exceed 30 to 45 seconds to the farthest sprinkler. Electric power must be available at all times to operate the automatic air compressor, low-air, and water-flow alarms.

Q. During routine inspection of buildings or for any other reasons, when fire department personnel are in sprinklered buildings,

what are some of the things they should look for?

A. They should look for obvious violations of sprinkler system regulations such as sprinkler heads painted, unauthorized suspension of objects from sprinkler piping, etc. They should also familiarize themselves with the location of outside fire department siamese connections and the location of dry pipe valves and shut-off valves. In this connection, it is appropriate that they advise the property owners to place a placard or some sort of sign at the shut-off valve showing the names and telephone numbers of any persons who should be notified if the sprinkler system must be left in an unserviceable condition after a fire in the building.

Q. What are the duties of the fire department with regard to leaving a sprinklered building after a fire in that building?

A. It is the duty of the fire department, if at all possible, to restore the system to a serviceable condition before leaving it. If a dry pipe system must unavoidably be left in a "wet" condition, or if a wet system is in danger of freezing in cold weather due to failure of the heating system of the building as a result of a fire or for any other reason, the fire department should make sure that the proper responsible person or persons are notified.

Q. What action can fire department personnel take if difficulty is encountered in removing the "caps" from an outside fire department connection?

A. Many "caps" on the fire department connection are made of cast iron or other brittle material and so designed that they can be broken by striking them with a hammer or similar tool. Care should be taken that the connections themselves are not damaged.

Q. Where are the shut-off valves of sprinkler systems usually found, and why is it advisable to shut off a sprinkler system water supply promptly as soon as it has been determined that the fire has been extinguished or can be controlled effectively by the fire department equipment at hand?

A. They are usually found in the basements of buildings at the wall adjacent to the street the building faces. They should be shut off promptly to reduce water damage.

Chapter 13

Cellar fires

PROBABLY MORE BUILDINGS are destroyed by fires that started in cellars than in any other place in a building. There are a number of reasons; the important ones are enumerated here:

1. As a rule the combustion process in cellars is slow. There is a lack of oxygen and draft effect. This creates huge amounts of smoke, making it difficult for firemen to advance to the fire area.

2. Discovery of such fires usually is delayed because the fire may be burning deep within the cellar. If the building is closed for the night (or weekend), the combustion process, even though slow, may have progressed to the point where the building is seriously threatened. This often takes place before the fire department is even called.

3. Ventilation is limited.

4. Men going down into a cellar fire are in essence moving down into a chimney—quite the opposite of moving in below a fast-moving fire with the heat and smoke moving up and away from the firemen.

5. Cellar fires usually require breathing masks. This limits free breathing and visibility.

6. The application of water to the seat of the fire is frequently inefficient. What cannot be seen is difficult to hit.

7. It is difficult to determine whether the fire is moving up beyond the reach of the hose streams.

8. The technique of handling such fires is not well understood.

9. A cellar fire exposes all floors above the cellar to the action of the combustion products which fill the upper floors rapidly. People above the fire may be seriously endangered. Fires on upper floors do not, as a rule, expose lower floors and people can exit quite safely.

10. It will be necessary to ventilate and search the upper floors both for fire involvement and for people who may have been overcome or are unable to get out without help.

11. This search procedure will demand the services of a good deal of your incoming manpower; it will delay your getting the required hand lines into position to combat the fire spread.

12. The materials stored in most cellars provide sufficient fuel for a hot fire.

Operations at cellar fires

Cellar fires are often difficult to penetrate with hand lines. Therefore firemen resort to lines from windows and doorways, or cellar pipes from above. Basements often become flooded to depths of several feet. In fact, with some cellar fires this is the only practical method of extinguishment. This is the case where the floor above is reinforced concrete,

FIGURE 114. *Two lines working abreast can push the combustion products ahead. But if you are going to use a wide fog pattern there must be* *ventilation ahead or trapped gases may ignite and flash back. Provide another line to protect the rear entrance.*

making it impossible to cut enough holes in the floor to cover the fire below with cellar pipes.

Self-contained breathing apparatus is an absolute necessity. It is the only way men can operate in such smoky conditions. Men should work in pairs, particularly in cellar fires. If a man becomes unconscious and falls, he can drown in the accumulated water from the hose lines. Do not use filter masks in cellar fires, for two reasons: There may be too much toxic gas for the filter mask to handle (above two percent of carbon monoxide, three percent ammonia). There may be, and often is, an oxygen deficiency—less than 16 percent will not support life.

In operating at cellar fires, watch for fire travel. Consider the possibility of fire traveling up sidewalls and vertical arteries such as light shafts, vent shafts, or dumbwaiters. Fire also can move horizontally in cellar fires. It can extend into adjoining cellars through poorly fire-stopped floor joists that may rest

on common party walls separating the two cellars. Check these possible routes of fire extension and cover them by lines if such extension appears likely.

In the average residential or small commercial structure, lines should be moved into the cellar or basement by the inside stairway. The hottest and smokiest part of the fire will be at the top of this stairway leading to the basement. If conditions are so severe that this line cannot be moved down, close the door. Leave the hose line in the hall to cover the inside stairway should fire burn through the door or come up via the stairway or side walls.

It is of primary importance to retain the use of the inside stairway. Occupants may need it to escape from the building. It also is vital that this avenue of communication be kept open for the fire department to advance lines, ventilate, search, and rescue. If it appears the fire may move up and threaten the first floor (or higher), you must lay addi-

136

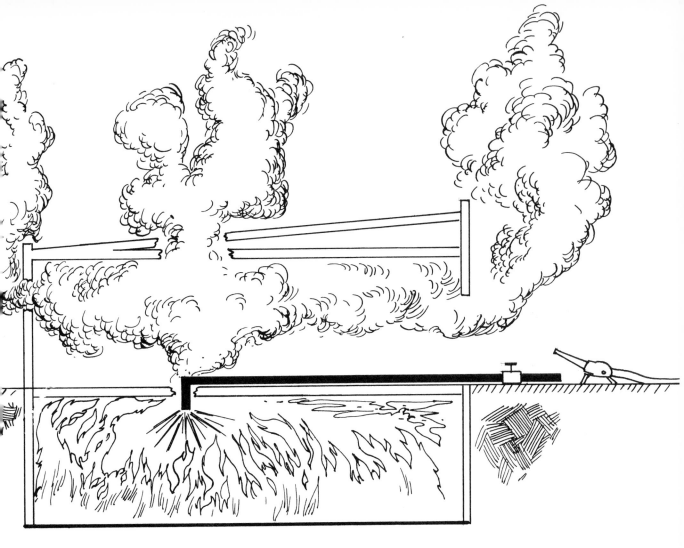

FIGURE 115 (Above). *A cellar nozzle with revolving fog head requires no manpower to operate the nozzle. If the floor goes, no life is jeopardized. In this example the floor above the cellar has been vented and a heavy stream appliance is ready in case fire breaks through the floor.*

FIGURE 116 (Left). *To give a visual demonstration of the water distribution pattern of a revolving fog head nozzle on a 2½-inch cellar pipe, the cellar pipe was dropped through the rungs of an aerial ladder extended about 20 feet to the rear. The stream covered a diameter of 35 feet, flowing at about 300 gpm at 100 psi.*

FIGURE 117. *Large amounts of foam can be generated rapidly. This took about two minutes.*

tional hose lines to head it off. You should not wait for positive signs of involvements on upper floors. By then you may be too late. When you suspect such upper floor involvement, get the lines upstairs. Ventilate thoroughly so that men can hold their positions and examine vertical channels for fire spread.

If the cellar is large and the fire is hot, one hose line may be insufficient to handle the blaze. Men cannot move in against the fierce heat. Remember, masks are not designed to protect against heat!

Often in these hot cellar fires another line is stretched and advanced via a rear cellar entrance. This drives the heat and smoke toward the opposing crew. Neither crew will be able to advance and the fire will continue to burn upward. It is better to have both lines abreast and move in this way, pushing the heat and smoke ahead with a fog stream. But be careful. Remember these two points: ventilate and provide a second line at the rear. There must be ventilation ahead of the fog stream. Otherwise the heated gases may be trapped ahead of you, ignite, and flash

back. Provide another line at the rear of the cellar, but not to move in with. This line is to protect the rear entrance and check any fire from extending up this channel unnoticed. (See Figure 114.)

The cellar nozzle. There are additional techniques to use in cellar fires. One is the cellar nozzle through holes cut in the floor above the fire.

You can feel the floor for hot spots. This will indicate where to cut. If there are rugs on the floor remove them. They will insulate the floor from the heat of the fire, nullifying your best guide as to where to cut.

It is extremely helpful if there is someone familiar with the arrangement of partitions and the type of materials stored in the cellar. It will guide you in making efficient use of water on the fire with your cellar nozzles. You must keep in mind the urgent need for complete ventilation of all floors above the fire.

The use of cellar nozzles indicates it was not possible to advance lines into the cellar. It follows then that physical examination of

FIGURE 118. *A stubborn cellar fire was set in this abandoned building for training. It was given a 10-minute preburn; then high-expansion foam* *was started. In about five minutes the fire began to darken and was under control shortly thereafter. (See Figure 119).*

the structural supports was not possible either. Control of cellar fires may take a long time. If men are to continue operating the cellar nozzles they may be working on a floor that is, or might become, seriously weakened by the fire below.

If the cellar nozzles have a revolving distributor head, it is not necessary to keep men on such floors. The head will distribute the water up, down, and in a circle automatically. If the cellar nozzle is not designed for such automatic distribution, change to a distributor and back your men out. You should plan on covering an area about 30 to 35 feet in diameter (about 900 square feet) with a 2½-inch distributor nozzle. If the cellar is considerably larger, plan on more distributors. Try to keep the distributor head about two feet below the ceiling joists.

Plan for the possibility of the fire getting away from you. Check the possible exposures. Start setting up heavy stream equipment if there is a possibility of such exposures being threatened by a forced withdrawal of interior streams. (See Figure 115-116.)

Large commercial structures may have sprinklers. If so with a cellar fire your first lines should be connected to the fire department connection—the outside sprinkler siamese. Supply the sprinkler system until the fire is under control. Water damage is preferable to the loss of the entire building and its contents.

High expansion foam. A new and promising technique for the stubborn cellar fire is foam with up to 1,000 to 1 expansion. This foam can fill a small cellar and smother a fire in minutes. Water damage is nil. The bubbles

FIGURE 119. *Foam has now completely filled the cellar and is pushing out of the first floor (window at left). This is an effective technique for fighting cellar fires, but it does require these considerations: (1) The windows and other openings should be closed to allow foam to build up. (2) Be sure fire has not traveled up side walls, ducts, etc., or that it has not burned through the floor to* *ignite materials above. (3) Search must be made for people overcome. (4) Ventilation must be provided for floors above. (5) Foam will extinguish fire in gas meters, but gas will continue to leak and may explode. Shut off gas and electricity at street. (6) Make sure you have sufficient foam on hand to handle the job. (7) Lay out conventional hose lines in case foam is not effective.*

break down in a few hours, leaving only a harmless water residue. The material is non-toxic.

During the winter of 1964 the Chicago Fire Department used the technique on a fire in the Goldblatt warehouse. The warehouse, 460x510 feet, was one in a complex of similar large buildings. The fire originated in the cellar at about 5 P.M. on a workday. The Chicago Fire Department contained the fire in the cellar for more than 12 hours despite efforts to pierce 10 inches of reinforced concrete to insert cellar pipes. The water supply was brought to the scene by relays.

Late that night when it appeared all else would fail, the decision was made to try to fill the cellar with expanded foam. After foam

was pumped into the cellar for several hours, the heat, smoke, and fire subsided. It appeared to be under control. But the supply of foam ran out. The fire increased in intensity and floors began to show huge cracks. Steps were taken to protect exposures if the fire broke out of the cellar and all men were ordered out of the building. At 7 A.M. the next day the fire did break out of the basement and the warehouse was destroyed. The fire department succeeded in containing the fire to this single unit—no mean feat considering the near conflagration they faced. (See Figures 117-119.)

There are two methods which are not ordinarily used in firefighting that can be employed in stubborn cellar fires. The first is to

140

play heavy hose streams onto the first floor (if the floor is wooden). Enough water may seep through the floor to act as a makeshift sprinkler system. The second method: breech adjoining cellar walls to get hose lines to the seat of the fire.

Remember, do not keep companies on a floor above a hot cellar fire too long. Be particularly cautious where there are unprotected metal structural members. The floor may collapse and bury your men in the fire below. If you are concerned about the stability of the floor, yet it is important to keep hose lines in operation, use distributing nozzles at the end of hose lines into the cellar. Back your men out.

Some building codes require what are called "basement pipe inlets." These are cir-cular openings in the floor above the cellar. They are covered by some type of metal plate with provisions for ready removal. Their purpose is for the insertion of cellar nozzles or distributors.

At first glance basement pipe inlets appear to be of material aid in fighting inaccessible cellar fires. They may indeed prove useful at times. But usually they are of questionable value. They would nullify the value of a fire-resistant floor because of the openings. They could be difficult to locate during a fire—when they are needed. They might be covered by storage and therefore inaccessible, or you might not be able to find them because of heavy smoke conditions. Heat could communicate through the metal covers and ignite combustible materials stored above the openings.

Chapter 14

High-rise fires

HIGH-RISE FIRES are a strange breed of cat to the average fire department. Since there are relatively few major fires in tall structures, expertise built up by trial and error is lacking—except in the large cities. But with the rapid proliferation of high-rise buildings in the small urban areas, the problem is now becoming more common.

Lest the fire chief with a new high-rise in his area feel he is inheriting an insoluble problem, he can feel somewhat assured if the building is constructed under good building codes. If so the high-rise will give him less trouble than any other structure in his city. If the building code was vague or enforcement was lax during the planning and construction, he will inherit a headache.

There are thousands of high-rise buildings in the United States, and more are being built every day. Yet up to this time no high-rise has suffered a fire of sufficiently disastrous proportions to endanger the building structurally. True, there have been serious fires—loss of life and large financial losses. But as you will see later in this chapter and in your own examination of such fires, there is a consistent pattern that emerges.

How high is a high-rise?

First let us define what we mean by the term high-rise. Then we should determine what is different about fires in these buildings and why they constitute an unusual problem.

Any fire that is beyond the reach of your portable equipment should be considered a high-rise fire. If you have a 100-foot aerial ladder which can reach to the eighth or ninth floors, any structure above that height is beyond your portable equipment for rescue purposes. If you use a ladder pipe from the fly ladder which can penetrate the floor area two stories above the ladder pipe, then for stream penetration anything higher than the eleventh floor is beyond your reach and should be considered a high-rise.

You may have buildings in your city which are not higher than your aerial ladders, but because they are set back excessively from the street (as in housing projects) your aerial ladder will not reach the objective. For all purposes such set-back buildings may well require high-rise operational techniques.

The basic difference in fighting fire in a high-rise is that you must rely on standpipes for your streams. Men require special training in such operations. (See Chapter 4, ladder company operations, and Chapter 11, standpipes.)

Another difference is that you have to rely on elevators. You may have to wait for them, slowing your operation considerably.

High-rise fires are more difficult to fight

because normal ventilation procedures cannot be easily employed. There can be no top venting. In order to clear corridors you have to rely on cross ventilation by way of windows on each side of the halls.

The construction of high-rise buildings is usually fire-resistant. This means that stairs and elevators are enclosed in fire-protected assemblies of three or more hours' duration. Main structural members (columns, beams, girders, floors) will be protected with more than three hours of fire-safe-rated materials.

The enclosed stairway is one reason you cannot ventilate by way of vertical arteries such as stair shafts. Certainly, though, one would have to admit this kind of construction is advantageous insofar as the occupants are concerned.

People above the fire are usually quite safe, although there may be some smoke involvement of the upper floors. These buildings are rarely occupied by heavy manufacturing or warehouse type of operations. Therefore the fire loading will not produce a hot enough fire to endanger the structural stability of the building. Usually the occupancies are residential or offices. In the residence type high-rise the fire usually is confined to a single apartment, though the smoke and heat may travel hundreds of feet down all the halls.

While there is no question of the superior qualities of fire-resistant construction, there are some definite disadvantages for the firefighters. The structural features (enclosed elevator and stairway shafts, fire-resistant floors and walls) which do not allow the fire to extend also serve to retain the heat. The entire floor and in particular the fire area build up heat and hold it like an oven. Firemen have to undergo severe punishment to reach the seat of the fire. Keep in mind that masks are not designed to protect firemen from heat.

Fires have been known to spread to upper floors in fire-resistant structures—even those with enclosed stairs. The reason is faulty construction. In nearly every such case the fire spread because of nonfire-stopped pipe shafts or duct networks. These are often lined with combustible insulation, in contact with framing, or heavily coated inside with grease from cooking stoves. Even where such ducts will not carry fire, they may spread smoke, sparks, and heat from the fire floor to many floors above.

One other method of fire communication to upper floors should be mentioned. It is by fire billowing out of windows and lapping into windows of the floor above. This is readily combatted by getting men to the floor above, closing the windows, getting standpipe hose lines into operation to extinguish any fire that has already started.

Smoke can be spread by elevators to floors above and below the fire. The air movement created by the travel of high-speed elevators acts as a huge piston pulling and pushing the smoke into and out of the elevator shaft onto the various floors.

Another difficulty in these fires is the slow egress of large numbers of people trying to escape. If the people exit via the elevators, this delays the use of elevators by the fire department.

While the more modern high-rise, built under adequate codes, will have enclosed stairways, there still are many structures with open stair shafts leading from the lowest to the highest floors. In these buildings the problems are magnified. Combustion products from a fire on the lower floors can create hazardous conditions and cause loss of life 20 stories above the fire floor. Such conditions did occur in the Winecoff Hotel fire in Georgia, the LaSalle Hotel fire in Chicago, and the Times Tower office building fire in New York City.

In buildings with open stairways, people above the fire are in serious jeopardy. The firemen you send to ventilate, search, and rescue on upper floors may be endangered. Self-contained breathing masks are essential. An attempt must be made to ventilate the stair shaft at the roof level to pull the combustion products clear of the halls below.

Every effort must be made to get hose lines to the fire area to cut off the upward spread as rapidly as possible. These lines should be manned with extra personnel so that firemen at the nozzle can be relieved frequently. This is so the firemen will be sure to hold their positions. If firemen are working above, these firemen must hold their positions or the men above may be cut off. If for any reason firemen on the hose lines cannot hold their position, the men operating above should be notified to get down before the lines are withdrawn.

Even if the hose streams cannot immediately attack the fire in the individual office or apartment, the stream should still operate in the halls to keep the combustion products from sweeping up the stairs. A sufficient number of hose streams should be brought into play to make sure this objective is assured. Lines must also be moved to the floor above to combat any extension here.

High-rise rescue

Rescue at fires beyond the reach of the aerial ladder is possible by one of these three methods:

1. Carrying a scaling ladder to the top of the aerial and climbing it to the trapped victim, then taking him down the same way. (See Figures 120-122.)

2. Lowering a firemen by rope from the floor above to reach the victim. The fireman and victim then are either lowered to the ground or pulled back to the floor above.

3. The firemen make the floor with a hose line from the standpipe and extinguish the fire in time to save the trapped person.

Even getting out of the apartment into the hall is no guarantee of reaching an exit by way of the halls. In some cases the secondary means of egress is so close to the primary means that both exits are cut off by one fire. Poor architectural planning is the source of the problem. In some cases apartment buildings are laid out with "dead end" corridors with no exit at the ends. In order to reach an exit, the person may have to pass the fire apartment. If the fire is blowing out of the apartment into the hall, the person cannot reach the exit and is trapped.

Involvement by smoke and heat may make any corridor untenable—even for trained firemen. Such smoke and heat can penetrate high up in these buildings from fires in lower floors because of the defective construction features previously mentioned.

Some operational guidelines

There are conditions that complicate operations at high-rise fires, and because of the complications it is important that firemen report properly equipped.

Normally ardous fire duty is further complicated in high-rise fires because of several conditions:

First, line advancement is slow. Men have to bring up rolled lengths of hose by elevators, stopping at the floor below to connect to the standpipe floor valve. They then have to stretch up to the fire floor.

Search and rescue is a time-consuming process. It takes considerable time for firemen to search along smoky corridors and rooms for persons who may be trapped. Frequently rooms are locked, requiring forcible entry with its attendant difficulties and delay.

Should electric power fail, the elevators may stop running. This means firemen must walk up to the fire floor, carrying hose lines and equipment.

Communications between operating units and the chief may be erratic because of the building's steel skeleton construction.

High-rise buildings are equipped with standpipes. They may also be equipped with sprinklers. In sprinklered occupancies one of the first hose lines should be connected to the sprinkler siamese for supply by a fire department pumper. Be careful when the hose line is connected that it is to the proper siamese. Unless the siamese is color-coded to distinguish the difference between the supply to the standpipe and to the sprinkler, it is easy to make a mistake. True, the purpose of the siamese is stamped onto the casting but in the dark it is difficult to read.

In tall buildings the height of the roof supply tank above the floor outlet valve to which the hose line will be connected may result in excessive pressures. To prevent people from being injured by this excessive pressure, a device is screwed into the outlet which cuts down on the flow, reducing the back pressure. If greater flow is desired, simply remove this pressure-reducing valve and reconnect your hose line.

FIGURE 120. *Rescue with the scaling ladder is an extremely difficult, dangerous undertaking to be used only when the situation is desperate. It requires coordinated training. The long toothed hook is swung around into the window and set firmly on the sill. One fireman climbs to make the rescue; the other fireman steadies the base of the scaling ladder. Both men cooperate in bringing the victim down.*

FIGURE 121. *In this rescue the fireman scales the building by himself. He sits across the sill when moving the ladder to the floor above. In this case he brings the victim down to the floor below. Victim waits on window sill until ladder is lowered another floor. This is repeated until safety is reached. In most cases he only has to bring the person down one floor below the fire. From there he can use the interior stairway.*

146

Firemen must carry equipment. An efficient officer reporting for an assignment will report with his men properly equipped. This is particularly important in high-rise operations, where men must operate at some distance from their apparatus. Carrying the proper equipment initially avoids the inexcusable delay that results when men have to go back to the apparatus to get what is needed after being assigned a position.

In any procedure which will require men to function a considerable distance from their trucks and to insure the continued efficient operations without loss of time, here is a list of the equipment firemen should carry:

All units—firemen assigned to ladder companies and engine companies should carry this equipment:

1. Self-contained breathing equipment for each man.
2. Portable radios.
3. Searchlights.
4. Life belts and ropes to be able to remove any victims safely or for escape of firemen.
5. Wooden door wedges. These may be used to hold doors open or to remove doors by inserting the wedge between the door and the jamb under the hinge and slamming the door shut, springing the hinge screws.
6. Spanner wrenches. To remove or connect hose lines to standpipe valves.
7. Forcible entry tool.

Engine companies should carry, in addition to items above:

1. Sufficient number of rolled or folded lengths of hose.
2. Nozzles.

Ladder companies should carry, in addition to items above:

1. A complete set of forcible entry tools including power saws, door forcers, etc.
2. Inhalators. If an unconscious person is found, valuable time can be saved by bringing the victim down one floor and beginning treatment there. Why go down possibly 20 floors and then to the truck before starting to revive the victim?

Whenever there is a shortage of manpower at these fires, the use of 1½-inch hose instead of the customary 2½-inch line is indicated. The increased mobility of the lighter lines and the speed with which they can be placed in service are usually sufficient reason for their use. As a general rule, fire loading is not sufficiently heavy in such fires to rule out the use of 1½-inch hose. However, if the fire is obviously of major proportions, the 2½-inch line should be used from the onset.

Fire officers operating at high-rise fires should keep a list of the men under their command and frequently refer to it. Of course they should do this at any serious fire where men are scattered or operating at distances from their apparatus. If the officers have a list, there will be little delay if a man is lost before he is missed and search for him can be started.

Real high-rise fires

A look at actual high-rise fires will give some indications of where the firefighting problems lie, and how best to handle them. It also can provide some guidelines for code requirements.

The major problem and the one most responsible for the spread of fires in high-rise buildings is the flue effect of the vertical openings—such as open interior stairways, elevator shafts, dumbwaiter shafts, and pipe chases. The higher the building, the greater the draft. Because of the height of these buildings, and, in most cases, with no way to ventilate the top of these open shafts, many fire officials have pressed for mechanical skylights which would open automatically in case of fire. This viewpoint gained considerable support after the Winecoff Hotel fire in Atlanta, Ga., in December, 1946, and the LaSalle Hotel fire in Chicago in June, 1946.*

In these hotel fires there were open stairways which allowed toxic gases to extend upward. There they spread laterally via the corridors and into the individual guest rooms, mainly by open transoms.

---

*These case histories are from American Insurance Association Bulletins No. 241 and No. 245.

FIGURE 122. *In this attempt at a scaling ladder rescue, the victim was trapped on the 12th floor in a fire-resistive high-rise. The fire was between the person and the hall door. Fortunately the engine company reached the apartment door in time* *to force the door and extinguish the fire before the fireman on the scaling ladder reached the trapped victim. He was brought to safety and required no medical aid.*

148

The argument has been posed that in such cases it would be improper, until all the people above the fire had been evacuated, to produce a draft, which would be very strong in a tall building, by opening up the enclosure at the top of such a stairway; the same would be true of an elevator shaft.

In connection with the above, it is worthwhile to consider both the LaSalle and Winecoff hotel fires. In both, there were ample ventilation openings above the fire, considerably more than would have been provided by any skylight at the top of the stairway. These venting facilities were provided by the open transoms and doors of rooms where windows were open, and in the case of the LaSalle, by the doors to the fire escapes, which were frequently opened during the fire.

Even with these numerous openings in the 20 stories above the lobby fire in the LaSalle, it should be noted that the loss of life occurred largely below the seventh floor. In like manner, the destructive effect of fire in the Winecoff was greatest between the sixth and twelfth floors, and even the toxic effect was less on the fifteenth.

It seems desirable, therefore, that consideration be given to the property and behavior of smoke or the products of combustion. Where there is fire burning with plenty of air, the product of combustion is largely carbon dioxide, which has a normal weight, or specific gravity, at ordinary room temperatures of about $1\frac{1}{2}$-times that of air. With this will be carbon particles, or soot, some carbon monoxide, and nitrogen.

All of these will be heated to a temperature, probably up to or above 1,200° F.; at this temperature the mixture of gases has much less weight, or specific gravity, than the air surrounding the gases; therefore they tend to rise. As anyone knows who has built a fire in a fireplace, these gases are cooled by contact with the walls and thus at some point above they lose their buoyancy. When this happens the gases no longer rise but instead tend to stratify. Succeeding masses of heated gases do not push through the strata but slip out from under if there is any space on the sides. Where there is no opening, the heated gases bank down and ultimately exude through the opening from which the fire was receiving its supply of air. This may slow down the burning rate and, if the shaft above is tight, may even extinguish the fire, as can be demonstrated by closing the top of a lamp chimney.

At just what height this stratification of smoke will take place will depend upon many things. The intensity and amount of the fire —that is, the heat units evolved—the size and length of the passageway, the temperature of the air and of the walls, the amount of carbon dioxide and soot produced, and the normal upward draft in the passageway all are factors. That a hot fire, fed by the paint on the walls, will travel upward four to six stories has been demonstrated in many fires, including those in the LaSalle and Winecoff hotels; but there also are many fires where conditions, especially a deficiency in heat, are such that smoke will not rise more than a few feet, or may settle to the ground. Such conditions are common with basement fires and fires involving rubber. The most common fire in which this occurs is where people burn fairly compact piles of leaves.

There is evidence then that the idea of fire and heat going to the top of an unvented shaft and mushrooming, then backing down to the floor below, may not always be true in every tall building. This behavior of smoke and toxic gases of combustion where they are cooled by the materials of incombustible construction of the building for considerable distance could nullify the probability of sufficient heat reaching any fusible link or other thermal device located at the skylight, in time to improve conditions from a safety to life standpoint.

Other cases on record, however, show that the toxic products of combustion will rise to great heights.

On November 22, 1961, a fire in the Times Tower building* in New York City caused the death of a civilian and two firemen. The building was 56 years old, 25 stories high, with cellars and subcellars below the subway.

---

*This description is in part from WNYF, the magazine of the New York City Fire Department.

An open-well double-run stairway extends from the first to the sixteenth floor. Access to the stories above the sixteenth floor was by an open single stair on the east side of the building. Elevator shafts extend between the first and sixteenth floors adjacent to stairs with only two of these shafts going up to the twenty-fourth floor. A circular stair extends from the twenty-fourth to the twenty-fifth floor; a wall ladder and scuttle lead to the small roof area of the tower.

Below street level was a subway arcade, and two lower storage levels. The fire started in the lowest level, 70 feet down, in some fluffy, flammable toys. It apparently smoldered unnoticed for a considerable time.

Responding units were met by smoke pushing out of the subway stair, located at the southwest corner of the building, and from other shaft and pipe openings at street level, on both the inside and outside of the building. Excited citizens reported that the fire was in a barbershop in the subway arcade on the Broadway side.

After ventilation and examination it was determined the heat and smoke apparently were rising from lower levels of the building via ducts and a service dumbwaiter shaft that passed through the barbershop and terminated at the first-floor drugstore.

Access to these lower levels could be had only from a stair (steel double-run) that began on the first floor, bypassed the arcade on the way down, and gave access to second- and third-level storage areas.

As discovered later, the fire was in the lowest level, in a large room that covered the entire subsurface of the Times Tower. This sub-basement contained the control boards, drums, and motors for the elevators; a carpenter shop; an area for storage; and various other operating equipment, including standpipe pump and sump pump. But the greatest area was used for storing toys made from kapok, excelsior, and plastics. Six vaulted rooms, used for additional toy storage, extended out beneath the Seventh Avenue sidewalk.

The fierce heat and smoke soon communicated to the shaftways, including the elevator shaft and stairwell and thence upward throughout the building, and actually started a fire on the second-lowest level. The stairwell leading from the fire area was directly adjacent to the open stairway on the first floor that went up through the building.

In the initial stage of the fire, units were dispatched throughout the building to search for occupants, two of whom were reported to be trapped on the twenty-second floor. The heat and smoke were so intense that it went through the building via the stairs and elevator shafts and, finding no outlet at the roof, mushroomed and banked down several floors from the top, creating a hot toxic atmosphere.

Two firemen apparently were taken to an upper floor in an elevator to search for the occupants. Both men were later found unconscious by their comrades. Despite mouth-to-mouth resuscitation both firemen succumbed. The porter who had taken them up was later found dead in the elevator car, stopped between the first and second floors.

A 36-story office building in Montreal less than a year old had a fire in a pipe shaft which produced sufficient smoke to warrant evacuation of the entire structure. The pipe shaft carried the fuel oil and natural gas pipe lines, air-conditioning ducts, soil lines, and water lines. There were no fire stops in the entire shaft.

A welder's spark ignited some combustible lining which was carried up by the strong natural draft and soon spewed out fire and smoke into the lower floors. This was picked up by the air-conditioning ducts which spread the smoke over the lower part of the building. The smoke spread to the upper floors by way of open stair shaft doors where it was again redistributed by the upper-floor air-conditioning duct networks. The ducts were protected by fusible link dampers but they failed to operate. Three thousand people left the building safely.

Twenty-two people died and a score were injured at a Jacksonville, Fla., hotel fire in December, 1963. The fire started in a dropped ceiling space in the hotel ballroom on the second floor of the 13-story hotel. The fire spread to pipe shafts which carried the combustion products, like chimneys, to the upper floors. The smoke built up in the pipe shafts and at 7:45 A.M. burst out into the corridors through small access panels. The hallways almost immediately were impassable and the smoke began to fill the rooms, trapping the occupants. One of the two enclosed stairways filled with smoke and could not be used.

Hundreds of people were able to reach the usable stairway. Some who made their way to the roof were rescued by helicopter. Others on lower floors were rescued by ladders. People were saved by sliding down the drain pipes or on bed sheets tied together. Although the fire was confined to the second floor, 20 persons above died of smoke poisoning. Most of them died on the top floor.

Buildings built with unprotected or poorly protected vertical openings, which produce the same effect as a chimney flue, will cause alarming smoke conditions on upper floors from even small fires.

A test in Paris, France, in 1962 is a case in point. A test fire in a ground-floor room of a 20-story building created such severe smoke buildup that people were driven from the twentieth floor. The main stairway, which was open, and the halls were impassable down to the twelfth floor within 10 minutes.

On August 5, 1970, a most alarming and unusual high-rise fire occurred in New York City, taxing the efforts of the New York Fire Department for more than five hours and killing two building guards who were trapped in a stalled elevator.

The fire started in the large concealed ceiling spaces of the thirty-third floor. There was no subdivision of these spaces whatever. Fire feeding on plastic pipe and wire insulation allowed burning drippings to fall on the upholstered furniture below, which began to burn. The heat and smoke were now pulled into the return air-conditioning ducts (the fans continued to run for almost two hours after the start of the fire). It spread rapidly to the thirty-fourth and thirty-fifth floors by way of poorly fire-stopped vertical arteries.

Smoke so dense it required evacuation of people on almost all floors spread through the building by air-conditioning ducts. Some of the firemen were trapped in an elevator

on the fourth floor by elevator malfunction and had to chop their way to safety.

High temperatures caused severe damage to the structure and its contents. Steel beams on the thirty-third and thirty-fourth floors were damaged. Apparently the sprayed-on asbestos fibre fire-retarding did not adhere in some places and had been removed during construction in other places. Therefore it becomes obvious that required built-in protective features, even though called for by the plans, may be less than adequate.

The firefighting technique in this fire is similar to that in other high-rise fires except that this operation was extremely difficult and punishing.

This fire only proves again that regardless of structural components, if there is excessive fire loading in a building, if careless workmanship allows unprotected or poorly protected vertical openings, and if interconnected ducts run horizontally and vertically throughout, disastrous fires can occur. In this case, poor design and construction methods allowed a fire to seriously threaten structural stability of parts of the building, an unusual situation for a modern high-rise. It makes one wonder how many other buildings now standing or to be built are as vulnerable.*

Another high-rise fire occurred on the thirty-sixth floor of a two-year-old 40-story apartment building on the lake front in Chicago in the predawn hours of January 24, 1969. Three people died from the fire and a fourth died later of a heart attack in the lobby.

The building was completely fire-resistant. The stairs and elevators were enclosed in fire-resistant partitions as per the Chicago code. The fire started in the living room of apartment 3612. It was a corner apartment, a contributing factor in that when the apartment's Thermopane windows broke, a wild draft was created from both sides of the apartment. The two occupants died, though the husband managed to get past the fire in the living room into the hall to warn the people in the next apartment and to ask them

---

*For complete details on this fire see, "One New York Plaza Fire," published by the American Insurance Association.

FIGURE 123 (Above). *Corner apartment on 36th floor of a Chicago apartment building after the fire. Plywood covers broken windows which were broken by the heat of fire. Prevailing winds blew fire like a fire storm out into the hall via the open apartment door. Fierce heat incinerated every living thing in the room.*

FIGURE 124 (Right). *This is a result of the same fire as shown in Figure 123. Note the heavy char on the face of this door. It leads to the apartment across the hall from the fire apartment. People trapped in this apartment were safe all through the fire. The transom (composition board) held during the fire but was removed later for observation. The plywood shown here was used as a temporary covering.*

FIGURE 125. *The fire fed on the wood faces of the apartment doors as it moved down the hall. Firemen undergo intense punishment moving in against such heat. There is no way to ventilate these halls except through apartment windows in the apartment across the hall from the fire apartment. Smoke ejector fans are helpful. In many cases the windows are fixed and cannot be opened.*

FIGURE 126. *This is an apartment on the fire floor. The occupant escaped, leaving the door open. This is a common occurrence and is frequently the reason fire involves other apartments. Note how fire has begun to involve the entrance to the apartment and how the heat buckled the metal door frames.*

to call the fire department. A man in the apartment two doors down the hall also died.

When the fire in the living room got hot enough, it broke the large Thermopane windows on both walls of the apartment. The resulting fierce draft blew the fire through the apartment door into the hall like a blow torch. The husband had left the door open in his escape to the corridor. Fire fed on the wood face of the solid core doors of each apartment and the heat wave penetrated the entire length of the corridor to the opposite fire door of the emergency stairs.

This emergency fire stairway has a novel shaft in the entrance. When heat actuates a thermostatic device it opens windows in the shaft, pulling the smoke from the stair shaft and allowing the people to exit in safety. (See figures 111 and 112.) Smoke permeated to the thirty-ninth floor via the duct system and elevator shafts. People on the floors above the fire were uncomfortable from the smoke but in no danger. In fact, if the people on the fire floor had stayed in their apartments and held their heads out the windows, they too would have been perfectly safe.

One factor which contributed to the problem was this: three policemen rushed up in the elevators before the fire department's arrival with the intent of saving lives. They made the classic mistake of going directly to the fire floor. They were in immediate trouble when the elevator doors opened and they were met by a pall of smoke and heat and were eventually overcome. The policemen did arouse occupants, both on the fire floor and the floors above. This turned out to be a mistake. Those people who remained in their apartments with doors closed were safe. The others rushed into the corridor and were in serious danger. They also left the doors to their apartments open, allowing the fire to penetrate the apartments to some extent.

The Chicago Fire Department did excellent work by moving in with a 2½-inch line taken off the standpipe from the floor below. A second line was stretched from the emergency stairs but the first line succeeded in halting the fire spread. This firemen took a great deal of punishment during their operation. (See Figures 123 to 126.)

Probably the most significant point to be made from these fires is that normal hazards are in most cases seriously aggravated in high-rise structures.

Summary of high-rise fire problem

In studying these fires and other high-rise fires, a general pattern emerges. Let us recapitulate and summarize these problems in most high-rise fires as they concern both the occupants and the fire departments involved:

1. Fires occur well beyond the reach of our portable equipment—ladders, exterior streams.

2. Elevators in the building have to be used to reach the fire, but they also are being used by fleeing residents.

3. The fire floor, because of fire-resistant construction and enclosed stairs, will retain the heat like an oven.

4. There is no way for combustion products to vent. Therefore these products fill the corridors and apartments by way of open doors and elevator shafts. This makes the job of firemen extremely punishing.

5. It is difficult to find the fire in the intense heat and smoke.

6. The work of extinguishment is slow and arduous. Firemen have to advance down long corridors to reach the fire and search apartments for people who have been overcome.

7. Co-ordination of operating forces under these conditions is a nightmare. Radios do not operate well in steel skeleton buildings. Men may be cut off, lost, and overcome.

8. Visibility is severely limited.

9. Any additional equipment needed to operate will require as much as 15 minutes to return with it.

10. There may be literally dozens of people overcome, requiring much more help than is available on the original response. Greater alarms for manpower will be needed.

11. The floor above may become involved by fire lapping out of a window and into apartments above.

12. There may be smoke involvement of upper floors by way of exhaust ducts from bathrooms and kitchens (negative pressure

here), poorly fire-stopped pipe chases, the up and down piston effect of high-speed elevators.

13. No fire alarm systems are required in high-rise residential buildings. There is no way hundreds of occupants can be advised what to do.

14. If firemen do get into the individual apartments on the fire floor and are instructed to vent by way of the windows, can they do so? Imagine the terrible injuries that could be inflicted on people in the street by large sheets of plate glass falling from hundreds of feet above. Some way has to be found to alleviate this problem. One way is to have smaller windows beside the large panes. The small window should be made removable from the inside.

15. If the elevator doors are operated by electric eyes, be careful. They are designed to open when the light beam is interrupted by a person passing through. If smoke buildup is heavy on a floor it may be enough to prevent the elevator doors from closing and you will not be able to operate the elevators. This is another reason why you should always stop the elevator at the floor below the fire.

16. The chances are that you will not be able to take control of the elevators because people on every floor will be pressing the button to summon the elevator. There should be a manual override installed on all elevators for emergency use.

17. There is a possibility that fire operations may burn electric wires or that water streams may short out electric circuits. This may stall elevators between floors, trapping people.

Summary of operations at high-rise fires

Your operational techniques will generally follow these procedures:

1. Stretch lines from the standpipe on the floor below the fire. Move up to the fire floor, charge the line, and move in on the floor. It is vital that this line be advanced to the fire area. Use as many men as you can to move the line in and relieve the nozzlemen frequently.

2. Stretch a second line from the second floor below the fire and back up the first line.

In this way the first line can move in rapidly, knowing that if they do pass any incipient fires they will be taken care of by the second line.

3. If the fire and heat are too severe for one line, have both lines advance together.

4. Get a third line in by way of the rear stairway. Stretch it from the standpipe in similar manner to the first line. Back up this line, just as you did the first line. Neither of these lines going in the rear stairway would use water until they came to the fire area. Avoid operating lines toward each other. Use water from one direction only. The opposing lines would use water only to halt extension of the fire in their direction.

5. If the fire conditions are not too severe or if you have a shortage of manpower, use 1½-inch hose.

6. Check corridors and apartments for people overcome and remove them to the floor below for medical attention. It may not be necessary to take them all the way down.

7. Ventilate by opening windows in individual apartments to create a cross draft. Use wedges to keep apartment doors open.

8. Check the floors above for any fire extension by way of exterior windows (use lines off standpipe for such extension, which is usually minor).

9. Ventilate upper floors and search for people overcome or in difficulty.

10. Use a public address system and loudspeakers to shout instructions to residents. Ask them to stay in their apartments and close the doors but keep them unlocked. This will make it easier for firemen to search apartments.

11. If examination of the floor above shows major involvement, call for additional hose lines to this floor and the floors above as needed.

Recommended built-in safety features

At the beginning of this chapter we said that there is a pattern of problems that reveals similar hazards in most high-rise fires. In the modern high-rise large numbers of occupants are beyond the reach of today's portable fire department equipment, so their safety depends on the built-in protective features of the structure.

Areas of potential hazard such as heating, power generating, air-conditioning, and storage must be properly segregated and sprinklered. There must be absolute fire-resistant cut-offs between potential hazard areas and the remainder of the structure.

There is no question that unprotected vertical and horizontal openings allow smoke and heat to spread rapidly to involve higher and adjacent areas in fire. These unprotected openings are pipe shafts, stairways, elevators, duct systems, laundry and trash chutes, and false dropped ceilings.

High-rise buildings may be made perfectly safe from fire spread, although it is true that so long as the contents of an apartment are combustible we will continue to have fires that can kill the occupants. But proper construction and forethought can insure that the fire will not extend beyond the individual apartment.

The following recommendations will provide the kind of safety that is needed:

1. In commercial occupancies (offices, showrooms) regardless of structural fire-resistant construction, limit the fire-loading below that which can endanger the structural stability of the building.

2. Allow no combustible materials to be used in the structure or the exterior finish.

3. Eliminate any materials which give off noxious fumes—regardless of their nonflammable characteristics.

4. Vertical arteries (pipe shafts, ducts, etc.) should be enclosed in fire-safe materials and fire-stopped at each floor; ducts which pass through floors should be check-dampered at each such point and protected by heat- and smoke-sensitive devices which will not only close off the duct but shut down the blower motors.

5. Vertical arteries (stairs, elevators, dumbwaiter shafts, etc.) should be enclosed and segregated from the rest of the floor area by fire-resistant materials.

6. Do not allow the use of combustible insulation anywhere (including pipe coverings) in the building.

7. Provide an emergency source of power to operate elevators, lights, standpipe, and sprinkler pumps in case of power failure.

8. Provide interior alarm systems. These should be combined with public address systems to instruct occupants in proper emergency procedures.

9. Provide corridor smoke barrier doors held open by magnetic catches which will close upon sounding the interior alarm—either manually or by smoke- or heat-sensitive devices.

10. Make doors to individual apartments, office, storage areas, etc., self-closing and of one hour fire-resistant rating.

11. Make all windows of wired glass to resist exposure from fire in apartments or offices below.

12. Provide complete automatic sprinkler protection for every square foot of floor area.

Chapter 15

Metal fires

MODERN METALLURGY has pioneered many new metals with their associated hazards. Some of the more common combustible metals are: aluminum, iron shavings or turnings, lithium, magnesium, potassium, sodium, sodium potassium alloy (NaK), titanium, triethylaluminum, uranium, uranium hydride, thorium hydride, zirconium.

Not only are these metals combustible, in the form of dust they are an explosive hazard. The relative explosive pressures and flammability depend on the nature of the metal, its purity, and the shape and size of particles. The smaller the size the greater the danger of explosion.

One of the basic difficulties with a fire in these metals is that they burn at very high temperatures—some high enough to break down water into hydrogen and oxygen. If free hydrogen is liberated, then the theory follows: using water on metal fires will cause violent explosions. This theory may be true, but the fears are somewhat exaggerated. It is true that there can be (and often is) a violent reaction when water is used on such fires, but this usually occurs when the metal is in dust form, chip form, or in a molten state.

Let us examine what happens when water is applied to highly heated or molten iron. In order to obtain this high heat there must have been enough air present to supply oxygen to the burning material. Under these condi-tions, if there is any decomposition of the water and a liberation of hydrogen there would be a sufficient supply of oxygen in the air to permit immediate burning of the hydrogen. That is, as fast as hydrogen was liberated it would burn, because of the oxygen in the air. No free hydrogen would be liberated, to collect somewhere else. Under such conditions there cannot be a hydrogen explosion.

Hydrogen-air mixtures readily burn over a very wide range, from four percent of hydrogen to 74 percent, and the ignition temperature is only 1,085° F., which is well below the temperature of ordinary flame. When water is applied to any mass of highly heated material, even wood, there is an instant production and liberation of steam (water to steam expansion ratio is 1 to 1,600) which is often mistaken for a hydrogen explosion. In a closed room or other confined space, this quick liberation of steam may blow out windows and even blow down walls. This is one reason why ample ventilation is vital before using water on any hot fire.*

The general rule is to avoid applying water on these metals, if possible. It may be wise to let the metal burn out. If it is feasible, scoop up the burning metal and remove it from the building to a place where it can burn

---

*Some of the material on the reaction of water with combustible metals on fire is from American Insurance Association Bulletins 166 and 178.

itself out without danger of extension. If the fire is isolated inside a structure, you can allow it to burn itself out where it is if proper precautions are taken. Open doors and windows for ventilation and for dissipation of heat. Where there is a likelihood of the fire spreading (it may melt and spread this way), try to ring the area with dry sand, salt, talc, or any other inert dry material. Do not disturb the burning metal—particularly if it is in dust form.

Of course, if extinguishers designed specifically for metal fires are available, use them. They usually contain salt with a special additive to render the extinguishing agent free-flowing. They may contain dry graphite for this purpose. As a rule, these extinguishing agents will not absorb water from the air. Therefore they may be stored in containers with loose covers. Although extinguishing agents designed for metal fires are intended to handle small fires, if available in sufficient quantities they also can handle large metal fires. An interesting point is that these special extinguishing agents can adhere to vertical surfaces.

Most combustible metals burn fiercely with a brilliant white light and little smoke. Steel, however, is usually in the form of chips or turnings and burns rather quietly. If there is smoke, avoid it if possible. If it is necessary to operate inside the smoke cloud, the men should wear masks. The danger is that tiny metal particles are caught up in the smoke and ash and can be breathed in and deposited in the lungs of firemen.

Magnesium

One of the most familiar metals involved in fire is magnesium. If magnesium is hot enough it will react violently with water. The following quotation from American Insurance Association Bulletin 178 describes the characteristics of magnesium which are of interest to the fireman:

Magnesium is a silvery-white combustible metal weighing only two-thirds as much as aluminum and having good structural properties when suitably alloyed. For this reason, magnesium al-

loys find widespread use in the construction of aircraft, automobiles and trucks, household appliances, furniture, office equipment, machine parts, and numerous other applications. Powdered magnesium is used in signal flares and other fireworks to produce an intense white light.

The melting point of pure magnesium is 1,204° F. The ignition temperature is generally considered to be very close to the melting point, but ignition of magnesium in certain forms may occur at lower air temperatures. Magnesium ribbon and fine magnesium shavings can be ignited under some conditions at temperatures of 950° F., and very finely divided magnesium powder has been ignited at an air temperature below 900° F.

Metal marketed under a variety of trade names and designations and commonly referred to as magnesium may be one of a large number of alloys containing widely different percentages of magnesium, aluminum, zinc, and manganese. Some of these alloys have melting points and ignition temperatures considerably lower than that of pure magnesium.

The ease of ignition of magnesium depends to a large extent upon the size and shape of the material as well as the intensity of the ignition source. The flame of a match may be sufficient to ignite magnesium ribbon, shavings, or chips with thin feather edges; a spark will ignite fine dust such as is produced in grinding operations.

Heavier pieces, such as ingots or thick-walled castings, are difficult to ignite because heat is rapidly conducted away from a localized ignition source. If the entire piece of metal can be raised to the ignition temperature, however, self-sustained burning will occur.

If practicable, any magnesium not yet involved in the fire should be moved to a safe distance. In this way, if the fire cannot be extinguished readily, it may burn itself out before serious damage has been done.

Where a considerable quantity of magnesium in the form of chips, turnings or shavings has ignited from any cause, the impact of a stream of water is likely to cause considerable scattering of molten and burning particles. Magnesium in these forms burns readily, and water penetrating to the burning magnesium underneath causes explosions and scattering of molten and burning particles.

In fighting fires where magnesium is in sheets, casting shapes and manufactured articles, if enough water can be applied quickly to burning magnesium to lower the temperature sufficiently to prevent the reaction with water, there is no explosion and the fire is extinguished. Due caution must be taken in the use of hose streams and it is well to apply such streams from as great a distance as possible and still have a good solid stream at not very high nozzle pressure.

Magnesium in its solid form melts as it burns, and if the fire has been burning long enough to produce considerable molten magnesium, application of water will present the hazard of steam explosions associated with all hot molten metal in contact with water but increased by magnesium's greater affinity for oxygen. Several explosions occur when a mass of highly heated metal is poured onto a water-wet surface, or is dropped into water; also when water is injected under the surface of the molten metal. Whether with molten magnesium these explosions are hydrogen or steam explosions may make little difference.

The danger from any resulting explosion may be lessened by providing as much vent area as possible, as by opening windows, doors and skylights.

Two interesting fires* involving combustible metals illustrate several important points on operations at these fires:

This fire occurred at the plant of Magnesium Products, Inc., in Los Angeles, California, on December 14, 1942, and is of special interest in showing the value of hose streams on fires involving magnesium.

The fire started in the section of the plant occupied by the finishing and shipping departments, and by effective fire department use of hose streams was largely confined to this section. This section of the plant was one story, about 50x45 feet, with brick walls, concrete floor and wood roof; not sprinklered. It was separated from the foundry section by a brick wall with fire doors which either closed automatically or were closed manually early in the fire. A wooden partition partly enclosed the shipping department. There were large windows along the two street fronts.

Equipment in the finishing room consisted of various types of machines used in finishing magnesium castings, also various types of woodworking machines used for pattern making. Some machines were equipped with dust-collecting equipment but others were not, which resulted in accumulations of fine magnesium and wood dust on ledges and other horizontal surfaces. It was the practice to sweep up magnesium filings and sawdust every few hours, but fine dust had been collecting on ledges, etc., since the building had been opened six months previously.

The fire was started by a spark which resulted when an attachment plug for an electric drill was plugged into a wall outlet by a maintenance man. Accumulated dust allowed fire to flash along the top of the work bench, up the adjacent

*Reported in Bulletins 94 and 171, American Insurance Association.

FIGURE 127. *A truck carrying magnesium crashed and burned on a major highway exposing a bridge overhead to the fierce heat of the magnesium fire. Straight streams of water early enough (before the magnesium began to melt and run) controlled the fire and saved the bridge. The reaction of water on magnesium is less violent in an unconfined space.*

wood partition and along ledges, quickly involving the wooden roof and spreading to filings and sawdust on the floor and to combustible cartons. With the collapse of a portion of the roof some of the magnesium castings, of which there was at least 10,000 pounds in the finishing rooms, were ignited.

Employees attempted to fight the fire with sand but without success. All fifty employees escaped without injury.

The Los Angeles fire department was called promptly. The first companies to arrive saw fire coming out the front windows and through roof skylights. Company officers had made recent inspections of the plant and were familiar with the contents. Realizing the situation and the need for many heavy streams, a second alarm was sent in immediately on arrival. Brilliant white light appearing in the flames confirmed the fact that magnesium was involved.

The fire was skillfully fought and in less than two hours was completely under control. Hose lines were taken into adjoining sections of the building and onto the roof to stop fire which was beginning to spread to these sections; other streams were directed from the street directly into the fire area, first to extinguish the burning roof structure, then to attack the burning magnesium itself. As the fire in the structure came under control, hose lines were moved in closer on all sides toward the seat of the fire in the

FIGURE 128. *Even in an open space, water causes magnesium to react violently. Firemen should* *take shelter behind a substantial object and use water from a distance until the reactions are over.*

stocks of magnesium castings until these were completely extinguished. Twelve 2½-inch hose lines with 1⅛- or 1¼-inch nozzles were used on the fire.

At first, when water applied to the burning roof fell on burning magnesium there were minor puffs with some spattering of particles of burning magnesium. Later, as heavy streams were applied directly to the burning magnesium, heavier explosions occurred. Early collapse of the wooden roof allowed these to vent upward. Pieces of burning magnesium and metal containers were hurled a hundred feet or so into the air by some of the explosions, and some windows up to a block away were broken, but no personal injuries were sustained. Some pieces of burning magnesium fell on roofs of other buildings but were readily extinguished; many pieces seemed to burn out before they landed.

The large quantity of water applied to the fire built up to a depth of several inches on the floor and submerged pieces of burning magnesium. Some were seen to bubble when covered with water and to ignite again when raised to the air, but being kept under water the reaction soon ceased.

Through the effective work of the fire department in applying water to this magnesium fire, the fire was confined to the section of the building in which it originated and approximately 8,500 pounds of magnesium castings in the fire area were saved from damage. Many of these were finished castings ready for shipment.

If, as some have advocated, the fire department in this case had declined to put water on burning magnesium for fear of explosions, it is evident that all the magnesium in the fire area would have been destroyed, and it is likely that the fire would have spread to buildings across the street and would have severely damaged if not destroyed other sections of the plant.

Reports made by the various fire department captains and chiefs who fought this fire are unanimous that only by the use of water applied in large quantity could this fire have been brought under control and extinguished. Water quite obviously cooled and extinguished many magnesium castings, and prevented many others from igniting. It was the consensus, however, that in a building offering more confinement to the fire the explosions produced by application of water would be more serious, indicating that buildings for foundry and machine shop operations on magnesium should preferably be one story, with large window or skylight area, and be located outside of congested city districts.

The fire department did contain this fire as described. However there are some dangerous oversimplifications in the story. These points should be considered:

1. There is an overemphasis on saving the magnesium castings at a potential cost in human life. Note there were explosions which hurled pieces a hundred feet in the air and broke windows a block away. Unless men were operating hose lines behind strong protective barriers they were dangerously exposed.

2. There is no reason why buildings across the street could not be saved by protective hose lines even though the fire building burned. This is common procedure in protecting exposures.

3. If it becomes obvious that severe explosions will take place (or are taking place), men exposed to such explosions should be withdrawn and efforts made to cover exposures, letting the magnesium burn itself out.

The author agrees that water may at times be used on magnesium fires, but not when they will cause major explosions—even if it means losing the entire stock and structure. Where fire departments have the equipment to project heavy streams from more than 200 feet away, (New York's Super Pumper and Chicago's special heavy stream appliance, for example) then water may be fully used on magnesium without endangering personnel. (See Figures 127-128.)

Metal turnings

A second fire is of interest for two reasons—its cause and the method of extinguishment. The material involved was oily metal borings and turnings. Such metal turnings, when saturated with oil, are subject to spontaneous ignition, but large-scale fires of this kind are so infrequent that there is little information concerning proper methods of extinguishment. Authoritative sources throughout the country have offered many divergent suggestions on how to handle this type of fire. There is general agreement, however, in cautioning against the use of water. This warning proves to be justified in the following example of such a fire:

Steel turnings had been purchased and stored for two years on a dock in a city in Michigan. On October 8, a steamer moved 2,400 tons of these turnings, unloading them on a railroad dock of a small lakefront city in Ohio. This dock had a concrete floor and concrete retaining walls eight feet high on two sides, open at both ends. The pile of turnings was originally about 30 feet high and remote from any combustible material. Of the original 2,400-ton cargo, 1,322 tons were still on the dock at the time of the fire. Private policemen patrolled the dock at night.

The dock superintendent noticed evidence of heating in the pile about noon on October 18, and on the evening of October 20 definite knowledge existed that the pile was burning. Firefighting did not begin until October 30 as it was realized that improper means of extinguishment might result in a major explosion, and further, the fire did not expose other property.

Following the 20th, no time was lost in contacting authoritative fire protection organizations to learn of safe and effective means of extinguishment to employ. In one instance the use of steam as a fire extinguishing agent was advocated, but steam was not available. In another, the fire department was advised to cover the pile of steel turnings with clay and apply carbon tetrachloride through a hole bored in the top of the pile. This plan was rejected because it was costly, of dubious practicability, and would tend to impair the value of the stock.

Finally, the Cardox Corporation was called in because of that company's experience in coal mine fires. Its engineers conducted a test in Chicago, using about a barrel of oily metal turnings and a blow torch to simulate conditions attending the dock fire. Following their experiments, two engineers came to the Ohio city with a seven-ton truck load of carbon dioxide and a three-man crew to operate the system. The local fire department was called in and the chief detailed two shifts of six firemen each.

About noon on October 30, plans for combatting the fire were agreed upon. The dock owners furnished a clam-shell bucket unloader and a Caterpillar tractor snow plow. The technique developed and used was to scoop into the burning pile with the clam-shell bucket, pick up about three tons of hot turnings, and deposit the load well away from the burning pile. Carbon dioxide was sprayed almost continuously on the bucket and its contents to prevent damage to the equipment.

As soon as the clam-shell bucket dumped its contents, the tractor snow plow scattered the hot metal which was then subjected to carbon dioxide through a long fog nozzle, and subsequently cooled down with water. This process continued until the evening of November 1 when the turnings, well scattered, had practically ceased burning. On November 2, water was used all day and by evening the fire was extinguished.

The fire was not spectacular. Large volumes of smoke were emitted, the burning being internal. Each time the clam-shell bucket dipped into the pile, flames would shoot up as high as the cab, making it difficult for the operator. This was due to the oil having decomposed into charcoal and, being far above the ignition temperature, burst into flame as soon as oxygen was supplied from the air.

A pyrometer inserted about one foot inside the pile recorded a temperature of 1,700° F., hence the steel did not reach the fusion point, a fact confirmed by the absence of slag after the fire.

The fire was fought for more than 50 hours. During this time five tons of carbon dioxide and approximately 600,000 gallons of water were used. A single hydrant located 800 feet from the fire was used, both hydrant hose connections were siamesed into a single 2½-inch line, necessitating the use of 1,300 feet of hose to which a fog nozzle was attached. No pumper was needed.

When the stream from a 2½-inch line was discharged experimentally on the main pile, a reaction took place of the nature of an explosion. This confirmed the advice not to use water on the pile. A 2½-inch by 1½-inch wye was then attached to the end of the hose line to obtain two 1½-inch lines; these streams resulted in less violent reaction when directed around the base of the pile.

Had this fire been permitted to burn out, there would have been little if any salvage. About two-thirds of the stock was reclaimed and shipped to a buyer with this method of extinguishment.

The pile of turnings had lain on the docks in Michigan for two years with no signs of heating, yet only a 12-day period was required for it to heat to the point of ignition after it had been deposited on the railroad dock in Ohio. In theory, it is possible that while on the docks in Michigan some slight degree of oxidation developed and that this was accelerated by a fresh supply of oxygen obtained during the loading and unloading operations. Assuming this to be so, it is readily conceivable that after delivery this heating process increased to the point of actual ignition within a relatively short period.

In conclusion, it is well to remember that material of this kind should be stored in low, well-separated piles. Further, that for fires involving such large amounts of oily metal turnings, water should not be used initially, but only in connection with a technique such as described, and preferably including carbon dioxide.

Other common metals

There are many other metals which you may encounter. The following information is excerpted from the *Manual of Firemanship*.* It gives details of important properties, from a firefighting standpoint, of several commonly encountered metals. No mention is made in this listing of a number of metallic elements such as radium, uranium, plutonium, neptunium, strontium, and thallium. These are either naturally radioactive or occur more commonly as the radioactive isotope than as the stable element. Since these metals are not necessarily found in the metal-working industries as such but are used in many different fields for special purposes, they are regarded as radioactive hazards rather than as metal fire hazards.

Aluminum. A light, ductile metal of good electrical conductivity and good resistance to corrosion. It is used in a wide variety of industries including aircraft, motor, and electrical engineering and utensil manufacture. It is often alloyed with copper, silicone, etc. Its melting point is 1,220° F. Heated aluminum gives off hydrogen when in contact with solutions of potassium hydroxide or sodium hydroxide, and reacts explosively with carbon tetrachloride and methyl bromide. Aluminum has been known to ignite spontaneously with sodium peroxide. It burns vigorously at 1,472° F. Aluminum dust is a severe explosion hazard, since it ignites in cloud form at 1,193° F. and also decomposes water, producing hydrogen. It is not liable to spontaneous heating and is not regarded as an industrial poison.

Beryllium. This light steely metal is used mainly in atomic work. Its melting point is

*Manual of Firemanship, Part 6C, Practical Firemanship—III, Her Majesty's Stationery Office, London.

2,336° F. When in contact with water, hydrogen is given off. Beryllium is a moderate fire hazard when exposed to flame. Beryllium dust offers a slight explosion hazard. The metal is highly toxic; the inhalation of dust or vapors from combustion can cause death.

Brass-Bronze. While not generally a fire hazard, these metals in dust form have a dust explosion hazard.

Cadmium. A soft white metal used for coating small steel articles against corrosion and a common constituent of fusible alloys. Its melting point is 610° F. It reacts vigorously with oxidizing agents, releasing hydrogen, and will ignite when exposed to flame in the form of a dust. This metal, when heated, emits poisonous fumes which can cause acute pain.

Caesium. Caesium is an alkali metal; it is silvery-white and ductile. It is used in photoelectric cells. The radioactive isotope is used in hospital therapy treatment. The melting point is 84° F. Caesium reacts with oxidizing agents and can ignite spontaneously in moist air, liberating hydrogen. It is thus a dangerous fire and explosion hazard.

Cobalt is a silvery metal, similar to iron but harder. It is used extensively in alloys. Its melting point is 2,696° F. It can be ignited by exposure to heat or flame, and especially in small fragments or finely divided, will heat and ignite by spontaneous chemical reaction.

Copper is a red metal, tough, malleable, and ductile. It has high electrical and thermal conductivity plus good resistance to corrosion. It is used widely for electric wires and for piping. It is also the basis of many alloys. Its melting point is 1,985° F. Copper is a negligible fire hazard, but copper oxide is irritating to the eyes.

Iron and steel. Iron in its pure state is a white metal—soft, malleable, tenacious, and ductile. The melting point is 2,795° F. Normally the ore is treated by roasting and then put in a blast furnace to produce pig or cast iron (combination of iron and carbon). Pig iron is very hard and brittle. Carbon may be almost entirely omitted from the pig iron to give wrought iron, or added in varying degrees to give steel. The properties of steel vary, and it may be treated in various additional ways to provide combinations of strength and toughness. It melts at 2,939° F. Special steels are made by combining other metals (such as chromium, nickel, tungsten, or manganese) with the iron and carbon. Contact between red-hot iron and steam or water liberates hydrogen. The same effect is produced on contact between iron and strong acids e.g. hydrochloric or sulphuric. There is a fire and explosion hazard when iron dust is exposed to heat or flame. Iron pyrites have a spontaneous heating risk.

Lead is a heavy, grey metal, soft and plastic. It is used for roofing, cable sheathing, lining chemical vessels, in storage batteries, metal bearings, and for piping. The melting point is 621° F. Especially when in finely divided form, lead can react vigorously with oxidizing agents, and it offers some fire and explosion hazard as a dust. When heated, lead gives off toxic fumes; inhalation of these or of lead dust is dangerous.

Lithium is a silvery, light, alkali metal which resembles sodium. It is used as an alloy in metal bearings. Its melting point is 367° F. Lithium is a severe fire hazard when exposed to heat or flame and it reacts violently with water, acids, and oxidizing agents, producing hydrogen in reaction with water or steam. It is usually kept beneath the surface of paraffin or toluene, but can be stored with safety under inert gases such as helium or argon. (Nitrogen, recommended for some dangerous metals, is not suitable for lithium.) Lithium offers a severe toxic hazard when burning.

Manganese is a hard, brittle metal, reddish-grey or silvery in appearance. It is mainly used in steel manufacture for purifying steel and as an alloy. Its melting point is 2,273° F. Manganese decomposes water, producing hydrogen, and dissolves in dilute acids to do the same. It reacts with oxidizing agents. It also offers a fire and explosion hazard when in dust or powder form. Dispersed in air the dust ignites at 842° F.

Nickel is a silver-white metal, used in the pure form for electroplating, for coinage, and for the linings of chemical vessels. It is used very widely as an alloy with steel and chromium, and with copper it makes Monel metal. The alloys give high working temperatures. The melting point of nickel is 2,642° F. In solid form it offers only slight fire hazard. It can be ignited, however, and offers an explosion hazard when exposed to flame in the form of dust.

Platinum is a rare, heavy, soft and ductile metal. It is immune to most chemical reagents and to oxidation up to high temperatures. Platinum wire is used in laboratory instruments. Only the salts are in common industrial use. The melting point is 3,223° F. While normal fire and toxic hazards are negligible, platinum dust has been known to explode with a mixture of hydrogen and oxygen.

Potassium is an alkali metal, silvery in color and highly reactive. As a metal, it has few applications but the salts are used extensively. The melting point is 144° F. Potassium is a very dangerous fire hazard since it reacts violently with all moisture, producing much heat, and evolved hydrogen; there is thus a severe explosion hazard. In air, the reaction is slower, but it is violent with oxidizing agents. Potassium may form an explosive compound in contact with carbon dioxide. The toxic hazard of potassium under reaction is very great. It can be safely stored under inert gases.

Sodium Potassium Alloy (NaK) is a shiny silverlike metal which resembles mercury. When exposed to air, oxides form quickly, changing the color to various shades of white, orange, yellow. NaK will react violently with moisture. It can generate enough heat to break down the water to hydrogen and oxygen. The heat is sufficiently high to ignite the hydrogen.

Sodium is a silver-white metal—light, soft, ductile, and malleable. Sodium is an alkali metal; its melting point is 204° F. It is very reactive and easily ignites; heated, it will ignite spontaneously in air. By chemical reaction with water or any moisture, with air or with oxidizing agents it will decompose violently, evolving great heat, and the hydrogen which is liberated will ignite. It also reacts violently with halogens, acids, and halogenated hydrocarbons. Hot sodium reacts violently with carbon dioxide. It is not liable to spontaneous heating, but toxic hazards in all circumstances are severe. Sodium is usually stored below the surface of naphtha, paraffin, or other liquids not containing oxygen. It may also be stored under inert gases. It may, however, be transported or kept for short periods in sealed air-tight drums.

Tin is a white metal with a yellowish tinge —malleable but not very ductile. It is used as a foil in coating copper, lead, iron, and steel and as an alloy with bronze, pewter, etc. Its melting point is 449° F. Normally, it offers no fire hazard but as a dust it can be ignited. It presents an explosion hazard when exposed to a flame or chemical reaction. Tin is not regarded as a toxic hazard.

Titanium is a strong white metal. It is lighter than steel and used in alloys with steel to give high working temperatures— mostly in the aircraft industry. Its melting point is 3,632° F. Titanium is easily ignited when in the form of thin chips, drillings, or turnings. The larger pieces present only a slight fire hazard except in heat treatment baths. It offers a severe dust explosion hazard, however, being ignitable in cloud form at 896° F. It has also exploded with concentrated nitro-acids. Spontaneous ignition can occur when fire chips or dust are covered with oil, and spontaneous ignition has occurred in titanium dust when dispersed in air. There is no noteworthy toxic hazard.

Triethylaluminum is a pyroforic liquid metal. This means it ignites spontaneously in air. Other than water and carbon tetrachloride, the standard extinguishers will be effective. Again, use self-contained breathing masks and guard against burns. Triethylaluminum is very corrosive to body tissue. If you do spill some on you, flush it off with copious quantities of water.

Zinc is a white metallic element with a bluish tint. It has very high resistance to atmospheric corrosion. It is used as a protective coating (e.g. in galvanized iron), and is also used in sheets and as a constituent of alloys with aluminum, copper, magnesium, and others. The melting point is 786° F. The metal itself is not considered to have a fire risk, but it can be ignited. It also offers an explosion hazard when in the form of a dust. It is not liable to spontaneous heating, and toxicity hazards are low.

Zirconium. The melting point of this metal is 3,452° F. In most respects it may be regarded as similar to titanium, though the fire and explosion hazards are much more severe. It ignites as a dust cloud, for instance, at a temperature of 68° F.

Salt baths. This is a widely used method of heat treating metals, particularly aluminum alloys. The metal is immersed in a bath containing a molten mixture of potassium and sodium nitrates and a small proportion of nitrites. Various types of baths employing different chemicals and different temperature ranges are used for varying purposes. Accidents have occurred with these baths from these three distinct causes:

1. Explosion resulting from the reaction of hot nitrates with the metal of the bath or with the metal articles under treatment.

2. Explosion resulting from the dipping of wet or greasy articles in the molten nitrates.

3. Gassing by nitrous fumes given off when the hot nitrates come into contact with oxidizable substances such as oil, tar, or soot in the furnace, if the bath leaks or breaks down under the action of the nitrates.

In the low-temperature range (300° to 1,000° F.), which embraces the common nitrate bath, the mixture of molten nitrates is stable up to 900° F., the temperature at which it is generally used. If the temperature reaches 1,100° F., the nitrates begin to decompose and to react with the metal of the bath or with the articles under treatment. Above 1,100° F. this reaction becomes very violent, and cannot be controlled. Finally, the reaction attains explosive violence. Fatal in-

FIGURE 129. *The results of an explosion caused by the overheating of a sodium nitrate salt bath in which aluminum was being treated. The explosion was produced by the chemical reaction which followed the decomposition of the aluminum.*

FIGURE 130. *The interior of the factory shown in Figure 129. Note the many salt and plating baths, crowded together.*

juries have been caused by explosions occurring in this way. (See Figures 129-130.)

While the contents of these baths are not in themselves flammable, they are strong oxidizing agents, and their temperature is sufficiently high to ignite any combustible substance with which they come in contact. The most important danger from the baths to the fireman, however, is the fact that if the water is allowed to come into contact with the molten salts, the instantaneous generation of steam will result in an explosion.

A fire in the vicinity of the baths therefore presents considerable risk. Every precaution should be taken to prevent water from entering the bath and, if the bath itself should become damaged, to prevent the contents of the bath from flowing toward combustible articles. Because of this danger, it may be wise to prohibit the installation of any type of fire extinguisher in the vicinity of the baths.

In modern heat treatment shops, medium-temperature (1,000° to 1,750° F.) cyanide hardening baths may be found. These are much smaller than nitrate baths but from a firefighting point of view present similar risks. The use of water in their vicinity is exceptionally dangerous. This applies also to high-temperature baths.

Generally speaking, most combustible metals will act and react somewhat similarly in fires. Some of course are much more hazardous, displaying greater sensitivity to heat. Others are highly toxic.

Extinguishing agents for metals

There are several extinguishing agents which have proved to be effective in small combustible metal fires. It would be wise to familiarize yourself with them:

Pyrene G-1 powder is composed of a graphitized foundry coke to which organic phosphates have been added. This extinguishing agent is applied evenly and gently to cover the burning material with scoops, shovels, etc.

Met-L-X powder is composed of a sodium chloride base plus special additives. It is stored in low-pressure extinguishers and is applied gently but heavily to coat the burning metal.

Lith-X powder is composed of a special graphite base and was designed for lithium fires. It also works well on magnesium, zirconium and sodium. It is applied with low-pressure extinguishers as Met-L-X powder.

Trimethoxyboroxine (TMB) is a new flammable liquid compound developed by the Navy for use on magnesium castings and structural shapes under aircraft crash conditions. It is applied from a 2½-gallon stored pressure extinguisher as a solid stream or spray. The application of TMB on a metal fire produces a secondary Class B fire with large quantities of dense white fumes. As the organic matter in this material is burned away, it leaves a glossy boric oxide coating on the metal. This coating excludes air which results in extinguishment.

Soda ash, talc powder and very dry sand will likewise serve to control combustible metal fires. They are also applied gently with scoops or shovels to avoid scattering the burning metal.

Avoid the use of water, carbon tetrachloride, carbon dioxide, foam, and sodium bicarbonate extinguishers. They will cause violent reactions with most combustible metal fires though large amounts of foam will help control small zirconium fires.

Remember that combinations of combustible metals may behave differently than when isolated. Here are some examples:

1. Spontaneous ignition results when aluminum and sodium peroxide are exposed in damp air.

2. Finely divided platinum will cause a mixture of oxygen and hydrogen to explode at room temperature.

3. Carbon dioxide and sodium react violently.

An important safety measure against structural damage by explosions is the provision of pressure-relief vents in equipment

168

and other affected structures. The function of these vents is to release gases during the initial stages of an explosion, preventing the development of high pressures.

Apart from the risks of explosion which have been mentioned, the danger to fire-fighting personnel of severe and painful burns from metal fires should be guarded against. There are many toxic hazards from the products of combustion and other reactions. Cadmium, beryllium, and NaK are particularly dangerous in this respect. Breathing apparatus should be worn in fighting fires known or thought to involve these and other metals.

Again, as with most combustible metals, when possible protect men and exposures and allow the fire to burn itself out.

As a final precaution when fighting fires in combustible metals, if it is necessary to direct hose streams onto materials which may react violently with water, apply the streams from a sheltered position. Use straight streams with sufficient reach to keep men as far from the fire area as possible. Set up heavy stream appliances which can be handled by one or two men. Deluge guns can be aimed and left in position with frequent checks to insure that the stream is reaching its objective.

Chapter 16

Closed front or windowless buildings

THE DESCRIPTION, closed front or windowless building, may seem ambiguous. What it means is a structure either originally designed with no windows or one which has been converted to such by adding false fronts or large signs. (See Figures 131 and 132.) As far as the business community is concerned, there is much to be said in favor of this type of construction. Such buildings are cheaper to build and maintain. There are no windows to wash, break, or maintain. The buildings are easier to heat and keep clean. Floor space is used more efficiently because there is no concern about blocking windows with stock, displays, or furnishings. As with most innovations, when the trend is established others soon follow. More new buildings are of the so-called windowless construction and many old buildings are covered with false fronts, giving them a new look.

Unique problems for firefighters

With this type of building it is more difficult for the firefighter to carry out the fundamentals of his work—ventilating and getting a hose line to the fire floor.

There is no practical, rapid way to remove the toxic combustion products from closed front buildings. Normal air supply to such buildings is by ducts that supply heated or cooled air to the entire structure. But these channels are not designed to take care of fires. Any attempt to rid a building of heat and smoke via these ducts would be unsatisfactory. Far from being helpful at fires, the duct network complicates the problem. It may distribute smoke and sparks throughout the building, into areas not originally involved with fire.

Fires on the top floor and involved stair shafts may be ventilated by opening at the roof level, but this ventilation procedure will not be sufficient for lower floors which are heavily charged with smoke.

Standard practices call for operation of a line through windows to extinguish fire on a floor that cannot be reached with inside streams. In windowless buildings this obviously cannot be done. It is not even possible to judge the fire extent and travel from outside. If the building is modern it will have enclosed stairs with self-closing fire-resistant doors. This should help confine the fire to the floor of origin (be careful for interior shafts, however). But we all know how often occupants block open the self-closing doors. This then would rule out the protective feature of the enclosed stairs and floor separation.

Another difficulty in fighting fires in these buildings is that firemen will need to use self-contained breathing equipment. These cut down on a man's efficiency and they offer no protection from the heat. Therefore, even though the men are wearing them they may

FIGURE 131. *These are examples of new facades covering older buildings. Unless special provisions are made there is no way to ventilate and no way to get exterior stream penetration.*

FIGURE 132. *This metal screen type facade is also a deterrent to effective fire-fighting. Ventilation is ineffective and water from exterior streams will not penetrate to reach the interior of the fire floor.*

be unable to advance under severe heat conditions. In such cases, with little or no interior line operation and no way to get exterior streams into operation through windows, the building in all probability will be lost. The fire department will be relegated to covering exposures.

Suppose a fire in such a structure disrupts the electrical system. The air movement system will fail, lights will go out, elevators will not operate. People will be in total darkness. The standpipe and sprinkler pumps may not work, and interior alarm systems may not function.

A serious loss of life can occur under these conditions—even in a modern fire-resistant building. Consider an office building or department store with hundreds of people inside who are unfamiliar with the location of

the stairways because they never use them. The fire department may be unaware of the number of people trapped or where they may be because there are no exterior windows through which the trapped occupants can call for help.

Firemen working at such fires will be in greater danger than at the usual fire. They will have to bring in hose lines in total darkness. They will stumble over objects, hose lines will become tangled, and there will be no windows to open for some needed air.

Old buildings which have been remodeled to appear as modern windowless structures are a greater problem by far than those so designed. While the building may appear to be new, behind the new wall you will find a number of faults. The building is basically the same old fire trap. There will be open stairs, wood lath and plaster partitions, poor exit facilities, wood panelling, overloaded electric circuits, leaky chimneys. Add to all this a lack of access by windows and you have a tough problem to deal with.

Because a fire may burn within such a structure without being seen from the street, the alarm usually will be delayed—with the expected fire spread. The same problems of advancing hose lines, ventilation, search, rescue, examination for fire spread that exist in the modern windowless building exist in the old building, but to a far greater degree, primarily because of the open stair shafts. The lines have to be advanced under extremely arduous circumstances.

Another similar structure is the old building with a large sign covering its front. In many large cities commercial property is not only very expensive, but space is at a premium. The owners of such properties take every opportunity to increase their income from these buildings. In some areas, owners can no longer rent upper-floor apartments because of neighborhood changes. The street level store is rented to some business enterprise. To increase their income, owners at times rent the front of their buildings for advertising purposes. A high sign may cover the front of the building from just above the street-level store to the roof, and from side wall to side wall.

While this is not technically the windowless building, it nevertheless presents identical problems. The sign seals off access to the upper floors by way of windows. Since the upper floors are not used, maintenance is neglected. To further complicate the problem, the interior stairs are sometimes removed to avoid access to burglars via the roof. It prevents anyone from getting into the upper floors from the roof—including firemen. Usually such precautions are accompanied by boarding up the rear windows as well. If the building is between and part of a row of similar buildings, no access to the upper floors is possible except by cutting through the sign at front, removing the boarding at the rear, or cutting the roof and lowering a ladder from it to the floor below. Depending on the construction of the sign

and the amount of space between the sign and the front of the building, it may be possible to climb behind the sign to reach the unused windows. This is problematical, however, and very risky. It does not allow for effective ventilation or stream penetration from the exterior.

If there is a common hanging ceiling with the adjoining buildings, fire extension to these buildings is likely, unless rapid line placement into the threatened areas and opening the ceilings heads it off.

Access panels—a partial answer

Some building codes require access panels in blank exterior walls. The locations of the panels and method of marking will vary. Some may not be marked. Memphis, Tenn., requires that two means of access be provided in blank exterior walls. They must be marked in red. Depending on the size of the panel, they will be marked "fire doors" or "fire." The purpose is to allow firemen to gain entrance via the fire doors or for stream penetration via the fire panel. Both can be opened from the outside. Inside the building at a point opposite the "fire door" panel is another door which communicates with the door in the blank wall. In this manner a man could go from the exterior side of the blank wall into the structure. The interior side of the door is similarly marked with its purpose. (See Figure 133.)

A fireman trying to enter the building from such an access door in a blank wall must be very careful, particularly under the limited vision of a night fire or one producing heavy smoke. The new wall usually is built out from the old wall for a distance of three to six feet and is constructed on a frame much like scaffolding. This holds the new front in place. Inside the new front there may be only a narrow catwalk for the firemen to walk on. What the fireman finds between the new front and the exterior of the old front wall is impossible to predict—unless the building was previously inspected with this purpose in mind. Windows may be nailed shut or boarded up.

Access panels are a step in the right direction. They do provide some means for stream penetration. Yet, they are inadequate as presently allowed. First, the small panel is neither wide enough nor high enough for efficient exterior stream penetration. It simply will not allow a stream from outside at lower levels to sweep widely enough (or from top to bottom) to gain good coverage of the floor area.

Even where such penetration may be partially successful, the interior wall opening may be blocked with stock, sealing off the opening and effectively blocking the stream. Second, there is no way of knowing whether a partition may have been built to block out the unsightly view of old walls and unused windows. This will also block stream penetration. Third, the firemen getting inside the window off the catwalk may have difficulty finding their way through this same partition to get onto the store floor. Finally, men entering such access panels from off ladders under heavy smoke conditions could be overcome or fall from the catwalk.

Good codes the only effective answer

Closed-front or windowless buildings can be effectively safeguarded, but this begins in the blueprint stage. The following recommendations should help achieve this objective:

1. Complete cutoff of one floor from another with fire-resistant construction and enclosed, smokeproof stairs not more than 100 feet apart in any such building more than one story high.

2. Complete automatic sprinkler protection.

3. Standpipe system.

4. Interior alarm system with connection to fire department.

5. Special smoke venting system which will carry smoke and heat directly to the outside without connections to any other ducts.

6. Emergency lighting systems on separate battery and electric circuits.

7. Noncombustible ceiling and wall finishes.

8. Installation of fire department access panels as follows: (A) In every building higher than one story. (B) On any floor exceeding 3,000 square feet in area. (C) On every wall facing a street or alley. (D) No

FIGURE 133. *Some cities require removable panels on exterior face of windowless walls. They may be marked either as a fire door or fire window. The purpose is to be able to remove panels for exterior stream operation.*

more than 50 feet apart horizontally. (E) Panels to be at least 32 inches wide, 48 inches high, and not more than 32 inches above the floor. (F) Panels to be suitably marked as to purpose. (G) If any space exists between the exterior wall and inner wall, such space shall be suitably guarded to prevent a person from falling through.

Windowless buildings have existed in some cities for many years. But these were generally substantial structures with heavy blank masonry walls such as breweries, bonded liquor warehouses, dead storage warehouses, etc. The heavy blank walls are extremely effective in providing fire stops in closely built-up areas. Usually such buildings had little or no human occupancy. Even though serious fires in these buildings were almost impossible to fight successfully, the life hazard was low. In the modern windowless building—or one converted to such use —the situation is far different. The converted buildings are not of substantial construction, the occupancies vary greatly, and hundreds of people may be inside at the time of the fire.

Three examples illustrate the problem

The AIA has reported on three fires which help point out the complexities of the problem of the so-called windowless buildings.*

The first example is a five-story department store which experienced damage to its entire stock from smoke and water. Damage amounted to more than $1 million, even though the flames were contained to a 25-foot area on the top floor. Because of the vaultlike structure, it took firefighters 30 minutes to locate the seat of the blaze. A build-up of heat caused 169 sprinklers to open. Although enough heads were opened to overtax the water supply, connection of fire department pumpers to the system controlled the fire. The main difficulty firefighters faced in this fire was poor ventilation.

A second example was a fire in a mercantile occupancy. The building was 310x180 feet, constructed of concrete blocks and sheet metal. The unprotected, undivided windowless building was heavily loaded with stock in preparation for the Christmas season. Combustible trash piled outside, near the metal side of the building, was ignited. The sheet metal soon conducted heat from the rubbish fire to the interior, where flammable stock was piled high. Fire quickly spread to the wooden roof and engulfed the entire structure. The blaze was not immediately lo-

cated because of limited access to the point of origin. By the time firefighters arrived nearly the entire building was in flames. Windowless walls and a large quantity of stock hindered firefighting efforts to such an extent that only a sales area in the front could be saved.

A third example was a shopping center fire.* This 375x300-foot building had concrete block walls with a reinforced concrete roof. The fire, starting in the receiving area, quickly involved a recent shipment of paint, thinners, and other products in aerosol cans. Since firefighters were blocked from entering through service or exit doors that were locked, hose lines had to be brought into the building by way of a main aisle through the sales area of the store. By that time, heat and smoke prevented entry to the storage area. Hose streams could not reach the base of the fire. Firefighters used acetylene torches and other forcible entry tools to open outside steel doors to gain access. A tractor was used to knock down portions of the windowless exterior wall. Before the flames were extinguished, the building and its contents were severely damaged. Loss was estimated at approximately $2.5 million.

In all of these fires the pattern is clear. There is heavy smoke involvement, making it impossible to find the seat of the fire. The heat build-up drives the operating forces outside, if they ever get in at all. The only alternative is to revert to an exterior stream operation. But stream penetration is not possible because of the lack of exterior openings, so the fire continues to spread and the structure is destroyed.

Firefighting tactics for windowless buildings

Even though the problems are serious, there are some techniques that may prove to be successful in the windowless building fire. The following techniques may be the answer in certain situations:

1. If the building is sprinklered, begin immediately to supply the system through the fire department connection. If there is more

*American Insurance Association, Bulletin No. 246.

*While shopping centers are not generally considered to be closed-front buildings, they do present many of the same hazards. Shopping center fires are covered in Chapter 24.

than one such connection, supply the additional connections with pumping engines.

2. Call for help early.

3. Use self-contained breathing equipment immediately to try to get to the seat of the fire with hose lines.

4. If the building is one story high, send men to the roof to cut for ventilation of the store below—remember to push down the ceiling or you will not ventilate the store.

5. Break out front show windows to help ventilate the fire floor.

6. If lines cannot penetrate from the street floor, use cellar nozzles through roof space.

7. Use distributors instead of cellar pipes if roof stability is suspect.

8. Don't forget to search for people overcome or trapped.

9. Provide good lighting.

10. Breeching side walls is perfectly feasible in trying to get lines operating onto the fire area, particularly where forcible entry via steel doors is not successful.

11. Top floor fires may be fought by using cellar nozzles through holes in the roof if hand lines are not successful. Vent top-floor fires by cutting the roof (see No. 4 above).

12. Fires on intermediate floors will be more troublesome because there may be vertical as well as horizontal spread.

13. If there are access panels in the closed front, remove them either by ladder or off the elevating platform basket. Get the stream close to the opening provided by removal of the panel and sweep the floor both sideways and up and down. Do the same with the other panels in an attempt to get total floor coverage.

14. If it appears that your tactics will not be successful, start protecting buildings that may be exposed if the fire building becomes more seriously involved.

15. If there are common party walls and shafts close by, cover these early in the fight by placing hose lines in such exposed areas.

16. Give thought to breeching walls on upper floors by working off the basket of the elevating platform.

In conclusion, remember this: The smoke, heat, and gases which normally vent via windows will remain in the windowless building. Some will push out at the doors through which you entered. The stage may be set for a serious smoke explosion. Therefore, in this type of fire, when the structure is well involved upon arrival, where there is heavy smoke and heat build-up and it is evident the conditions have been mounting for some time, it is a wise precaution not to attempt an immediate inside attack. The peril may be too great. Surround the fire with hose lines. Protect the exposures and wait for the fire to vent itself.

When the fire burns through the roof, it will pull the smoke and gases with it. It then may be feasible to move in with hand lines from below. If this attack is decided upon, do not beat the fire showing through the roof back down again with heavy streams from ladder pipes or elevating platforms. This will only drive the combustion products back into the building and consequently also drive the men making the top floor back out. Use these exterior streams to cover exposures, knock down flying brands, break up heat waves, and protect the remaining roof surface from burning.

Chapter 17

Overhauling the fire

THE OVERHAULING process may be defined as an orderly examination of a fire building and its contents to insure that the fire is completely out. This begins as soon as the fire is under control. It may require a good deal of opening up of partitions, ceilings, and shifting of contents. Therefore the job should be well-thought-out in advance, otherwise you will find much duplication of effort.

The officer in charge bears a heavy responsibility when he finally dismisses the last company. People who were evacuated during the fire may now start to reoccupy the building. The building itself is more vulnerable to a secondary fire because the walls, ceilings, and floors have been opened. The sprinkler system may be inoperative. It will be difficult for laymen to distinguish between the residual smoke odor and that of any rekindled fire just starting up. A rekindled fire may be far more destructive than the original fire, and people who now reoccupy the building may lose their lives to the secondary fire. Therefore the decision to say the fire is out should not be taken lightly.

Special precautions

There are some situations when it is extremely important to be sure before the decision is made that the fire is out. This is true when baled, tightly compressed fibres, mattresses, upholstered furniture, rubber products, built-up wooden girders, columns, or lapped wooden beams have been involved. Sparks may burrow into some of these materials and stay alive for days.

Bales of burning cotton have been submerged in water for days, yet when pulled out and opened they burst into flame. To a lesser degree this also applies to upholstered furniture. Furniture is often upholstered with kapok as padding. This material sheds water and retains embers for a long time.

Be particularly careful with rubber products such as tires. There may be no fire showing whatsoever, yet they may reignite spontaneously as much as an hour later. Some types of rubber buffings have a self-ignition temperature as low as 320° F. If it is not possible to remove such suspect materials to the outside for complete soaking and cooling, keep a watch line for at least six hours.

The overhauling procedure

Generally the overhaul will begin at the point of fire origin. You must check to see whether fire has involved areas which are not visible to the eye. (See Chapter 7, "Fires in concealed spaces.") In order to successfully control the fire and head it off, you probably did a great deal of opening up. Now continue (though with less urgency) to explore these avenues of potential fire travel.

Continue to follow the course of charred

woodwork until you come to clear wood which is obviously not involved in this fire. The old technique of looking in blind spaces to see whether cobwebs exist is still valid. No cobweb could resist passage of fire or high heat. Obviously, then, if you see cobwebs no further opening is necessary at this point.

When fire has burned around soil lines, piping, pipe chases, or involved chimneys, check every floor, the attic and the roof. (See Figure 134.)

Make sure there is no suspicion of arson before you begin to overhaul. In your overhauling operations you may destroy the evidence. Wait until the arson investigator has finished his examination.

See that the building is structurally safe. If it was a night fire and the building was seriously damaged, wait until daylight to begin overhauling. If daylight reveals questionable conditions, obtain the advice of the city engineer as to whether it is safe to continue overhauling operations. Don't cut with axes if supports have been weakened. The jarring blows may further weaken the structure. Use power saws for this purpose.

Now for the mechanics of the job. Make sure gas and electricity are secured before you begin, then follow these steps:

1. Clear a large space at your beginning point.

2. Assemble the tools you will need, as follows:

> Hose lines (small nozzle tips).
> Forcible entry tools.
> Good lighting equipment.
> Large barrels (to fill with water and soak burned materials and to carry debris out of the building).
> Shovels.
> Salvage covers.

3. If the building is a home, fill the bathtub with water to soak burned materials. Protect the drain from clogging with absorbent materials. Don't spray burned articles with hose lines inside the building.

4. Where practical, make troughs of salvage covers for soaking materials.

5. Personal records, books, pictures, and similar items should not be soaked. Put them in a separate safe place where they may be observed.

6. Don't pull ceilings and side walls onto salvageable material or material that has to be examined. In the first place, you will do unnecessary damage. In the second place, you will have to uncover the material to examine it for any residual fire. That means double work. This is one of the reasons for good planning. Never cover suspected articles with other materials. If the fire rekindles underneath these materials, you will only have to uncover it and start all over again.

7. Avoid unnecessary water damage. If your nozzles leak or you have to keep a small flow going because of freezing weather, put the nozzle in a sink or tub, or hold it out a window.

8. Don't discard bolts of burned cloth. They usually burn or scorch only at the outer roll and ends. Dipping them will be sufficient and the remainder of the cloth will be salvaged.

9. Don't overhaul substantially involved mattresses or upholstered furniture indoors. Remove them to the outside for examination. Don't leave the resulting debris alongside the building. It might rekindle. For that matter, no combustible debris should be left near any building.

10. Be particularly careful in removing mattresses from the building. Roll the mattress and tie it with a hose strap or rope tool. Now, if you are close to an outside window and you will do no damage by throwing it out the window, do so. The reason is this. If you attempt to drag a water-soaked smoldering mattress down the stairway, you will find it clumsy and heavy, and you will be dragging it over the stairs and carpets. If, while carrying it down the stairs, the mattress breaks out into flame, you will have to drop it. Now there will be a fire on the stairs. You will have to call for the line and do additional water damage—possibly to a part of the house which had not previously been damaged.

11. Be particularly wary of places where there is a possibility of dust explosions. Before starting to overhaul, open doors and windows to relieve pressures should an ex-

FIGURE 134. *This fire ran the space around the soil line. When a serious fire involves bathrooms or kitchens always check for involvement of these spaces or a fire may run floor to floor into the hanging ceiling spaces.*

plosion occur. Flood containers or bins containing smoldering dusts with very low-pressure fog streams.

12. If you have to move containers of chemicals whose contents are not obvious or where reactions may occur, handle them carefully. Hold such containers by the bottom to prevent them from falling apart. They may have become weakened by the fire.

13. Many men insist that the only way to

overhaul a lumber yard fire is to break down the lumber piles board by board. Anyone who has tried this at an extensive fire in a large lumber yard knows the result—you end up with a sea of boards covering roadways, on top of other piles, frequently requiring reshifting because of the lack of space. Lumber so handled will be broken, dirty, and useless. The result is an unnecessarily large loss. (See Figure 135.)

FIGURE 135. *It is not necessary to break down all the lumber piles when overhauling a lumber yard* *fire as was done here. The result is a large, unnecessary property loss.*

Try this technique instead: Poke a small garden hose as far as you can between the boards. Use good pressure. Also try the piercing nozzle with a long extension to accomplish the same objective. Do this in dozens of places, wherever you suspect fire has entered. In particularly suspicious lumber piles use a wetting agent in the water. After

this has been done, leave a company with several watch lines for a day or two.

Break down only those piles which show definite involvement, but plan carefully if you intend to break down some of the piles. You will need a great deal of space to store the boards you remove from the piles. Make sure no burned boards are covered until they have

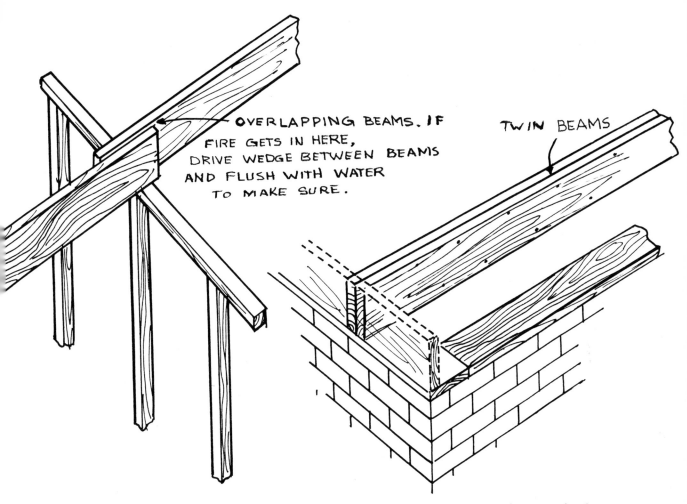

OVERLAPPING BEAMS. IF FIRE GETS IN HERE, DRIVE WEDGE BETWEEN BEAMS AND FLUSH WITH WATER TO MAKE SURE.

TWIN BEAMS

FIGURE 136. *It is important to check overlapping beams and twin beams for fire spread. Beams such* *as these commonly warp, leaving space for fire to burrow in and smolder for hours.*

been thoroughly wetted down by hose streams or you may have to do the job all over again.

The labor involved in these operations is enormous. Where you have plenty of yard space, use a bulldozer or fork lift truck to move the burned lumber. Move the lumber to a remote area of the yard and wet it down before piling or restacking.

The men in charge of the watch lines should be instructed to call for assistance the moment they see serious involvement. This rarely happens. The end result of this strategy will be fewer men injured by piles of lumber falling on them or tripping over slippery wet piles. The fire will be just as completely extinguished and there will be far less monetary loss.

14. Where arson is a possibility or is suspected, do not allow the removal of any records except by authorized persons.

15. If food stocks have been involved in the fire, notify the health authorities.

How to avoid unnecessary damage

Many officers do unnecessary structural and water damage because they are overly concerned or inexperienced. A good deal of this damage is caused by the thorough soaking of suspect areas by hose streams. If fire has burned deeply into concealed areas or between two beams, there must be some opening and application of water. However, it should be kept to a minimum.

Fire often burrows deeply into timbers,

particularly when they are overlapped. This is often the case when a common party wall is the support for floor or ceiling joists from adjoining buildings. You also see such joists overlapping on a girder in the same structure. Such joist ends are rarely spiked together. There often is some space between the two inside "faces" of the joists and fire can hide in this space for a long time. A cautious fire officer on seeing such conditions (where considerable fire has involved the area) will drive small wooden wedges between the ends. By spreading the ends he can be sure that some water will reach the hidden fire. (See Figure 136.)

It is completely practical in many cases to take time to observe conditions—to exercise a little patience. If time is important, where some areas are suspect and water damage is to be avoided, use a watch line. This means leaving a fireman or two (depending on the size of the fire) with a hose line attached to a hydrant. These men stay on watch several hours or up to several days depending on the situation. In the event of heavy baled materials it would be several days.

Often firemen have read or have been taught to keep pulling ceilings until clean wood appears. This is not always the proper procedure. It may do considerable unnecessary damage, particularly in the following situation: A building may have had a previous fire. The burned wooden members were still strong enough to carry the load, therefore they were not replaced. It may never

happen to you but it could. It is not uncommon for slum tenements to have had more than one fire. Further, it is quite common to find that no one knows there had been a previous fire.

In overhauling, the officer continues to have the ceiling pulled without questioning whether this fire could have burned this far. As a result, he continues to do considerable damage as well as exhausting his men.

The way to determine the need of further examination is to see whether there is a continuity of charring. This would indicate a progression of burning; if not, then some of the burn may be from a previous fire.

Throughout the overhauling operation the officer in charge must watch for signs of structural weakness. He should periodically examine all conditions mentioned in Chapter 8 on structural collapse. Water should not be allowed to build up on a floor. Floors should be drained. Water only 2 inches deep on a 40x80-foot floor will add 16 tons of weight to the structure.

Since no one expects a building to be completely torn down to insure that no burning embers remain, the officer in charge will always assume some calculated risk in dismissing the last company. If he is knowledgeable, prudent, and conscientious—and he follows the guidelines given here—he will have few rekindles, and those he does have will be of minor nature. In 35 years I have had fewer than five rekindles, none of them serious.

Section III

Specific fire problems

Chapter 18

Churches

FIRES IN OLD churches are extremely difficult to fight and constitute unusual dangers to the operating forces. Some churches are close to 100 years old. Once seriously involved, a church fire generally continues until the church is destroyed. These fires also present a severe exposure hazard to nearby buildings. The commanding officer must consider this early in his strategy. If the roof and walls collapse there will be severe heat radiation; sparks and brands will fly hundreds of feet. There may be an instant threat to an area far greater than the original fire.

Troublesome structural features

Some of the esthetic features present unusual and difficult firefighting problems. The heavy ornamental plaster ceilings and sharply pitched roofs (with their attendant difficulty of ventilation) combine to present major obstacles for fire control. (See Figure 137.)

The average church is a high single-story structure with poor fire-resistant qualities. There usually is a masonry outer wall (though many of the smaller churches are completely wood) with a massive peaked slate roof on heavy wooden sheathing. The roof supporting members are actually a form of truss construction. The rafters are tied to the ridge beam which in turn is supported by uprights resting on the cross girder below. Wood sheathing (at the corner where the cross girder meets the rafter) helps stiffen the truss effect. This cross girder in turn is supported by columns which end below as ornamental pillars. Throughout the structure there are large concealed spaces where fire can enter and travel out of sight and beyond ready reach of streams. Common to this construction is an organ loft and high steeple. (See Figure 138.)

Rarely are there window openings at the rear. The front may have one or two smaller windows up high near the peak. The sides may have some stained glass windows, which firemen are usually reluctant to break out.

The church floor is usually wood over a large cellar. Wooden wainscoating part-way up the side walls is common. Wood is also profusely evident in trim, pews, benches, balconies, and choir lofts. The interior walls are of wood lath and plaster.

To conceal old and often-large heating ducts and piping, inside walls are often furred out almost 12 inches. This leaves wide channels for fire spread to side walls and the attic.

The sharply peaked roof is practically inaccessible. Raising and placing ladders is a questionable effort. Not only is it difficult, but if the roof is inaccessible and there are few windows, what is the purpose of ladder placement? Certainly it is not for rescue from the church auditorium.

FIGURE 137. *The exceptionally steep roofs of the typical church structure are difficult to open for ventilation. The height of this church roof from the ridge beam is at least 35 feet, making it impossible to work off a ladder to cut for ventilation. The only other way would be to lay the aerial* *ladder alongside the roof much in the same manner as a hooked roof ladder. If it is impossible to get the aerial truck into proper position to do this, try the elevating platform. If all this fails then the roof cannot be vented and the chances are that, if seriously involved, it will go for a total loss.*

The church often is set so far back from the street that even the aerial ladder loses its limited effectiveness. If the aerial does reach, it may be possible to lay the ladder on the roof so that men may work off it much in the manner of using a hooked roof ladder. The use of the articulating boom may make such operations more effective.

Even when men succeed in cutting the roof, the combustion products in the church auditorium are not relieved unless it is possible not only to cut the roof but to push down the ceiling as well. Because of the height of the hanging ceiling space (as much as 12 to 18 feet) it is almost impossible to do so. The ceiling height from the church floor

can reach 50 feet. It is obviously impossible to pull ceilings from below.

The interior of the church is one large undivided area with a high ceiling. As in most large open spaces, fire conditions are difficult to handle because of the inability to ventilate at the roof level and the limited approach. Over the auditorium we not only find the hazard of a very heavy ornamental plaster ceiling, but it is common to find huge chandeliers hanging by supporting chains. These may weigh hundreds of pounds. Above the ceiling is the large attic (cockloft) with the accumulated dust of many years. Usually there is only a catwalk to walk on.

Church basements and cellars develop hot

A ▮ HANGING CEILING SPACE

B ▮ TRUSS CONSTRUCTION

C ▮ WOOD SHEATHING

D ▮ ORNAMENTAL PLASTER CEILINGS

E ▮ ORNAMENTAL PILLARS

FIGURE 138. *This church being demolished illustrates several of the problems of fighting fires in old churches: (A) High, wide open hanging ceiling space. When fire gets in here the church usually goes for a total loss. (B) Truss construction. Roof rafters are tied to the ridge beam which in turn is supported by uprights resting on cross girder below. (C) Wood corner sheathing acts as brace. (D) Ornamental plaster ceilings are enormously heavy. If pieces fall they can seriously injure people below. (E) The supporting pillars are made of built-up wooden members covered with ornamental plaster. The pillars usually have hollow spaces within them.*

smoky fires which are difficult to handle. They are inaccessible, difficult to ventilate, cover a large area, and are heavily stocked with combustible materials. In addition, they often are partitioned off into schoolrooms, meeting halls, and miscellaneous storage areas. Exits are poor and present a particular hazard when used by large numbers of people.

Where church fires originate

It is because of these undesirable features that once a fire does spread to involve the church interior it becomes a sea of flames, smoke, and hot gases. Spread to the hanging ceiling space must be anticipated along with the potential of roof collapse.

189

Statistics show that most church fires originate in the heating plant, for several reasons. Old churches are usually heated by gravity hot-air systems. They are poorly maintained and the plant is too small for the job it has to do. As the church ages the conditions worsen.

Fires starting in the furnace room can move quickly to the rest of the cellar and upper floors by way of the nonfire-stopped side walls, heating ducts, and direct flame contact with combustible materials in the cellar.

Next in importance as a fire cause is the defective chimney. This hazardous construction feature prevails in the basement and upper portions of the church. The trouble with the chimney may be due to its inadequacy for the system to which it is attached. Forcing any heating system will eventually bring to light defects in the construction of the chimney. The chimney may have floor beams built into it, or its weakness may lie in the aggregate of the mortar used in its construction. A mortar with too much sand and not enough cement will not hold up.

Defective electric wiring is another principal fire cause in the church fire record. This is mainly due to alterations and additions made after the original installation. Defective wiring is a difficult matter to control in a church because of its frequent use for entertainment and affairs requiring special lighting. Temporary extensions for lighting turn out to be permanent and soon the church contains numerous code violations. These range from general misuse of flexible cords for line wire to overfusing.

Firefighting tactics in churches

We said most church fires originate in the cellar. If upon arrival there is evidence of a working fire, get additional help in early. Try to advance hose lines down via the inside stairway to the cellar. Don't use less than 2½-inch hose and back up the first line as soon as possible. If these lines cannot penetrate to the fire, try to have them hold their position to prevent fire from coming up the stairs to involve the auditorium. Start to cut

openings for cellar nozzles and distributors.

Ventilate the cellar and auditorium floor at every conceivable point to hold positions in the main floor. Get a minimum of two 2½-inch hose lines in on the church floor to cover front and rear. These are large floors and the rear of the auditorium is usually partitioned off into various rooms. There may be a rear stairway to the cellar or basement.

Some churches may have both a cellar and basement. If the fire is in the cellar, try to move the lines down from the basement into the cellar; or at least hold the fire to the cellar until cellar nozzles can cool the fire and darken it sufficiently to start moving the hand lines down again.

Check to see if fire is running the side walls via nonfire-stopped partitions, heating and ventilation ducts, or pipe recesses. Open up any suspicious areas and use the lines in on this floor to kill any fire showing. Have a fireman check on the stairway to the attic, organ loft, and steeple. Men should use self-contained breathing masks and work in pairs.

It is extremely dangerous to send men to the interior of the church if the fire has seriously involved the hanging ceiling—even when the main roof has not fallen and the ceiling appears to be intact. There always is the possibility that the massive plaster ceiling with its chandeliers and ornamental plaster will fall. Under such conditions withdraw your men and fight the fire with heavy streams from the outside. Start setting up secondary lines of defense and begin to protect exposures.

Exterior stream operation into a large church is seldom efficient. Even though there are some windows, they may be inaccessible or too high to reach without ladders. Since these would probably have to be portable ladders, the size of the stream would be limited. Line operation from the rear also is restricted to the smaller hand lines because it is usually difficult or impossible to bring apparatus to these rear positions. Where there are rear windows, portable deluge guns may be feasible. But this is seldom the case.

Exterior streams cannot reach the hanging ceiling except through the small vent window. If there is one, this window is on the front wall, just under the peak of the roof. There may be a Rose window (a small oval window high on the front gable wall of the church) just below this vent. This window opens into the auditorium. In both cases stream penetration is extremely limited because of the small size of these openings, particularly the vent. Not only is penetration limited, but there is practically no way to move the stream back and forth to cover a greater area.

It may be possible to set up deluge guns just inside the large front doors. Here men may get some protection from archways to operate the stream without having to expose themselves to the hazards of the main auditorium. These positions will be difficult to hold. Since the roof is not vented, heat and smoke will try to vent toward the doors.

Another possibility is to get stream penetration with ladder pipes and elevating platforms through the vent and rose windows. It is wise to have this equipment set up even though it is not immediately necessary. Should the roof collapse, the equipment may have to be used to cover exposures and hold down sparks and flying brands.

Many church fires have roared beyond control because firemen try to avoid breaking the costly stained-glass windows for ventilation. Where this can be avoided, naturally it should be. But if necessary to save the church, the windows should be broken.

Should the roof collapse, it will probably cause the side walls to fall. Generally when a church fire of this type has serious involvement of the roof area, total loss of the church must be anticipated.

While loss of life to the parishioners has been gratifyingly small, it does not mean such life hazard does not exist. If a fire should occur during church services, a panic condition could readily take place. It is common to find a rectory, parish house, or nuns' quarters connected by passageway to the church proper. Should fire occur during the night, ventilation and search of these connecting quarters is vital. Protective hose lines should be laid to protect these areas from being involved in fire spread.

Summary of church fire hazards

The problem of church fires may be summed up under the following headings:

Life hazard. Be alert for potential life hazard in the following three categories:

1. To church occupants. Life hazard is severe when congregation is present. There is the possibility of panic, and inadequate exit facilities contribute to the hazard.

2. To the firemen the potential hazard is in two areas: (A) The danger of interior or exterior structural collapse, and (B) back drafts.

3. To occupants of adjoining buildings when wall or steeple failure occurs.

Rapid fire travel. Four factors contribute to rapid fire travel in church fires:

1. Concealed spaces beneath floors, in walls, hanging ceiling, organ interiors, and behind ornamental features.

2. Steeple interior provides a high flue.

3. Most interior construction is of frame. The furnishings are usually of wood.

4. Large open areas create tremendous drafts.

Exposures. Be alert for these potential exposure problems:

1. To adjoining and adjacent structures not church connected.

2. To rectory and similar structures connected with church proper by passageways.

3. By high temperatures—the hazard of flying sparks and brands.

Fire control problems. This is a summary of the numerous obstacles and hazards that will affect your ability to control the fire.

1. The inability to make interior attack if fire is intense or covers a large area.

2. Approach to fire is usually confined to front and rear.

3. Small exterior openings limit the effectiveness of exterior streams.

4. It is often impossible to ventilate at the roof.

5. The inability to pull hanging ceilings if the fire gains in this location.

6. Potential failure of balcony and organ loft structures which inhibit interior approach.

7. The hot-air heating system can carry fire throughout the building.

8. The heavy dense smoke makes fire-fighting more hazardous.

9. Back drafts often occur.

10. Rarely can a church fire be controlled without multiple alarms.

11. It is difficult to provide heavy street streams because of the possibility of structural failure which prevents proper placement of apparatus.

12. Heavy cellar fire nearly always assures failure of the first floor if it is made of wood.

13. High winds and fire involving the steeple intensify the hazard of flying brands.

14. Altars constructed of marble or combustible materials with many voids and open spaces contribute to spread of fire.

15. Heavy lighting fixtures may fail, injuring persons beneath.

16. Heat and flame endanger nearby structures.

17. Laddering of the building is usually impractical.

18. The hazard of roof collapse.

19. Heavy lead window panes separate, shattering glass—a potential source of injury to firemen.

20. The hazard of candles, tapers, oils and flammable decorations. These add fuel to the fire.

Chapter 19

Factories

THE WORD FACTORY is a broad term used loosely to indicate a structure used for manufacturing. Factories range from the small one- or two-man woodworking shop to the giant industrial complex employing thousands of people. It would be impossible to discuss all types of possible factory fires in a book this size. Therefore, we will devote most of this chapter to the factory fires that are most likely to occur.

The modern industrial complex is usually a one-story relatively fire-resistant structure. Employees work around the clock so the possibility of delayed alarm is remote. There will be some sort of fire brigade. Plant inspection for fire breeding conditions is a continuing process. Serious fire incidence in this kind of occupancy is low. This is not to say disastrous fires do not happen in such plants. They do. But there is much greater likelihood of serious fires occurring in the older factory common to all areas.

The nonfire-resistant factory

The nonfire-resistant factory building is a brick, wood joisted structure with wood floors, open wooden stairs, wood lath and plaster interior walls and air and light shafts. Regardless of contents, the structure is highly combustible. Some of them are more than 100 years old.

These buildings are three or four stories high and may be more than 100 feet deep. If they exceed 25 feet in width, chances are there will be a center girder running from the front to the rear wall. This girder, which supports the floor joists, will be supported by columns. If it is a very old factory, the columns probably will be cast iron, which have a poor record in fires. They have no tensile strength; their failure is sudden and complete. Cast-iron columns are particularly dangerous if superimposed on one another. That is, a lower column supports not only its girder on the same floor but the column on the floor above as well. Should a column on a lower floor collapse, it will cause a loss of support for the columns on the upper floors. Once the column gives way, the girder will not have the strength to support the floor load. In this way every floor above may collapse within moments after the first lower column failure. This is one reason why older factories have such a sorry record under fire conditions.

Don't underestimate fire potential in one of these buildings. Because of the old, inferior construction (and most probably combustible contents) they make hot, smoky, difficult fires to fight. If you are unable to move in with hand lines, heavy exterior streams with large water supplies will be needed. We will therefore treat fires in old factories on two levels: the small fire on one floor, and the large fire where hand lines cannot be advanced onto the fire floor.

Fire confined to one floor

If fire is extending out of the windows upon arrival of the fire department, the first engine company should lay two lines. One should be 3-inch hose to supply either a deluge gun or other form of heavy stream appliance. This exterior stream will be effective in preventing the extending fire from getting into the floors above the front windows. (See Figure 35.)

The second line is used to move in on the fire floor via the inside stairway. As soon as possible this interior line should be backed up with another 2½-inch line.

The operator of the exterior stream must use judgment. As soon as he is aware the company has made the floor by way of the inside stairway, he must either redirect the stream or shut it down. Shut-down usually requires time, therefore it is simpler to aim the stream up and over the roof until shutdown is accomplished. There are two reasons for such concern over shut-down of the exterior stream: First, it prevents combustion products from blowing out the window; second, it tends to push the heated smoke and gases back in on the floor toward the company moving in.

If the outside stream continues to bore in on the floor, it may drive the inside line back out. The outside stream should be used to darken down the fire, prevent it from extending by burning through the floor, up vertical arteries, or by way of front windows until there is evidence the inside line is making progress.

At times it may be difficult to determine whether the inside line is making the floor. Here is what to look for: If the fire darkens, if the color of the smoke lightens, if you notice water spray from a window other than the one your stream is entering, then you know the inside line is making progress.

One of the reasons such teamwork is necessary is this: The engine company may have had to force the door from the stair side to the floor (or a ladder company may have done this for them). The door may have been badly damaged in the process and would no longer close the fire area off from the stairs.

If the engine company is driven back and has to retreat down—never up—the stairs, the fire may roar out the door, involving the stairs and floors above. Once the stairs are lost, generally the upper floors will be lost. Most of these old factories have one inside stairway and an exterior fire escape. Of course, additional hose lines should attempt another inside attack via the fire escape.

An experienced engine crew will operate in the following manner at such fires: They will stretch to the door of the fire floor. Surplus hose will be pulled up and distributed without kinks on the stairs above so that when they want to move in on the fire floor, they will be able to do so readily. The hose above will pay out without much effort. It is more difficult to pull surplus hose up a stairway and this would slow up the progress of the men moving in. While the door is being forced, orders would be given to charge the line. Never charge a line until it is in position. The charged line is stiff, unmanageable, and for each 50 feet of 2½-inch hose there will be more than 100 pounds of water.

The crew will assume a kneeling position to one side of the doorway so that when the door is forced they will not get the full effects of the heat and smoke in their faces. After waiting a few seconds (to give the fire a chance to light up before they move in and to avoid being trapped in a back draft), they start to advance.

They will be in a very rough position. If the floor was not vented, the only place the smoke and heat can go is to the opening in which they are standing. Usually they will not be able to spot the fire right away. The heat and smoke will be punishing. Vision will be nil. The following techniques have proven successful in such fires:

1. Keep the men quiet. All hands listen carefully for crackling, popping noises which will indicate the location of the fire.

2. Direct the stream in a wide sweeping arc toward the opposite wall. The chances are that windows heated by the fire will be hit and will break, ventilating the floor. This also serves to let the chief on the street know the inside line is on the floor and to shut

down the exterior stream if any is being used on this floor.

3. If the fire is or becomes visible and covers a large area, deflect the stream off the ceiling to serve as a giant sprinkler. Coverage of a wide area is achieved in this manner.

4. Trained men will know whether the stream is being obstructed by stock, partitions, or other obstacles. There will be a thudding sound when the stream hits a partition. The line must be moved in ahead of the obstruction or there will be no fire extinguishment, only water damage.

This position of the hose line on the fire floor is of crucial importance and plays a key part in the total fire strategy. If the line cannot advance, the fire on the floor will continue to burn. If the exterior streams were shut down to give this line a chance to move in, no water is hitting the fire. If so, the fire will continue to burn and will probably extend not only horizontally to involve the rest of the floor but upstairs as well. This is why the company at the doorway must do one of two things: Either move in to extinguish, or back out and use streams from the doorway. In the latter case, the heavy exterior streams should be started again.

Where the floor areas are large with a considerable body of fire, and the first inside line was not backed up previously, make sure it is backed up now.

Large fire—impossible to advance inside line

We have discussed small fires confined to one floor in old nonfire-resistant factories—fires where three to four lines are sufficient. Let us consider the fire where there is evidence of extension, where the inside line or lines will find it impossible to advance in on the fire floor. You will need help on this kind of fire and it should be called early.

One of the primary actions where the building is sprinklered is to supply the sprinkler by the outside fire department connection. Whether this is the first or second line is not terribly important, so long as the sprinkler is supplied. Try to place your apparatus so it doesn't block the front of the building. It may become necessary to place aerial ladder pipes or elevating platforms here later. If you will use an exterior heavy stream appliance from ground level or from a pumper mount, try and place the appliance at the opposite street curb so as to gain greater penetration on the fire floor.

Move hand lines in via the inside stairway to the fire floor and the floor above. Hand lines also are moved in via fire escape or the second interior stairway to the fire floor and floor above. These should be 2½-inch lines. Do not use smaller hose during the active firefighting phase. Set up one or two heavy streams in the front (depending on the width of the building). You must check whether the buildings alongside are in danger of exposure. If so, they must be protected by lines. The rear is another point to consider early in the fight. It must also be covered by lines.

Protect the firemen working on a fire escape. When hand lines are moved up by exterior fire escapes, give thought to protecting these positions. They would be seriously endangered if fire were to blow out from the floor below. Avoid the procedure of moving lines to floors above the fire with no protective lines to cut the fire off from below. Where upper and lower floors are involved and lines are operating on each floor, make sure that if it becomes necessary to withdraw the lower line this is not done until the men above are advised and brought down first. Where lines are working off fire escapes at the front, set up a heavy stream ready for instant use so that the men will be protected should fire blow out below them. Where it is impossible to cover men on fire escapes at the rear and sides, they must be doubly cautioned about this possibility of being trapped.

Remember, stream penetration on a fire floor is poor above the second floor, or on any floor two or more stories above the height of any exterior stream (ladder pipes or elevating platforms). A ladder pipe or elevating platform can be effective up to approximately 150 feet to prevent fire from floors below getting into upper stories by way of exterior windows.

In really bad cellar fires where companies experience great difficulty not only in getting

FIGURE 139. *This large skylight is ideal for ventilating the top floor or stair shaft. Try to lift the skylight or remove the glass panes instead of* *breaking the glass. Firemen below may be cut by falling glass. Remember, the skylight will not vent the hanging ceiling space.*

down into the cellar but in holding their position on the floor above, cellar nozzles are brought into use. Often heavy stock, partitions, or machinery are on top of the hot spots. This precludes efficient placement of the cellar nozzles.

This is why at such cellar fires, where the conditions are as outlined and the usual methods of operation on the floor above are not effective, the deluge gun should be used to flood the ground floor—and in extreme cases, the second floor. This may prevent fire from extending to upper floors. The deluge of water floods the floor and flows down through the floor cracks and pipe recesses,

acting as a sprinkler system over the fire. This method is the only one to be used in many cases, unless high expansion foam can be employed to fill the cellar.

In buildings of open-beam construction where the floor boards have cracks or openings in them, always examine the stock on the floor above for fire. In cases where fire has possession of a floor and it is impossible to examine the floor above the fire floor because of heat and smoke conditions, it is advisable to wet down this floor as well. In such cases keep the stream as low as possible so as not to wet the stock more than necessary.

Ladder companies at such fires should go

to the roof by way of the least exposed means to ventilate over top floor fires and over the stair shafts. (See Figure 139.) The stair shaft is particularly important when engine company crews are attempting to move in on the fire floor. Roof ventilation will help clear the stair shaft of smoke and heat coming from the door on the fire floor. Ladder men should also move down exterior fire escapes to ventilate, and search floors for fire extension and people overcome. Part of the ladder company crew is dispatched with the first engine company to force entrance for them and to open ceiling and side walls as necessary.

Ladder company men must be instructed carefully regarding the fire extension problems of air and light shafts. Particularly deep buildings (more than 75 feet) will almost certainly have them. There is only one sure way to check against fire extension via shafts and that is to place lines in these threatened positions. Such vulnerable features must be checked early in the fight and continually re-inspected if no protective lines can be spared for these areas.

Fire on one floor will often break a window facing on a shaft. Now the fire is pulled into and up the shaft by the natural flue effect. The radiated heat will break windows on the course of the shaft, allowing fire to get in on the floors of the adjoining building or other parts of the same building. This generally takes place at the side or rear—often without knowledge of the fire chief. Serious involvement of adjoining structures in this manner is fairly common. (See Figures 27-34.)

Operations at these older buildings are fraught with danger. Floors may be overloaded. Years of vibration from large machines may have weakened the structure. Remodeling may have cut away supports. Walls may be out of plumb. The occupancy may be just about anything from a dress shop to metal fabricating, from radioactive experimentation to printing with its massive presses. Buildings stocked with absorbent materials can absorb enough water to overload a fire-weakened floor. Moreover, the expansion of such tightly packed materials can push walls out far enough to cause loss of

support for floor joists where they rest on these side walls. Literally dozens of other hazards can exist.

This is why when a fire is burning out of control on more than one floor for more than 20 minutes, you should back all inside units out. In such cases rely on heavy exterior streams to darken the fire down. Then have the building thoroughly checked for stability before moving in the hand lines for final mopup.

Fire-resistant factories

Fire-resistant factories are not only higher, but they have larger floor areas than the typical nonfire-resistant type. The fire-resistant factory is built with masonry walls, concrete floors, enclosed stairways, and elevators with an absence of concealed spaces. There may be light shafts. The stability of such buildings is excellent and collapse is not a problem. Spread of fire in such buildings beyond the floor of origin is uncommon. Air-conditioning ducts could account for fire and smoke extension to other areas.

Even though these buildings are far more fire-resistant than the older type of factory building, at times fires can be more difficult to handle. Because the stairs are enclosed, these buildings are difficult to ventilate. Venting into an enclosed stairway shaft is not good practice—particularly if people above are trying to get down. Since the floors are concrete, cutting for ventilation or insertion of cellar pipes is very, very slow. The only means left is cross-ventilation by way of the windows or mechanical ventilation. Reaching the windows from the inside may be difficult because of the accumulated heat and smoke. However, it is sometimes possible to break the windows by sweeping the stream from the door in an effort to hit the windows. This will of course cause some water damage. The next possibility is to break the windows with heavy exterior streams from deck guns, ladder pipes, or elevating platforms. If the height is beyond the reach of these appliances, go to the floor above the fire and try to open the windows from above. It is sometimes possible to reach shaft windows with long pike poles from adjoining buildings.

Doors to such floors are usually heavy. It may take 15 to 20 minutes to force them and it may require a cutting torch. If the partition is hollow block or hollow tile, it is more feasible to breach the partition than to try to force the door.

Without question, men will take a great deal of punishment at such fires—even if they are wearing masks. Don't rule out explosions or back drafts. While the building is well-constructed and structurally sound, the occupancy itself may be extremely hazardous.

In general, line placement at these fires is quite the same as for the nonfire-resistant factory with one exception: there is not the urgency to cover the floor above as quickly. Since there is less chance of extension to upper floors, there will be no need for as many covering lines. The exposure to adjoining buildings may be as severe, except that the fire will not go through the roof and expose the higher buildings and roofs alongside.

Tips on factory fire operations

These items are of concern at factory fires in buildings of either new or old construction.

The floor above the fire. When operating on the floor above the fire floor, keep these points in mind:

1. In searching for people who may have been overcome, look in restrooms, small mezzanine offices, behind and under tables.

2. Be careful of narrow, winding aisles with highly piled stock; the stock may fall over on you.

3. Check to make sure that combustible stock stored on the floor has not been ignited by heat or sparks through the floor.

4. Watch out for heavy machinery or safes resting on burned areas; they may come crashing through to the floor below.

5. Check for openings in the floor that may have communicated fire such as openings for power belting, chutes, open hoistways, or shafts.

6. Examine under cutting or storage tables for hidden fire.

7. Follow up on pipe recesses, particularly around soil and vent lines in toilets.

The roof. These pointers will help men working on the roof at a factory fire to operate more efficiently and safely:

1. Drain water from roof tanks if the supports below have been weakened.

2. Watch out for loose signs and awnings.

3. Check on chimney and any walls out of plumb or cracked.

4. If there is a penthouse where machinery is housed, examine it for fire spread.

5. If there is a roof hopper for dust collection, make sure fire has not gotten inside.

6. Check for fire involvement of hanging ceiling space.

7. Warn men to be extremely careful when working on roofs with no parapet walls at roof edges.

8. Don't rely on the stability of the gooseneck ladder leading from the fire escape onto the roof. Examine it carefully to see that it is not pulling from the supports.

9. Don't cut header beams around roof openings. The header may support three or more joists. Cutting the header may seriously weaken the roof. (See Figure 107.)

10. Don't use a vent stack as a support for ropes, etc. They are not strong enough to stand the strain.

Chapter 20

Flammable liquids and gases

Part I—Flammable Liquids

There are a few basic definitions and principles one must understand to handle the flammable liquid fire effectively. The first is that a flammable liquid does not in itself burn. It gives off a vapor or gas which can be ignited. The lower the temperature at which the gas is given off, the more dangerous the liquid.

Gasoline as an example

Everyone is familiar with gasoline. It will be our example to show the characteristics of flammable liquids.

Gasoline flashes at −45° F. This means that it gives off a vapor that can be ignited as low as −45° F. That is why it is so difficult to put out a gasoline fire with water. You never can cool it enough to stop the liquid from giving off flammable vapors. Even water fog cannot cool the gasoline fire sufficiently. If you do achieve extinguishment with water fog on gasoline, it is because you were able to completely cover the burning surface with the spray. Two things happened: (1) The spray helped prevent available oxygen from combining with the vapors, and (2) the burning vapors turned some of the water fog into steam. The steam expanded (1600 to 1) and also helped to keep the oxygen from the flammable vapors. This

is really extinguishment by smothering (excluding oxygen). Foam, dry chemical, and carbon dioxide (CO_2) achieve extinguishment in this way.

Gasoline has a flammable range of about 1.5 percent to 6 percent (the percent of vapor in air). This means the lower limit is 1.5 percent and the upper limit 6 percent. It also means that at the lower limit, gasoline will burn if mixed in the ratio of 1.5 percent gasoline to 98.5 percent air. And at the upper limit, 6 percent gasoline to 94 percent air, it will also burn. Outside of this narrow range, gasoline will not burn at all. Below the lower limit it is too lean and above the upper limit it is too rich. One of the qualities that makes gasoline so dangerous is its low flammable limit of 1.5 percent. Because this amount of vapor is easily reached, the potential of fire with gasoline is nearly always existent.

The terms explosive range and combustible range are synonymous with flammable range. The maximum energy in any flammable range always is toward the center. Therefore gasoline is most dangerous in a mixture of 3.5 percent gasoline to 96.5 percent air. This mixture will burn most furiously, but it will not explode unless confined in a vessel where the pressure build-up cannot be vented as fast as it is created. This is why you always have some form of automatic venting on gasoline storage tanks (as well as on other flammable liquids).

Gasoline vapors are three to four times heavier than air. Therefore, they will settle in low spots. They will not rise and dissipate, as will hydrogen, which has a flammable range of 4 to 74 percent. Hydrogen dissipates easily because it is lighter than air. It will rise and be blown away by the air currents.

Not only will gasoline vapors settle in low spots, they will travel hundreds of feet to reach low areas. If these vapors reach a source of ignition, they will ignite and flash back to the source of the vapor emission.

Now you can begin to appreciate the hazards of a gasoline tanker crash with hundreds of gallons of free gasoline flowing towards sewers, cellars, and subways with the vapors traveling even further.

If you have trained at flammable liquid fires you know that there is an immediate threat to nearby structures. The radiant heat energy of a gasoline fire is high, and you will understand why if you compare the combustion of wood with gasoline. The heat of combustion of wood is about 8,000 Btu's per pound; gasoline is about 20,000 Btu's per pound. Much more heat is released by the burning of gasoline compared to wood, and gasoline burns at a greater rate per pound of material. The heat units are released at a much faster rate. So we really have two factors: (1) the heat energy is much greater, and (2) the heat energy is released in less time. This adds up to a much hotter fire in a shorter time.

Another illustration of the difference in burning rates is that the average structural fire releases 3,000 Btu's per minute per square foot while a gasoline fire in an open container releases about 14,000 or about five times the energy release of wood in the same time.

We have been discussing gasoline and its hazards. It should be realized that all flammable liquids—and this includes crude oils—are just as dangerous as gasoline once they are heated enough to give off flammable vapors. The answer to the flammable liquid fire then seems obvious: confine such flammable materials so no vapors will be emitted. Yet this is not feasible. First, such liquids must at times be moved and transported.

When we buy gasoline for our car, the liquid is in transmission and temporarily in an open state. In industry where the liquid is taken from the buried storage system to be used in manufacture, the material often is in an open state.

Storage tanks

If closed containers of flammable liquids with high vapor pressure (such as gasoline) have no way to relieve the internal pressure they can become dangerous—especially if subjected to heat from a nearby fire. The release of some of the flammable vapors is necessary to keep the containers in a safe condition.

This is why flammable liquid tanks always are vented. This feature is particularly important in the large above-ground tanks. The record of buried storage tanks is excellent. The requirements for venting buried tanks is mainly to allow vapor movement as the tank is either being filled or fuel is being withdrawn. Buried tanks do not explode or go on fire. Tests show that a tank buried under two feet of earth is protected against any exposure to fire.

The objective in large above-ground tank storage is to keep the vapors in the tank at a minimum. There are four general types of above-ground storage tanks.

One has a solid roof which may be either flat or slightly cone-shaped. These roofs must have some type of emergency pressure relief devices (in addition to the normal vents). This may be in the form of a weak seam between the roof and sides of the tank, or hinged doors, or explosion hatches on the roof. The purpose of the doors or hatches is to relieve pressure build-up and then automatically fall back into the closed position, cutting off any air needed for combustion. Of course, if the explosion blows the roof at the weak seam, there is no way to prevent the mixture of air with flammable liquid. If the flammable liquid is gasoline or some other hazardous liquid, the chances are you will have a fire.

A second type is the floating roof tank. Here the roof rests upon the liquid in the tank and moves up and down with the level of the liquid.

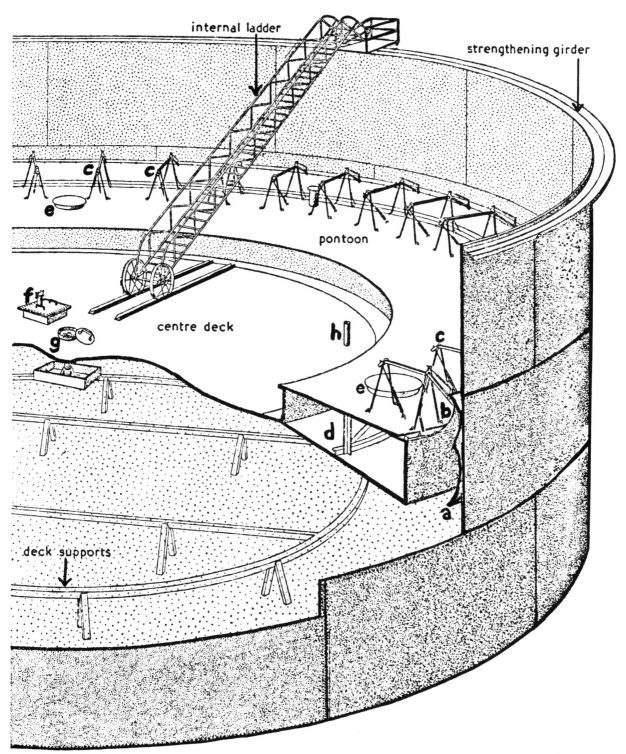

internal ladder

strengthening girder

c c

e

pontoon

centre deck

f

g

h

c

e

b

d

a

deck supports

FIGURE 139A. *The Wiggins floating roof tank (pontoon type). The following details are shown: (a) metal shoe, (b) fabric seal, (c) spring, (d)* *pontoon, (e) pontoon manhole, (f) deck manhole and diphole, (g) rainwater siphon drain, and (h) rainwater emergency overflow.*

201

FIGURE 139B. *An explosion sent flammable vapors straight up. Evidently the vapors were too "rich" to burn until they mixed with enough oxygen. This mixture occurred well above the burning tanks. If such vapor accumulation takes place at low points where men are working, they could be trapped in the explosion. In doubtful areas, men should operate from high ground with the wind at their backs. Each team should be covered by other hose lines.*

A third type, similar to the floating roof, is the liquid sealed type. It also moves up and down with any changes in the volume of the vapors inside the tank.

In both floating roof types there is some form of movable seal between the roof and the side walls of the tank. This prevents the formation of vapor space inside the tank.

The fourth type is called a vapor dome roof tank. This has a flexible diaphragm in a hemispherical roof that fluctuates with the vapor volume. It performs the same function as the floating roof types. That is to say it eliminates a vapor space build-up of flammable gases inside the tank.

Some leakage of vapors may occur around the seal of the floating roofs. If these vapors are ignited, they may be handled by the use of foam or dry powder. Such a fire is usually not of any significance. (See Figure 139A.)

Causes of fires in storage tanks

From the foregoing it seems perfectly obvious that if the vapors are not allowed to build up inside a tank or if there is not a major release of the flammable liquids, there will be little danger of a serious fire. This is generally quite true. However, major fires do occur in areas of flammable liquid storage and there are several causes:

1. Fire from a building exposes a tank. The vents are insufficient to relieve the internal pressure build-up and the tank ruptures.

2. A spill fire involves the tank, and that portion of the tank above the interior liquid level collapses from the heat of the spill fire. That portion of the tank below the liquid level is kept cool by the liquid inside the tank.

3. There is an explosion of the vapors inside the tank.

4. Tanks on unprotected metal support members are exposed to the heat of an adjacent fire. This could be from a tanker loading or unloading at the filling platform. The metal supporting members fail, the tank drops, breaking open at the seam or tearing piping, etc.

5. Above ground piping is struck by trucks or breaks from explosion or stresses.

6. Lightning strikes on the old wood roof tanks.

7. Fire burning at the vents is pulled into the tank and explodes the shell.

The problem, then, appears to be a large release and ignition of flammable vapors emanating from an explosion or spillage of flammable liquids. (See Figure 139B.)

Firefighting operations at tank fires

Operational techniques will vary depending upon nine situations: (1) burning liquid in an open tank, (2) fire exposing nearby flammable liquid tanks, (3) the burning liquid is crude oil, (4) the burning liquid is heavier than water, (5) the feasibility of using subsurface or foam injection, (6) spill fire, (7) extinguishing mediums that are available, (8) the availability of trained help from plant fire brigade, and (9) the availability of adequate fire department personnel and equipment. Let us discuss these nine points and the operating techniques for each.

1. The burning liquid is contained within an open tank.

A. Begin to cool the exposed tank shell with heavy water streams. Be careful not to get water inside the tank and overflow burning contents onto the ground.

B. Use foam, powder, Light Water, etc., to extinguish the fire.

C. If extinguishment is impossible, pump tank contents into another tank and let the remaining contents burn out while continuing to cool the exterior tank walls.

2. The previous fire is also exposing nearby flammable liquid tanks.

A. Take all actions as listed in A, B, C, in the first fire above.

B. Immediately cool the exposed tanks with heavy streams.

C. Keep the stream moving to insure against spot heating of some parts of the exposed tank.

D. Don't pump out the contents of an exposed tank unless the person in charge of the plant advises this. A full tank tends to stay cooler because of the temperature of the liquid therein.

TABLE IV*

BURNING CHARACTERISTICS OF FOUR FUELS

Flammable Liquid	Rate of Expansion of Heat Wave Downward (inches per hour)	Burns Off at Rate of (inches per hour)	Boil-Over or Slop-Over** Potential
Gasoline	None	6 - 12	None
Kerosene	None	5 - 8	None
Crude Oil (light)	15 - 35†	4 - 18	Yes
Crude Oil (heavy)	3 - 20†	3 - 5	Yes

*This table is from Fire Protection in Refineries prepared by The American Petroleum Institute.
†The greater the amount of moisture contained in the oil, the greater the heat wave travel.
**Slop-over is an overflow in similar oils which may be caused by the application of extinguishing agents like foam or fog. It is at times preceded by a lighter smoke color.

3. **The burning liquid in the first fire (No. 1, above) is heavy crude oil.**

A. There is potential for a boil-over or slop-over. A boil-over is a violent eruption of part of the burning tank contents. Crude oils generally contain some moisture which settles at the bottom of the tank. As the crude oil burns, a heat wave begins to extend downward toward the bottom of the tank. This wave of heated oil may reach 400° to 500° F. When the heated oil reaches the moisture, it turns the water into steam which expands more than 1,600 times. The steam will either erupt to the surface in large bubbles or become trapped in the oil, causing a huge increase in volume. This expanded volume will swell up to throw out a burning wave of oil over the sides of the tank. It may trap firemen operating nearby. This is one reason why men should not operate at such fires inside the diked areas. They should remain on top of the diked wall and even then they must remain alert. Where burning oils contain no moisture but are capable of creating heat waves downward, allowing water from hose streams to get into the tank will create the same danger. As long as any moisture remains at the bottom of the tank, boil-overs may continue to occur. Thus, if one boil-over occurred this is no guarantee against another.

Table IV lists the burning characteristics of four fuels. Use this table as a guide to estimate the boil-over possibility of these fuels.

B. Use foam or water fog to try to extinguish fire in the tank.

C. Cool sides of tank with heavy streams.

D. When boil-over is probable, remove all men from nearby areas. Boil-over may cause the area surrounding the tank to become involved in fire, increasing the hazard measurably.

E. Provision must be made to remove the water from inside diked areas or there may be an overflow as hose streams fill the dikes.

F. Protect exposed tanks with heavy streams.

4. **The burning liquid in a tank is heavier than water.**

A. Find out from the person in charge whether the use of water is dangerous.

B. If not (it usually isn't) apply a light film of water spray on top of the burning liquid.

C. The water spray will cool and the steam generated will help blanket the liquid, causing extinguishment.

D. Sometimes the use of water will cause a frothing or foaming which may slop over the tank's edge. Therefore, exercise caution in applying the stream.

E. With the exception of gasoline, kerosene, benzine, naphtha, and mineral oils, most flammable liquids which are on fire require the use of alcohol (all-purpose) type foam. Again, be guided by the person in charge of the plant.

F. Cool the outside of the burning tank with heavy streams.

5. Is sub-surface injection of air or foam feasible?

This technique was developed by the Mobil Oil Company. It is basically a method of injecting air, foam, or an inert gas into the bottom of the tank to induce an upward flow of cooler oil or foam to the burning surface. The cooling is sufficient to extinguish fires in high-flash-point oils and reduce the severity of fire in low-flash-point oils to where they may be controlled by other extinguishing agents. The rising foam blankets the oil and either extinguishes or reduces the height of the flames. Care must be taken to avoid slopover. This happens if agitation is too rapid. The subsurface injection method is not suitable for use on gasoline or other liquids of similar high vapor pressure. Of course, there must be a system of piping in use before the fire for such systems to be put in operation. Here again prior knowledge of the plant and its facilities is invaluable.

In designing the air supply equipment and piping*, the following rules should be observed:

A. The minimum air rate required for a group of tanks is the maximum rate required for any one tank in the group.

B. Air or gas storage capacity can be used as the source of agitation gas. With oils having flash points above their stored temperatures, the air storage capacity must be large enough to supply air at the required rate and pressure for 30 minutes. With oils having flash points below their stored temperatures, enough additional capacity (above 30 minutes) is required to supply air at the minimum rate long enough to put into use

_____
*The material given here on the design and special techniques of the air-agitation fire suppression method is from the Pamphlet, "Extinguishment in Control of Oil Fires by Air-Agitation," published by Socony-Vacuum Oil Company.

the equipment needed to complete extinguishment.

C. When air compressors are used, they must be able to provide air continuously at the required rate and pressure to supply the largest tank.

D. The regular plant air system can be used as the air supply, provided it can supply air at the required rate and pressure.

E. The minimum air pressure required at the tank is that necessary to overcome the static head of the greatest possible depth of oil in any tank. This pressure can be calculated on the basis of 1.0 psi of air pressure for each $2\frac{1}{2}$ feet of tank height. For example, a tank 50 feet high would require a minimum air pressure of 20 psi at the tank.

F. The air lines and the air inlet openings should be large enough to carry air at the required rate without appreciable back pressure. The use of a substantial margin of safety in the design of these pipes and inlets is recommended.

G. Check valves should be installed in lines at the tank when the air inlet valves are located outside the dike or otherwise at a distance from the tank. This may prevent oil spillage if the lines should be broken.

Air injection procedures. Not all conditions which might be encountered in a tank fire can be forecast, hence no rigid procedure can be recommended. However, the following are general steps of procedure which can be used as a guide:

Air should be started into the tank at a low initial rate to be certain that all connections are correct and there will be no slopover. When this is established, the air rate should be increased to the optimum as promptly as possible. These precautions are particularly essential for fires in small tanks containing viscous oils and in all crude tank fires. In the former, too high an initial rate might throw oil over the side and spread the fire; in the latter, water might be carried up into the heat wave, thus precipitating a slopover.

When the burning oil has a flash point above the stored temperature, the air rate should be increased to the point of best reduction of flame. This rate should be maintained until all flames are extinguished except those caused by the splashing of oil onto the hot tank plates above the liquid level. At this point the air rate should be reduced to cut down the splashing so that the upper tank shell will cool and not ignite the vapors.

When the burning oil has a flash point below the stored temperature, the air rate should be adjusted to give the greatest reduction of flame. This rate should be maintained while portable equipment is used to put the fire out. Where foam is used, agitation should be reduced gradually as the foam covers the surface of the oil.

In crude oil fires, promptness in the application of air agitation can prevent the development of a heat wave. If one has had time to develop, the air should be applied at an extremely low rate until the heat wave is eliminated. The air rate then may be increased for maximum fire control, and the fire put out with portable equipment. The gradual application of air will lessen the possibility of a slop-over caused by carrying water from the bottom of the tank into the heat wave. When air agitation is applied to a crude oil fire that has been burning for some time, a small amount of water reaching the heat wave will cause the flame to whiten and appear to increase temporarily. This does not mean that a slop-over is imminent, but the air rate should be reduced momentarily as a safeguard. The air rate should then be increased gradually until the fire is extinguished or under control.

After 5 to 10 minutes of uncontrolled burning in a tank more than 20 feet in diameter, the shell may buckle if several feet of it is exposed to the flames. Water applied to the outside of the tank shell in the flame area will help reduce tank damage. After the fire has been reduced to the best control level, extensive buckling should cease. Buckling of the shell will not prevent extinguishing the fire.

When the oil depth in a large tank is less than five feet, cold oil pumped into the tank simultaneously with air agitation will facilitate extinguishment or control. The air and oil may be introduced through the same or separate lines.

Precautions. In using the air agitation method there are several precautions to be taken:

Do not test the air mechanism in any tank by the introduction of air under any condition where vapors are present or may form above the surface. Air agitation under certain conditions can cause a static charge to build up at the surface of the oil faster than it can be dissipated. When this occurs, a spark may jump to the shell or other structure, causing ignition of any combustible vapors.

Before air is turned into the line (or lines) to a tank of burning oil, the valves to other tanks which may contain combustible vapor-air mixtures must be closed. (In some cases, closing such valves may be necessary to insure the correct flow of air to the burning tank.)

In case it becomes necessary to go to the top stairway platform of a tank in which a fire is burning under agitation control, make sure that the air rate to the tank is continued and control maintained while the platform or stairway is occupied.

Cool the sides of the burning tank with heavy water streams.

Get ready with foam, Light Water, and conventional extinguishing methods just in case the subsurface injection method should fail. Recommendations on the use of the air agitation method vary with field conditions such as the kind of oil stored, the availability of conventional portable and other extinguishing equipment, and the cost of installation. There may be a number of situations where the air agitation method is not justified. Use of the method may be indicated especially in crude oil storage where foam cannot be applied before the slop-over stage is reached, and where agitation could be used in time to prevent or to break up the heat wave before foam is applied.

The experience of the oil industry indicates that when tank fires occur, the initial explosion may rupture or remove all or part of the roof. Existing foam systems are frequently put out of service. In such cases and in those where no permanent system exists, portable equipment must be used to extinguish the fire. Effective air agitation at locations where it can readily be put into use will not only extinguish tank fires of high flash point oils but will also make portable equipment many times more effective on fires of low-flash-point oils.

6. Is it a spill fire and if so where is it traveling?

Where the spill occurs in a conventional bulk oil storage plant, it will be contained within the diked area. Dikes may be constructed of earth, concrete, or steel. They are generally of a capacity to contain all the spillage from the largest tank within the diked area. The space taken up by other tanks in the area is not considered in the calculation. Some cities require much more dike capacity than this. There will be (or should be) provisions to remove rain water or water from fire hoses to a safe area. Dikes should be limited in height. Some cities allow them to be built up to 40 percent of the tank height. This is too high for easy access and placement of hose streams. It allows accumulation of flammable vapors, and men will find it difficult to climb over high embankments if escape is necessary. The dikes should be no higher than six feet with adequate means of access to the diked areas every 100 feet.

The following are pointers on handling the spill fire:

A. Apply fog or foam, depending on the qualities of the burning liquid, to extinguish the flames.

B. Protect exposed tanks with heavy streams to keep them cool.

C. Spill fires which are flowing to an area where they may safely burn themselves out should be allowed to do so. However, if you wish to divert the flames from an exposure, you can do this by the use of heavy streams.

D. Be cognizant of the topography in spill fires. Don't place your men and apparatus either down wind or down hill. The vapors or a spill may trap them. A good rule: if you feel the wind at your face, you are in the wrong position for a flammable liquid fire.

There are exceptions, as when it is necessary to drive flaming spills back with heavy streams. In such cases sweep the streams up in the air occasionally and then in a knee-high-wide level arc to break up vapor concentrations. This stream should be backed up with another hose line to protect the crew should they be trapped.

7. Are there sufficient supplies of needed extinguishing mediums for the particular hazard?

A. There are a variety of agents and equipment which you may find on the site. They are:

Yard hydrant systems with hose and nozzles.

Fixed foam systems.

Steam extinguishing systems.

Dry powder (usually large wheeled units).

Carbon dioxide (usually large wheeled units).

Light Water (water which floats on flammable liquids).

High expansion foam generators.

Fixed fog systems (automatic or manual).

Subsurface injection piping.

B. A site familiarization tour before the fire is invaluable. You will know what extinguishing systems are available at the site.

C. Find the person in charge and learn what he has that will aid you in extinguishment. Call early for whatever may be needed. It is much wiser to have special equipment on hand and not used than to need it and find precious time spent in getting it.

8. Is trained help available from the plant fire brigade?

If so, use them and be guided by their advice.

9. Is there sufficient fire department personnel and equipment on hand for this fire?

If not call for help immediately and in adequate numbers.

Some pointers on tank fire operations.

In many cases vapors emanating from the vents of an exposed tank are ignited. Where such flames are burning steadily with a luminous, smoky red or orange color, there is no danger of explosion. The liquid inside the tank is giving off vapors in sufficient quantity to keep the flame going outside the tank. Where this flame is not causing any damage or not impinging on the tank itself, allowing it to burn is the safest procedure. When the danger is past, the vent fire can be extinguished.

However, conditions may change and it is wise to continually check for such changes. Hose streams cooling the exposed tank may cause a reduction in the amount of vapors issuing from the vent. Pumping the tank (removing liquid to another tank) may cause an inbreathing of the vapors. In either case, should the flame change to a snapping bright blue to colorless short flame with no smoke, extinguish the vent fire at once. This can be done by use of a straight stream directed at the vent or by use of dry powder. The change in the nature of the flame indicates that the vapors in the tank are at or near the explosive range. If the vent flame were drawn back into the tank, there could be an explosion.

Where vents are fitted with flame arrestors in good condition, it is safe to assume no flame will pass back through the vent into the tank. However, this is impossible to determine at the time of emergency. It is safer to assume there is no flame arrestor in place and so operate rather than take chances.

Tank fires have occurred at the seal on floating roof tanks. Two possible conditions at this kind of fire can make a simple fire unmanageable. The first is where the tank is completely filled and the roof is at its highest position, leaving little room for a foam build-up. In a high wind there will be a tendency to readily disturb what at best will be a very thin foam blanket.

The second condition can occur when heavy water streams are applied with the roof in either the topmost position or down several feet. In either case the water may overflow and spill burning gasoline down the sides of the tank, causing a running fire. If the tank diameter is not too large, dry powder will do the job. Otherwise have the tank pumped to lower the roof level sufficiently to build up a foam blanket at least 12 inches

thick to extinguish the fire. Light Water will be even more effective, if available. There is no need to build up a heavy blanket with Light Water (a 1/2-inch thick layer will do).

When using foam to provide a blanket over a burning liquid, apply it as smoothly as possible. You must avoid directing the extinguishing medium so as to plunge it into or under the surface of the burning material. This will defeat your purpose. If the burning liquid is confined in a tank, play the foam stream against the inside of the far wall of the tank. This will allow the foam to flow down and back over the burning liquid, building up the necessary foam blanket. Don't put water into the tank after the foam is applied; you will destroy the foam cover. Also make sure you do not use mechanical, protein foam with a detergent (high-expansion) foam. These are not compatible and the foam blanket will be broken up.

On some heavy viscous oils another operational technique is possible. These oils are subject to frothing and slop-over as well as boil-over later on. Before foam is applied, try to extinguish this fire with hose streams by whipping several streams across the top of the burning liquid. What is sometimes achieved by this is a frothy emulsification of oil and water which temporarily makes the oil surface nonflammable (like a foam). It may also cause a slop-over of this frothy mixture if the oil level is near the top of the tank. This slop-over could also be caused by applying foam which would carry the foam over the tank sides and prevent a successful build-up of the extinguishing medium. This is why the hose lines should be tried first. If the fire is not extinguished by the hose lines and the slop-over danger is past, then apply foam.

Tank collapse. Constant care and observation of changing conditions is a must at all fires. In the case of flammable liquids it is of even greater importance. Few fires carry greater danger of explosions and running fires.

Another hazard of tank fires to be alert for is that of tank collapse from the heat of the fire in it or the heat from an adjoining fire.

Look for color changes in the tank sides. When the tank walls are highly heated they may glow to a bright red, indicating either imminent explosion of interior vapors or tank failure if the color shows light yellow. The fact that such color is not obvious or present is no sure indication it may not occur. Where tanks are supported on unprotected steel or weak structural members, collapse of such supports would allow the tank to drop, causing pipes to tear. It can also cause rupture of the tank itself and spill the flammable liquid.

Horizontal tanks. Special care should be taken with horizontal tanks which contain either flammable liquids or gases. An exploding tank generally will relieve its pressure through the top or bottom. A vertical tank will usually blow the roof off. They have been known to explode and rocket through the air. The horizontal tank is even more prone to this type of explosive rocketing. Either the front or rear end of the tank blows off. The reaction propels the tank in the opposite direction with great force. The principle is that of the jet engine. A simple example is to take a toy balloon. Blow it up and allow the pressure suddenly to escape through the opening. The balloon will propel itself in a direction opposite to that which the air is released. In fighting horizontal tank fires of any kind, never work in front or in back of the tank body. Always work from the sides. This rule also applies to tank trucks.

Using heavy streams. Fires involving flammable liquid tanks require many heavy streams with the manpower to place and keep such streams operating. The technique involved generally calls for massive cooling of the tanks on fire and those seriously exposed. Whatever technique is employed, remember that a principal danger in tank fires is getting water from hose lines into the tank, causing an overflow onto surrounding ground.

Lines may be used from heavy stream appliances, elevating platforms, ladder pipes, and deluge guns. Where there is a question of safety, streams should be operated from deluge guns which may be set in place and function without the need of an operator.

Hand foam lines. Where hand foam lines are to be directed on the top of a tank, they may best be used from off an aerial ladder or elevating platform basket. In all cases where men will be operating streams in an exposed condition, they should be covered by another stream either in operation or ready for operation by opening the nozzle.

Line placement must also consider the topography and potential exposures. If an explosion were to cause a large flowing fire toward other tanks or buildings, the exposure would be almost instant. Therefore, protective lines should be placed to cover such potential before it becomes a reality.

Drums. It is common at bulk plants to find 55-gallon drums of flammable liquids (naphtha, benzene, etc.) stored indiscriminately in the open as well as in sheds. If involved in fire they may explode violently. If exposed, they must be kept cool by hose stream. If possible they should be moved from an exposed area to a safer place. Such drum storage should be in a diked or sunken pit area to contain any spillage. (See Figures 140-141.) Drum storage of flammable liquids is common to many industries.

Varnish and paint. A relatively common flammable liquid fire is one occurring in paint and varnish factories. In the older plants where open-kettle cooking is still used, the fire frequency is greater. In practice, the resins, thinners, and oils are poured in proper proportions into high kettles containing several hundred gallons. These kettles are on wheels and towed back and forth by small tow carts. Once filled, the kettle is towed into place in a small stall and placed over a large gas burner. The material is now cooked and stirred by an agitator in the bottom of the tank until the varnish is finished. Such cooking stalls are always vented to the outer air and usually are heavily coated with varnish residue.

The causes of fires in such industries are these:

1. Kettles are heated too rapidly or overheated, causing varnish to boil over and reach gas flames at the bottom of the kettle.

2. Moisture in the kettle causes a boil-over.

3. Agitation at bottom of kettle wears a hole in it.

4. Spot heating of deposits in kettle causes

FIGURE 140 (Right). *Note how the top of this 55-gallon drum containing flammable liquid is bulged from the heat of a fire. This drum is ready to blow.*

FIGURE 141 (Below). *This is the explosion of a partially filled 55-gallon drum of gasoline. Firemen are moving in with fog stream.*

weakening and, ultimately, breaks in the kettle.

5. Flammable vapors reach gas flames or other ignition source.

6. Kettle contains too much liquid; as kettle is towed out of the stall when cooking is finished, some hot varnish slops over, hitting the hot burner below.

Usually these fires are handled by the employees of the plant. They don't want the fire department in if they can help it. When the fire department is called, the chances are the employees have tried and failed to extinguish the fire—which by now is burning in the stack and roof vents and outside the cooking stall.

Be prepared to get your hose and tools covered with varnish residue. Floors with a mixture of varnish and water will be very slippery—particularly to men wearing boots. Men may slip and fall.

Engine companies should stretch two 2½-inch lines to the fire area but use care in handling water. Avoid getting water into heated varnish in the kettle. This may cause a boil-over and spill burning varnish all over the floor. Use dry powder before using water. If the kettle is still in its stall, the chances are that any fire will roar out the vent. The vent ducts may be burning but usually they will burn themselves clean. Have firemen check the roof to make sure no part of it or nearby areas are involved or in danger. Call for lines to the roof if needed.

Reflashes in the cooking area are common to this type of fire. Flowing liquid reaches the hot burners below and reignites. Most of your problem will be caused by spilled burning varnish flowing toward adjacent storage areas. It is important that such exposures be covered by hose lines. Make sure the solvent tanks are not endangered. Generally, the solvents employed are high-flash-point oils; but remember, once heated to the temperature where they give off flammable vapors, they are as dangerous as gasoline. Keep them cooled by hose streams if necessary.

Gasoline tankers. One of the most feared of flammable liquid fires is the gasoline tanker that has crashed and gone on fire. It is impossible to adopt a universal operational procedure; actions will vary depending on the size of the emergency, the location, danger to life, etc. Certainly a flowing gasoline fire on an isolated road presents a different picture than one in the heart of a shopping area.

On the isolated road these are the problems that would present themselves:

1. Lack of water supply.
2. Delayed alarm a probability.
3. Lack of sufficient help.

With a gasoline fire in the heart of a shopping area these conditions stand out:

1. Severe fire extension probability.
2. Crowds, panic.
3. Blocked streets.
4. People trapped in buildings.
5. Gasoline flowing into sewers, cellars.
6. Overhead power lines burn and fall.

Safety regulations regarding tank trucks vary from state to state. In general, though, there are safety features that will be of material aid in any such fires. They are:

1. Automatic vents in the fill caps at top of tanks.
2. Fusible plugs in fill caps at top of tanks.
3. Automatic valves to shut off flow in case of pipe rupture.
4. Remote control of valves from front of tank.
5. Heat-operated devices to shut off flow if flow valves are on fire.
6. Rigid construction of tank itself—individual tank compartments.

Generally, a tank truck will become involved in fire for one of these reasons: (1) It is exposed by being in a garage which catches fire. (2) It is parked near a building or vehicle which catches fire. (3) Careless smoking around tanker when loading and unloading.

The solutions to these situations may be simple:

1. Tow the truck out of the garage.
2. Tow the truck away from the other fire.
3. Extinguish the other fire by conventional means.
4. Cool the exposed tank body with hose streams.
5. If the pressure vents have opened and are burning at the vents, they will close when

FIGURE 142. *Fog stream begins to blow a path through the burning gasoline.*

FIGURE 143. *Rescue path is completed. This operation requires a minimum of two 2½-inch lines using a 45° fog pattern with good pressure to push flames away.*

the tank body is sufficiently cooled. The fire at the vents will die out.

But suppose the tank truck is involved in an accident. If the body is not ruptured there is little concern. If the tank does rupture and the contents ignite, they may burn fast enough to consume the spill. This then will be no problem so long as the tank body is cooled by hose streams. What must be avoided is allowing a flame to impinge onto the tank body, particularly above the liquid level. This will heat and soften the metal. Many new tankers have aluminum bodies. They can and do burn.

If the gasoline spillage is not ignited or is not burning fast enough to consume the gasoline, it becomes a matter of concern if the spillage will expose an area by liquid or vapor. Spillage or vapors flowing toward an empty field are not much of a problem. Just keep people away from the downwind area and make sure there is no smoking.

Let us discuss a specific example. Assume a tanker is ruptured on a highway and gasoline spillage has ignited. There is no water supply other than that in tankers of the fire department.

These are the points that must be considered immediately:

1. Rescue of driver and other persons involved in the crash.

2. Need to advance under cover of fog stream to rescue; you may need high-pressure fog to blast path through fire to reach victims. (See Figures 142-144.)

3. Need to work from high ground to avoid being caught in spill.

4. Need to work with wind at back.

5. If more than one line is used, work together, not opposite each other.

6. Caution for overhead high tension lines.

7. May have to call for mutual aid (more foam, tankers, medical aid, wrecking crews, police).

8. Are houses in the path of flowing gasoline or vapors?

9. Are houses or other buildings directly exposed by flames? You may be able to protect them with garden hose. Close the windows to protect against sparks and brands. Use portable extinguishers.

10. Flowing gasoline and vapors may be dissipated by fog streams—avoid use of heavy streams here because water supply is limited.

11. Give thought to relay operations if it looks as if fire operations might be extensive.

12. The use of foam to cover spill and extinguish.

13. Foam has insulating qualities—could be used to cover exposed windows, etc.

To carry the example of a tank truck fire a step further, assume there is a flow of gasoline toward a house. The following methods could be employed in such a case:

1. Evacuate all people in the path of danger.

2. Remove any vehicles in the path of danger.

3. Try to divert the gasoline flow from the house to a less exposed area by means of streams, a foam barrier, or by trenching. Heavy streams can divert flowing gasoline if water supplies are sufficient.

4. Shut off gas and electricity in exposed house.

5. Close all windows on exposed side, open them on unexposed side.

6. Remove combustible materials from exposed side, group them on unexposed side, and cover them with tarpaulins.

7. Notify electric company to cut service wires, or burning electric wires will fall and possibly start other fires.

8. Cover exposed side of house with fog stream or garden hose to keep cool. Windows will be greatest point of danger. Try to insulate them with foam and avoid washing off the foam with the fog streams.

9. Constantly check interior of house for involvement.

10. Remember, vapors may cause an explosive mixture to build up. Check for vapors with an explosimeter. If such a mixture exists, try and dissipate it with suction fans (explosion-proof motors!). Fog streams also may be used for this purpose.

11. Be careful of low spots in the terrain.

12. Allow no smoking in the area.

13. Check roofs in vicinity. Wood shingled roofs are quickly involved. Prepare to wet them down—use extinguishers, pails, pump cans, garden hose, etc.

213

FIGURE 144. *This training fire was set in two large metal troughs partially filled with gasoline. The object was to determine whether a man in a proximity (aluminized fabric) suit under cover of two* *1½-inch fog streams could make a rescue of a victim in a gasoline fire. The two fog lines were able to open a path long enough for the rescuer to retrieve a dummy in the blazing gasoline.*

Here are some additional points to consider on tanker fires:

1. If the tanker has a small hole from which gasoline is leaking, try one of these methods: Stop the flow with tapered wooden plugs, catch the gasoline in pails, or improvise chutes from salvage covers.

2. If the hole is near the bottom of the compartment, you may be able to pump water into the tank, thereby raising the gasoline level (gasoline will float on the water); now only water will flow from the hole, giving you time to plan your strategy.

3. Notify the oil company. They may be able to bring another tanker to pump off gasoline supply or they may be able to supply 55-gallon drums.

4. Notify building and other contractors in the area to bring supplies of sand to erect dams to contain the gasoline.

5. If in the vicinity of airports, request help of airport crash crews. They have special equipment for gasoline fires such as winches, crash trucks, turret nozzles, large supplies of foam, CO_2 trucks, entry suits, and proximity suits. They also will have a great deal of specialized knowledge.

Now let us take this tanker fire a step further. Consider the different problems if the tanker spill takes place in a populated residential area of the city.

The fire problem will be severe, with flames leaping high in the air. The fronts of many buildings may be involved. If it is late at night when people are asleep, if there are lodging houses or cheap hotels nearby, the situation is dangerous. There will not be enough manpower on any initial response to handle such a situation. Extra alarms should be transmitted immediately. Normal fire-fighting conditions do not prevail in this type of emergency situation.

All hands on the initial response may have to help get trapped people out of the buildings. This is a tough command decision to make. Often, getting a hose stream into immediate operation may save more lives than search and rescue operations. Flames from the burning gasoline lapping up the building fronts will cut off ready access to the interior stairway. Ladder placement to upper floors may be impossible. If heavy streams can be put into operation quickly, they may drive the fire from the exposed fronts and allow people to exit; however, there is strong doubt that such streams could be placed into operation quickly enough.

Try to get into the threatened buildings by rear stairs, ladders to rear windows, or through adjoining buildings if they are of same height, and down rear fire escapes. It may be possible to bridge narrow shafts with ladders. Hose lines may be brought in this way also. Whatever means were used to gain access can be used to remove people. Conditions will dictate your choice of action.

Life hazard will be severe not only to the people trapped but to the firefighting forces as well. Do not park apparatus in low spots where it may be engulfed in flows of burning gasoline, and keep men out of such spots. Advances should be made from high ground with your back to the wind, if possible.

If gasoline is flowing downgrade toward exposures, or the wind is blowing flame toward them, direct incoming companies by radio to approach from the exposed direction. They can take positions at hydrants toward the side of the path of the flow and use hose streams to divert the burning flow to a less dangerous direction.

Avoid washing unburnt gasoline down sewers unless it is a short sewer line leading directly to unexposed open water such as a river or bay. Washing unburnt gasoline down

sewers may make the sewers under several city blocks highly explosive. If the gasoline is burning, however, it is safe to wash it down. You will probably do minor damage to the masonry work, but this is preferable to an explosive mixture which may blow up several blocks of sewer under city streets.

Should you follow the procedure of washing burning gasoline down sewers, make sure you do not expose or create a worse situation. Where does the sewer line terminate? It may come out in a creek or bay with shipping, piers, or bulk oil plants. If you suspect such a problem, consult with the water department for advice. It may be feasible to have a pumper standby at the point where the sewer empties to break up the burning gasoline with strong hose streams. If you have fire boats, have them alerted to stand by.

As soon as companies start to arrive, have them set up heavy streams. Ladder pipes and elevating platforms will be particularly effective in sweeping the fire from the buildings. Roof streams can be similarly advantageous in wetting down the building fronts on the opposite side of the street.

Extreme danger points for possible explosions will be the low spots such as cellars, manholes, and sewers. Constant checks must be made with explosimeters. Cover accumulations in cellars with foam blankets to keep the vapors from igniting. Manholes may be covered with tarpaulins to prevent gasoline from spilling down storm, sanitary, or utility company sewers carrying electric or gas pipe lines. Set up explosion-proof fans or fog nozzles to ventilate all suspected areas.

Notify electric and gas companies immediately to respond to the area. Overhead power lines are particularly susceptible to fire damage. They may fall on roofs, causing fires, or to the ground, creating an additional hazard for the fire department. Don't order a general area shutdown of electric power unless it is a dire emergency. Indiscriminate shutting of power may cause failure of elevators, sprinkler and standpipe pumps, lighting. This can cause a serious problem in nearby hotels, hospitals, or business establishments.

FIGURE 145. *An example of how wrong technique can create a dangerous flame blast. The stream should not be directed into the fire but just over the surface of the burning liquid. (Also note the lack of protective clothing.)*

General rules for flammable liquids

The following are some general points to consider when operating at fires in flammable liquids. They are not necessarily in order of importance.

1. Keep men and equipment on high ground and upwind of fire, if possible.

2. Cut off the fuel supply, if possible.

3. Keep tanks cool with water streams.

4. Flush burning liquids from under and around tanks.

5. Co-ordinate use of hose streams. Back up firemen with water-fog protection.

6. Listen for whistling sound. A louder whistling sound indicates pressure build-up inside tanks.

7. Unprotected steel supports of tanks must be kept cool with water streams. This prevents collapse.

8. Protect exposures.

9. If more than one tank is burning, put out the fire on the windward side first to avoid reigniting tanks just extinguished.

10. Don't put foam on the walls of a burning tank. It will act as an insulator, preventing the heat from escaping through the tank walls.

11. If ladder pipes and elevating platforms are to be used, head them in the direction of escape from the area before putting them to work. They will be in a better position to get out in a hurry, if necessary.

12. Remember, the part of the tank wall

above the liquid level will fail rapidly unless hose streams are used to cool it. The part of the tank wall below the liquid level is kept cool by the liquid inside the tank.

13. If the flames suddenly get brighter and higher, it may indicate that a boil-over is imminent. Move men and equipment to safe positions.

14. If fire is in a hazardous building and it has made considerable headway, keep men out, surround it with lines, protect exposures.

15. Make use of the plant fire brigade.

16. Firefighters must wear proper protective clothing.

17. Use special firefighting equipment which is available at oil yards and similar hazardous places.

18. Provide a path of retreat for firefighters. Break open fences if necessary. At night keep the retreat path lighted.

19. Don't allow men to operate inside of a dike if there is any possibility of a boil-over. If operating from the top of the dike is satisfactory, keep the men there.

20. In hazardous areas use fixed lines instead of exposing the men, if this is possible.

21. Whenever men are operating in a precarious position, cover them with another line. If men are subjected to excess heat from the fire, a fog stream should be employed to cool them. Operators of such covering fog streams should be alert to use the various fog patterns to maximum efficiency. (See Figures 145-150.)

Foam and wetting agents

No chapter on flammable liquids would be complete without discussing foam. In the last decade a number of compounds designed for extinguishment of flammable liquids have appeared. The first successful use of foam on flammable liquids dates back more than 60 years. Essentially, this foam was a combination of aluminum sulphate, sodium bicarbonate, water, and a foam bubble stabilizing agent. The chemical union produced carbon dioxide gas inside bubbles of water. It proved to be successful in fighting flammable liquid fires.

In permanently installed systems, the two chemicals, called A and B powders, were stored in separate tanks. Operating a valve brought the solutions together. Mixed with water, the resulting foam was piped to the top of the burning tank.

There also were portable foam generators carried by fire apparatus. The A and B powders were dumped into a hopper and stirred vigorously. The powders then dropped into an orifice where they mixed with water being fed by a hose line. The result was a very stable foam with excellent extinguishing characteristics on flammable liquids. Later, a single powder was developed that contained both the A and B elements. It also used the foam hopper and hose line. These foams were formed by a chemical combination of ingredients and hence were called chemical foams. There was an additional advantage to using chemical foam, namely the expansion factor. Every gallon of water produced more than eight gallons of foam. However, there was a logistics problem. It took one pound of powder for every gallon of water to produce the eight gallons of foam. This meant that considerable manpower was required. The foam powder had to be carried to the scene in 50-pound pails opened, dumped, and mixed.

The next development was mechanical foam, a mixture of water, air and foam liquid. It had several advantages over chemical foam. It needed no hopper, but only a pickup to be inserted into the foam liquid. It was no longer necessary to carry a large amount of powder in cans. The mechanical foam was as efficient as chemical foam, and because of its simplicity of operation was more mobile. It operated simply by a proportioning device which drew up a small amount of the foam liquid concentrate and aerated it in a special nozzle to produce bubbles.

Mechanical foam (protein base) comes in two strengths—six percent and three percent. The six percent solution mixes six percent of foam concentrate with 94 percent of water. One five-gallon can of regular (six percent) foam concentrate will produce about 650 to 700 gallons of foam. The expansion ratio of concentrate to finished foam is about 1 to 130. The three percent solution mixes three percent of foam concentrate with 97 percent of water. One five-gallon container

FIGURE 146. *This photo illustrates how a straight stream fans a flammable liquid fire.*

of double strength (three percent) foam concentrate will produce approximately 1,300 gallons of foam. The expansion ratio of concentrate to finished foam product is about 1 to 270.

Don't be confused by the terms. Six percent and three percent can be misleading designations. They mean simply that one concentrate has twice the expansion capability of the other. An equal amount of three percent foam concentrate will produce nearly twice the amount of finished foam as the same amount of six percent concentrate.

The 650 gallons of foam produced by the five gallons of six percent foam will cover an area of nearly 200 square feet to a depth of

six inches. The same amount of three percent foam concentrate will produce 1,300 gallons of foam and would cover an area of almost 400 square feet to a depth of six inches.

Estimating foam requirements. In estimating the foam liquid requirements for a given fire risk, foam expansion is only one consideration. It depends on several variables —water pressure, efficiency of mixing, type of nozzle or eductor, and operational techniques, the flammable liquids involved, possible fire area, physical barriers to the path of the foam, wind, and topography.

To assure sufficient foam liquid for adequate fire protection, follow the National Fire

FIGURE 147. *Note how far this straight stream blew burning liquid from the confining vessel (arrow).*

Protection Association's "Standards for Foam Extinguishing Systems" (NFPA No. 11). The rate for foam solution is 1 to 1.6 gpm per 10 square feet of liquid surface area to be protected for an operating time of 20 to 75 minutes, depending on the risk and application.

Techniques for applying foam. Avoid agitating the surface of a burning flammable liquid when applying foam. Aiming a solid foam stream directly at a liquid surface causes agitation and drives the foam under the burning liquid. The fire will gain in intensity and foam will be wasted. The solid foam stream should be handled in one of two ways: (1) direct it toward some object to arrest its velocity so the foam will flow gently onto the burning surface, (2) direct stream into a high arc so the foam falls gently onto the burning surface.

Using foam in a fog pattern allows direct application without agitation or immersion. At the same time it effects rapid surface area coverage. In fighting a flammable liquid spill or running fire, agitation also should be avoided. Limit the spread or control the flow of the flammable liquid, and effect liquid surface coverage promptly to minimize exposures.

Fires in alcohols, ketones, esters, and other polar solvents cannot be extinguished by the

219

FIGURE 148. *The proper use of fog — playing the stream just over the surface of the burning liquid.*

regular protein type of mechanical foam liquid. It is necessary to use a special "alcohol or all purpose" type of foam which is used like regular foam concentrate.

Wetting agents. The next innovation in the special extinguishing liquids were the wetting agents (Wet Water). Normally water has surface tension. This is what makes water stay in the form of tiny drops or beads. Adding a wetting agent chemical reduces, or breaks down, the surface tension so the water will not form drops or beads but will run in all directions. It gives water the stability to penetrate tiny spaces, making it very effective on materials which ordinarily

shed water, such as baled materials, kapok, leaves, etc. Aerating a wetting agent produces foam which can be applied directly to the surface of burning flammable liquids. Applied in sufficient quantity, it has good extinguishing qualities. However, it lacks the tenacity and viscosity of the protein foam and will disintegrate more rapidly.

High expansion foams. The natural progression from a wetting agent foam was a product with a much greater expansion rate. These are known as high expansion foams which are similar to the wetting agent foams. One company adds some protein to its mixture and produces a high expansion foam with some greater stability. The expansion ratios are reported to be 1 to 1,000. To achieve this high rate of expansion, the foam concentrate mixed with water is aerated by blowing the liquid mixture against a mesh or net. The amount of expansion varies with the amount of air, water, and concentrate used.

Synthetic surfactants. In 1962 the U.S. Navy developed a product now manufactured under the name of Light Water. This is a synthetic agent that makes water float on flammable liquids to achieve a cooling and smothering effect. It was discovered while trying to develop a material which could prevent reignition of flammable liquids successfully extinguished by the new potassium carbonate (Purple K) dry chemical. This new chemical Light Water belongs to a class of materials called perfluoro-carbon surfactants. By using this additive it is possible to make a foam that will spread over gasoline quickly and reseal itself if the foam blanket is disturbed. Then as the water drains from the foam bubbles it floats on the surface of the gasoline, continuing to vaporproof the gasoline even after the foam is gone.

Light Water is ideal for use in combination with Purple K powder. Trucks now are available which carry the two agents for combined use in a twin nozzle with dual controls. The Light Water concentrate is used in a 25 percent solution (one gallon concentrate to three gallons of water).

Knockdown of the flammable liquid fire is first achieved by the use of the dry chemical. Then the Light Water is applied as a foam to seal the surface, preventing the flammable vapors from being given off. It has an expansion ratio of about 10 to 1. It is applied gently to the surface of the extinguished fuel. The securing rate is about one gallon of Light Water per 30 square feet of fuel area. A foam blanket ½-inch thick has proved adequate to secure a gasoline spill against reflash. There is absolute compatibility between dry chemical and Light Water. (See Figure 151.)

As with all new developments, improvements were made in the synthetic surfactants. Beginning in 1968, products appeared

FIGURE 149. *Typical example of cooling an exposed tank to the leeward of one that is burning. Note that the men are in proper position, near the top of the containing dike.*

FIGURE 150. *Burned-out oil tanks. Note the complete folding inwards of the sides of the tank in the foreground, and the pool of free oil lying at the base of the tanks.*

on the market which use one gallon of concentrate to about 16 gallons of water, compared to the former one gallon concentrate to three gallons of water. The new surfactant was applied in the same manner as foam to the burning liquid. Late in 1969 further improvements appeared. Expansion ratios increased. They could now be used as low, medium, or high expansion foams, and as wetting agents, too, depending on the eductor

221

FIGURE 151. *This photo shows the excellent extinguishing characteristics of Light Water on a gasoline spill. A blanket of the agent about ½-inch thick has proved adequate to secure a gasoline spill.*

settings and aeration. They could also be used as emulsifying agents.

Compatibility of various additives. Because of the multiplicity of extinguishing liquids, the problem of compatibility is very real. While most products appear similar, combining two or more different foam concentrates may spell disaster by breaking down the foam as quickly as it is generated. The general rule is: don't mix brands.

Don't use protein foams together with the synthetic surfactants (Light Water). Don't use wetting agents with protein foams. Don't use dry powder (unless it is foam compatible) with foam.

Before buying any extinguishing product in bulk, read the instructions and specifications carefully. Then try the medium in the way you intend to use it. Often the finished foam products (after generation) may be used against the same fire satisfactorily but the place to find this out is at the drill, not on the fireground.

Part II—Flammable gases

Flammable gases have flammable ranges, just as do the vapors given off by flammable liquids. The only difference is that these materials are gases in their natural state. Since they are normally in the gaseous state, there is no flash point rating. While there are some 25 common flammable gases, most fire departments will be confronted with fewer than half of them. Of this dozen or so, more than 90 percent of the fires encountered will be in either natural gas, liquefied petroleum gases, or acetylene. The physical characteristics of the dozen gases fire departments are most likely to meet in their work are given in Table V. The gases are listed in the table in descending order of probable frequency.

As with any flammable leaking substance (be it liquid or gas) which is feeding the fire, try to effect shutdown. Continue to cool cylinders exposed to heat. If possible, remove cylinders which are burning or leaking to a safe unexposed street and allow them to leak or burn off if you cannot effect a shutdown.

Any liquefied gas escaping to outer air will have a refrigerating effect at the leak area. If a cylinder valve is partially open, the leaking gas may form ice crystals under the valve seat. In such cases, the valve cannot be closed enough to shut the flow. Enough gas will get past to continue the refrigerating effect. Try this: Open the valve one full turn for a second or two. This may blow the ice crystals out and then the valve can be closed. All operations around leaking flammable gas cylinders should be under cover of charged hose lines.

Liquefied petroleum gases

Liquefied petroleum gases* (LPG or LP gas) are petroleum products. As crude oil comes out of the ground it is a mixture of many different liquids and gases. There are five principal petroleum gases: methane, ethane, propane, butane, and iso-butane. All have slightly different characteristics.

Methane and ethane can be liquefied but

---

*This material, in part, is reproduced with permission from the National LP Gas Association.

require high pressures to hold them in the liquid state at normal temperatures. This feature makes their use as liquefied petroleum gases impractical. Ethane and methane are used instead in city gas mains in vapor (gaseous) form and are known as natural gas.

That segment of the gas family which is a vapor at atmospheric pressure and normal temperature but can be changed to liquid form under moderate pressure is called liquefied petroleum gas (LPG). In its liquid form it occupies a volume of only 1/270 of the volume it requires in the gaseous state.

Liquefied petroleum gas is chemically stable, is not toxic, and is not subject to detonation by impact alone. LP gas usually is odorless when produced, and requires the addition of an odorant to warn of leaks. (This also is true of natural gas.) In a closed container the liquefied gas exerts a pressure. Gas is constantly boiling off, trying to reach a state of equilibrium. When the temperature of the liquid goes up, the pressure goes up. The reverse is also true.

The following basic information about LP gas is of interest to the fire service:

1. Liquefied petroleum gas storage tanks, whether mobile or stationary, are never completely filled. Approximately 13 percent of the capacity of the tank is vapor. This allows for the expansion of the liquid.

With a tank full of liquid, only a slight rise in temperature would produce a relatively high hydrostatic pressure. The relief valve would open and discharge liquid. Propane liquid, for example, expands at the rate of 1.6 percent for each 10° F. rise in temperature.

2. Most LPG tanks have openings in the vapor space and the liquid area. These openings are generally tagged or labeled to show whether they communicate with the vapor space or liquid space. The law in some states requires that tank openings be tagged or labeled.

3. Under ordinary circumstances it can be expected that a tank vapor outlet valve will discharge vapor when opened and a liquid outlet, liquid. However, if a tank is turned over, the vapor outlets can become liquid outlets and the liquid outlets can become

223

TABLE V

Characteristics of Common Flammable Gases

FLAMMABLE GAS		FLAMMABLE RANGE	WEIGHT AIR = 1	ODOR	HEALTH*	FLAMMABILITY*	REACTIVITY*
Carbon Monoxide		12.5 - 75	1	No	2	4	0
Butane	Liquefied Petroleum Gases	2 - 8.5	2	No—but is odorized by Gas Co.	1	4	0
Propane		2.2 - 9.5	1.6	No—but is odorized by Gas Co.	1	4	0
Ethane	Natural Gases	3 - 12	1	No—but is odorized by Gas Co.	1	4	0
Methane		5.3 - 14	.6	No—but is odorized by Gas Co.	1	4	0
Acetylene		2.5 - 81	2.7	Garlic	1	4	4
Cyclopropane	Anesthetics	2.4 - 10.4	1.5	No	1	4	0
Ethylene		3 - 32	1	Sweet smell	1	4	2
Hydrogen		4 - 75	.1	No	0	4	
Ammonia (Anhydrous)		16 - 25	.6	Very Pungent	3	1	0
Hydrogen Sulphide		4.3 - 45	1.2	Rotten Eggs	3	4	0
Ethylene Oxide		3 - 100	1.5	Like Ether	2	4	3

*The numbers shown under the headings of Health, Flammability, and Reactivity are borrowed by permission of the NFPA from Pamphlet 704M, Identification System of Fire Hazards of Materials 1969. (See explanatory chart on next page.)

Explanatory chart for Table V—Identification of materials*

Identification of Health Hazard Color Code: **BLUE**		Identification of Flammability Color Code: **RED**		Identification of Reactivity (Stability) Color Code: **YELLOW**	
Type of Possible Injury		Susceptibility of Materials to Burning		Susceptibility to Release of Energy	
Signal		Signal		Signal	
4	Materials which on very short exposure could cause death or major residual injury even though prompt medical treatment were given.	4	Materials which will rapidly or completely vaporize at atmospheric pressure and normal ambient temperature, or which are readily dispersed in air and which will burn readily.	4	Materials which in themselves are readily capable of detonation or of explosive decomposition or reaction at normal temperatures and pressures.
3	Materials which on short exposure could cause serious temporary or residual injury even though prompt medical treatment were given.	3	Liquids and solids that can be ignited under almost all ambient temperature conditions.	3	Materials which in themselves are capable of detonation or explosive reaction but require a strong initiating source or which must be heated under confinement before initiation or which react explosively with water.
2	Materials which on intense or continued exposure could cause temporary incapacitation or possible residual injury unless prompt medical treatment is given.	2	Materials that must be moderately heated or exposed to relatively high ambient temperatures before ignition can occur.	2	Materials which in themselves are normally unstable and readily undergo violent chemical change but do not detonate. Also materials which may react violently with water or which may form potentially explosive mixtures with water.
1	Materials which on exposure would cause irritation but only minor residual injury even if no treatment is given.	1	Materials that must be preheated before ignition can occur.	1	Materials which in themselves are normally stable, but which can become unstable at elevated temperatures and pressures or which may react with water with some release of energy but not violently.
0	Materials which on exposure under fire conditions would offer no hazard beyond that of ordinary combustible material.	0	Materials that will not burn.	0	Materials which in themselves are normally stable, even under fire exposure conditions, and which are not reactive with water.

*This explanatory chart is reproduced with permission of the NFPA.

vapor outlets. In certain positions all outlets could become liquid outlets.

To what extent any of these conditions could prevail would depend on the position of the tank and the amount of liquid in it. For example, if a tank contained no liquid, all openings would, in a sense, be vapor openings.

LPG vapors. Here are some facts about LPG vapors firemen should know:

1. LPG vapor issuing from a tank into the atmosphere (unless burning) is not readily visible. Under certain conditions it can be seen. It looks much like heat waves which rise from a pavement on a hot day.

2. If the leak is large enough, it can be located by the sound of the escaping gas.

3. Small leaks are found with a mixture of soap and water or any one of the many solutions made especially for this purpose.

4. LPG vapor spreads out as an invisible gas.

5. How far the gas will spread and how long it will persist as a flammable mixture depends on these conditions: (A) the quantity of gas escaping into the atmosphere, (B) the topography of the area, and (C) weather conditions.

The same volume of escaping gas: (A) Will persist longer in a hollow or low spot than on a hillside or open area. (B) Will thin out more rapidly if the air is in motion than on a calm day. (C) Will thin out less rapidly on a foggy day than on a bright sunny day. (There is little difference in the behavior of vapor on an overcast day versus a sunny day.) (D) Will linger longer in high grass or vegetation than on open ground. Various combinations of weather and topography will have a bearing on the distance traveled and time required to reduce the vapor to a nonflammable mixture.

As an example: On a calm day, LPG will disperse very slowly from a low spot. At the same location on a windy day much more air will mix with the gas, moving it along at a faster pace and thinning it out in less time.

LPG liquid. Here are some facts about LPG liquid that firemen should know:

1. A liquid leak is readily visible. Small liquid leaks will develop ice at the point of escape to the atmosphere. Large amounts of escaping liquid (such as from a hole or broken fitting) will spread to the atmosphere as a white fog. The liquid is vaporizing and expanding so rapidly it freezes the moisture in the air. The frozen fog, while for the most part a rich mixture, is flammable, especially at the outer edges. It will flash if brought in contact with a source of ignition.

2. Flammable gas mixtures also will be found beyond the outer fringe of the fog pattern. As the expanding gas moves further from the source of supply, it begins to warm. The frozen moisture previously seen as fog will no longer be visible. Only the invisible gas remains. As it moves out, it mixes with the air and finally reaches a point where it will no longer burn. When it reaches the invisible stage, it reacts to conditions in the same manner as gas escaping from the vapor space of the container. But there is one difference. The escaping liquid will vaporize more rapidly on a hot sunny day than on a cool overcast day. With escaping vapor, the amount of sunshine makes little difference. It is already in a gaseous state.

3. There is only one sure way to determine at what point gas in the atmosphere from either a liquid or vapor source has thinned to where it is no longer a flammable mixture; that is by the use of a combustible gas indicator.

4. A liquid propane fire is more difficult to control than straight vapor. One gallon of liquid propane will produce 36 cubic feet of vapor at 60° F.

5. Liquid propane coming in contact with the skin will cause a freeze burn. Propane vapor has no effect on the skin. The vapor from liquefied petroleum gas is not toxic.

LPG tank accident or fire. It is almost impossible to get up a definite procedure to follow where tanks are involved in an accident or fire. However, there are a few general procedures that would be of help in deciding on a plan of action.

Where a tank is not involved in a fire but subjected to excessive heat because of a fire close by, the best way to keep the pressure down is to cool the tank with a stream of water as soon as possible.

Use plenty of water on any part of a tank where there is impingement of flame on the metal. This is necessary to keep hot spots from developing. Hot spots have a tendency to weaken the tensile strength of the steel.

That part of a tank which does not contain liquid will heat up more rapidly than the part covered with liquid. Direct the water to the upper part of the tank, allowing it to run down the sides and ends. ASME-API propane tanks are built for a working pressure of 250 psi. They are hydrostatically tested to 500 psi, and are fabricated with a safety factor of four. That means that as an unfired pressure vessel, the shell and heads will withstand an internal pressure of 1,000 psi.

When a tank is involved in a fire, the tensile strength goes down as the temperature of the steel rises. Somewhere between 800° and 900° F. the safety factor of 1,000 psi has dropped 50 percent. At 1,000° F. it is down to 25 percent.

Up to this point, the importance of water has been stressed for controlling temperature and pressure in liquefied petroleum gas storage tanks involved in fire. However, there will be areas where water is not available. Without water it is a case of considering possibilities, forming a plan of action, and following through. One advantage where there is no water: rarely is there a built-up area nearby to consider.

No matter where or how it happens, there

always will be spectators. Evacuate the area. Spectators are not a part of any risk involved. Size up the situation. If it is vapor that is burning and the break or opening is pointed away from the tank, the flame will burn outward with great force. If there is no impingement of flame on the tank, the chances are the fuel will be consumed without incident. Under the circumstances named, the tank is receiving heat by convection and radiation only. At the same time, there is a refrigerating process going on in the liquid because of the expanding gas escaping through the break. As the liquid grows colder, the pressure lowers. As the pressure goes down, the size of the flame will go down and less heat will be concentrated on the shell of the tank. On the other hand, if the tank is involved with flame from the burning vapor, the internal pressure will rise.

Liquefied petroleum gas tanks are equipped with relief valves to relieve excess internal pressure.

Normally, the relief valves communicate with the vapor section of the tank, but in the case of a truck accident the tank could be far enough on its side for the relief valves to be in the liquid, and the outlet side of the valves could be buried in the pavement. Where the relief valves are buried, there is little chance for the excess pressure resulting from the fire to relieve itself to the atmosphere. You can reasonably expect the tank to rupture if the fire continues long enough.

If the relief valves are in a position to vent to the atmosphere but will be discharging liquid instead of vapor, their rated capacity, which is based on vapor, will be greatly impaired. Here again, you can reasonably expect the tank to rupture.

Where the tank is in a normal position, the relief valves will open and discharge vapor when the pressure reaches a predetermined setting based on the working pressure of the tank. The relief valves will keep the pressure down only to the limit of their capacity. The pressure can build faster than the valves can relieve it. If the pressure continues to rise rapidly, it can reach a point where the tank will rupture. How much below the safety

factor of 1,000 psi a rupture could occur will depend on the temperature of the surface of the steel shell.

Where an LPG tank is involved in fire, it is good practice (when possible) to stand clear of the heads. In the event of a boiler-type explosion, it is the heads that usually travel great distances while the shell has a tendency to flatten out. A boiler-type explosion is one in which the steel shell ruptures because the internal pressure is greater than the resistance of the steel shell.

We have been discussing vapor. What about a liquid leak? A liquid leak will not lower the pressure in a tank. Broadly speaking, where conditions remain the same the velocity flow of the liquid will continue at the same rate until all the liquid has been discharged. On a relative basis, if the pressure rises the velocity flow rises. If the pressure is reduced, the velocity flow drops. The amount of heat concentrated on the tank determines the temperature of the liquid in the tank. The temperature determines the pressure and the pressure determines the velocity of the flow. Liquid will behave the same as vapor when burning at an opening in the tank except that, for the same size opening, the fire from a liquid opening will be larger and spread out further.

When LP gas or liquid is escaping and has not been ignited, it is not a good policy to ignite it. By the time the fire department arrives, the gas already has spread and there is no way of telling how far it has traveled or exactly where.

If possible, put out sources of ignition in the immediate vicinity. Perhaps the best method for handling this type of incident would be to break up the gas vapor with water fog, which has been found to be very effective.

Heavy sweating or icing of an LPG tank is an indication that the liquid is going through a refrigeration process. As a hypothetical case, let us say that because of a broken fitting in the vapor area of the tank, large quantities of gas are escaping to the atmosphere. The gas is ignited and is burning at the broken fitting. The reserve supply of vapor in the tank is soon used up and the pressure starts to drop. The liquid continues to boil but with less and less ability to replace the escaping gas. The temperature of the liquid goes down and down. First a sweat line appears on the tank and finally a frost or ice ring. The flame is still burning at the broken fitting but in a lazy manner.

The tank is already cold, the pressure down, so turning a stream of water on the tank is not good practice. The water at this point would only tend to increase the activity of the flame because the tank is already colder than the water. In this case, perhaps it would be best to let the flame burn. It could very easily be extinguished at this stage, but that would create a problem of uncontrolled gas. As long as the fuel is being consumed, there is no chance for a combustible mixture to accumulate. A plug could also be inserted in the hole to stop the flow of gas, but with the hole plugged pressure starts to build up again. Should the plug blow out because of the increased pressure, a second hazard would be created.

The height of the frost or icing on the tank will indicate the level of the liquid in it. The icing on the tank will be slightly higher than the level of the liquid in it.

How to control LPG leaks

The following is a summary of the methods of controlling leaks at fires involving liquefied petroleum gases:

Basic precautions:

1. Approach the fire or gas lead from upwind.

2. Keep all persons out of vapor cloud area.

If necessary to evacuate any area which is in the path of the vapor cloud, do so immediately, eliminating all sources of ignition at the same time.

3. Policing the area, keep all persons at least 200 feet away, except those necessary to cope with the condition. (See Figure 152.)

Leakage without fire:

1. If escaping LP gas is not on fire, close any valve available that can stop the flow of gas. Small lines such as copper tubing could be flattened to stop the flow. If an LP-Gas vehicle is involved, consult the driver; or if storage facilities are involved, consult plant personnel regarding possibilities of shutting off leaks. (See Figure 153.)

2. Water spray is effective in dispersing LP gas vapor. If available, it should be used as soon as possible, directing the spray stream across the normal vapor path and dispersing the vapor into a safe location. Those handling the hose should avoid entering the vapor cloud and should keep low behind the spray so they will be somewhat protected from radiant heat if the vapor should be ignited unexpectedly.

3. If the flow of gas cannot be stopped, the vapor cloud should be dispersed by some other means. Controlled fire conditions involve applying sufficient water to keep the shell of the vessel and any exposed piping cool enough to allow the fire to burn up the product without danger of causing failure of the vessel or piping.

The escape of unburned gas forming a vapor cloud may present a greater danger to life and property than burning gas, particularly where there is no valve by which the gas can be shut off quickly. However, there are many factors to be considered, such as possible danger to persons and property from ignition of the gas and the serious liability that might result from setting the gas on fire. It is doubtful whether any fire officer would assume responsibility for starting a potentially serious fire with results of ignition so unpredictable. How would you start such a fire with assurance of getting away safely? If the leak occurred on the property of an LP gas plant under suitable isolation, deliberate ignition might be a solution. It would appear that the best normal solution for dispersing the unburned gas is the old reliable antidote—heavy streams of water from a maximum distance. Make certain pumpers are at a safe location.

4. In some instances of leakage from a tank without a fire, it may be desirable to move the tank to some remote area such as a blocked-off isolated roadway or open field where it can leak safely away from a source of ignition. However, if this is done, the tank should not be moved in any but an upright

position. Never drag the tank in a manner which might damage valves or piping. Any attempt to turn a tank upright for moving it to some remote location should be done carefully to avoid damage to valves and piping.

Leakage with fire:

1. Do not extinguish unless leakage can be stopped, except under certain conditions.

2. If the escaping gas is on fire, immediately apply large quantities of water as quickly as possible to all surfaces exposed to heat. Approach the tank from the sides. Concentrate on piping and metal surfaces of vessel or adjoining vessels, equipment, or combustible surfaces exposed to flame or intense radiant heat.

3. Consult driver of vehicle or plant operating personnel, as the case may be, regarding possibilities of shutting off fuel supply. Stopping the flow of gas should be the first consideration.

4. If the only valve that can be used to stop the flow of fuel is involved in the fire, consider the possibility of effecting shutoff by protecting firemen with water fog streams and protective clothing while they are closing the valve. Proceed slowly to avoid any flashbacks or trapping of firemen in the flames.

5. The controlled burning of escaping LP gas (which cannot be shut off by closing a valve) is a commonly accepted firefighting practice. Application of sufficient water to keep the shell of the vessel and piping cool will allow the fire to consume the product in the tank without danger of causing failure. (See Figure 154.)

6. Dry chemical portable extinguishers are effective for extinguishing small LP gas fires. Extinguishing agent should be directed toward point of vapor discharge. Carbon dioxide may also be used.

7. When sufficient water is not available to keep the tank cool, some warning of increased pressure may be noted from the increase in volume of fire or noise level. This should be a signal to consider withdrawal of all men to a safe area.

8. Failure of LP gas tanks usually occurs only when some portion of the metal surface in the vapor space of the vessel becomes

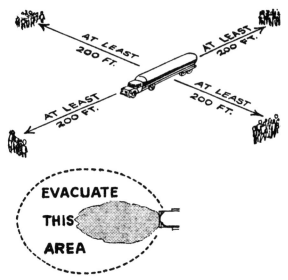

FIGURE 152. *Keep people at least 200 feet away from area. Evacuate any area in path of vapor cloud.*

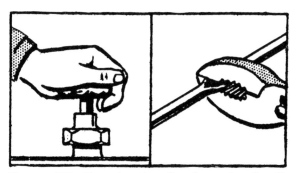

FIGURE 153. *If gas is not on fire close valve. Small lines can be flattened to stop the flow.*

overheated, softens, and weakens to the point where it will not contain the pressure of the product. In the absence of sufficient water to keep the metal surface cool where it is exposed to direct flames or extreme radiant heat, there is danger of the tank rupturing.

9. Shooting holes in an LP gas tank that is involved in fire does not serve any useful purpose and should not be permitted. (See Figure 155.)

10. Ordinarily, no attempt should be made to move any tank involved in a fire. Usually little would be gained in reducing the hazard. However, if specific conditions develop that make it desirable to move the tank, it should not be moved in any but an upright position. Never drag it in a manner tnat might further

FIGURE 154. *Controlled burning. Apply water to cool vessel and piping and allow fire to consume the product in the tank.*

FIGURE 155. *Do not attempt to shoot holes in LPG tank that is involved in fire.*

damage valves or piping. Any attempt to turn the tank upright to remove it to some remote location or to facilitate product withdrawal should be done carefully to avoid damage to valves and piping.

Exposure to fire:

1. It is always important to control any exposure fire. In addition, when LP gas storage vessels or equipment are subjected to serious fire exposure such as from a nearby burning building or a fire involving another fuel, it is of prime importance to apply sufficient water to keep the shell of the vessel and piping cool to avoid any unnecessary release of LP gas.

2. If the LP gas storage vessel becomes heated to the point of causing the relief valve to function, the discharge should be allowed to burn if it becomes ignited (or in some circumstances, as indicated previously, it is de-

sirable to ignite the discharge). At the same time, large volumes of water should continue to be applied to the vessel and piping to keep it cool and allow the relief valve to close after the excess pressure has been relieved.

3. Portable LP gas cylinders that are exposed to a serious fire should be moved to a safe location.

Natural gas

Natural gas is now the most common type of city gas. It is transmitted by high-pressure pipe lines to practically all of the United States and Canada. Natural gas is composed principally of methane with ethane, propane, butane, and small amounts of carbon dioxide and nitrogen. Natural gas does not contain carbon monoxide but in sufficient quantity it is suffocating. As with any combustible gas under conditions of incomplete combustion, it may produce carbon monoxide.

Normally, the hazards of natural gas are no greater than those of other city gases. The major difference is the high pressures (up to 900 psi) in some pipe lines. Proper precautions are not always strictly observed in laying pipe. Pipe is allowed to lie in the open where it is subject to rust, or it may be handled roughly. If weak points develop from rust or rough handling, the pressure may cause breaks. Even with simple pipe ruptures the high pressure shoots fragments of rock, dirt, and pipe with dangerous force. If there is a rupture, ignition of the gas is almost sure to follow.

Natural gas fires under these high pressures are exceedingly difficult to extinguish. By far the safest procedure is to protect personnel and exposures, letting the gas burn until shutdown is effected. Tests by the Ansul Company at Longview, Tex., proved that with proper techniques and ample amounts of powder, dry chemical was effective with openings as large as six inches in diameter flowing 800 cubic feet per second of gas. A test fire in which flames soared up to 170 feet was extinguished in 6½ seconds using two dry chemical hose lines.

Using dry powder on natural gas fires. The successful use of dry powder at natural gas fires requires special techniques, as follows:

1. Approach the fire with the wind at your back.

2. If the heat is too severe, discharge some of the powder in an up-and-down motion in front of you. This will produce a dust cloud which acts as a heat shield, allowing the operator to advance closer to the fire.

3. Direct the powder at the base of the escaping gas jet (even though the flame column is burning several feet above the leak area). The escaping gas will carry the powder up to the flame and extinguish it.

4. Immediately cool any hot metal with water to prevent reignition of the escaping gas.

5. Shut down the valve, closing off the gas supply.

6. Back away from the fire (never turn your back lest reignition occur and trap you) with the extinguisher at the ready position. (See Figures 156-161.)

A general conclusion may be drawn: with proper equipment and know-how, dry chemical can extinguish fires in natural gas at pressures to 850 psi. Impinging jet fires are more difficult to extinguish and would require more or larger equipment.

Under fire conditions, evacuate the area and keep men and equipment upwind. If people are enveloped in the cloud of fumes they will be in terrible danger.

On March 4, 1965, in Natchitoches, La., at 6 A.M., a 32-inch natural-gas pipeline under 750 psi ruptured with a deafening roar. Flames leaped 400 feet high. The explosion blew a crater 15 feet deep, 30 feet wide, and 75 feet long. Seventeen people more than 150 feet away in their homes were incinerated. Seven homes were burned down, six cars and three trucks were melted, and debris was scattered over a 20-acre area. It took gas company employees 30 minutes to shut down the flow of gas and control the fire.

Noise. There is another important factor in handling fires in high-pressure natural gas. It is the high noise level. If the break is large enough, the roar of escaping gas is sufficiently loud to practically eliminate any form of voice communication. This will be true up

to distances of hundreds of feet. The volume of noise can be so loud that it has a physical effect on the ability of involved personnel to act and think clearly. It robs the men of normal efficiency. The noise actually hurts.

Radiant heat. The radiant heat from these fires can be terribly dangerous. Severe burns can occur if men are not properly clothed. Exposures are in instant danger of ignition.

A natural gas break with fire

The following is a factual account of a major gas main break with fire.

At about 8:40 A.M. a front loader bulldozer, clearing land for an overpass at Route 83 and 55th Street, Hinsdale, Ill., hit and broke a buried 12-inch high-pressure natural gas main. (See Figure 162.) The location of the break was about 150 feet west of a one-story residence (845 South Jackson Street). For five to 10 minutes gas fed by a pressure of 155 psi roared from the resulting six-inch hole. During this time, the bulldozer operator and the driver of two semi-dump trucks being loaded by the bulldozer were able to escape from the area. Eventually from some unknown source (possibly sparks from the generator of the trucks or bulldozer), the gas ignited with an explosion which broke the front windows of number 845 South Jackson and shot a column of flame into the air about 100 feet high and 50 feet in diameter. Immediately the closest homes, numbers 845, 841, and 835 on the east side of Jackson, and number 830 on the west side were in danger of igniting from the radiant heat of the fire column. The interesting point is that none of these houses were seriously damaged even though they were instantly and directly exposed.

At 8:49 A.M. the Hinsdale Fire Department received a phone call reporting the fire and responded with three fire trucks and six men, reaching the scene in about four minutes. Strategy determined on arrival was to cover the exposed homes with hose streams, and allow the gas fire to safely burn up its flammable vapors pending a shutdown by the gas company. Homes within 500 feet were ordered evacuated. A box alarm was sounded,

FIGURE 156. *Burning gas escaping at 150 psi from a 2-inch pipe is controlled by injecting dry powder at the point of the leak. The powder is carried into the burning gas cloud, effecting con-* *trol. Approaching from any other direction would simply blow the powder away before it hits the fire. Do not extinguish the flame if the leak cannot be shut down within a few seconds.*

calling help from the mutual aid organization. This brought the cities of Clarendon Hills and Western Springs to the fire. The City of Westmont dispatched a pumper to cover Hinsdale's now-vacant fire station.

The first three hose lines were placed in operation by Hinsdale and covered 845 and 841 South Jackson Street. These three hose lines from Hinsdale's Engine No. 342 used up 18,000 gallons of water in 40 minutes. As volunteers reported in, they laid the next two hose lines from Hinsdale's Engine 343 into a deck gun which was directed against 835 and partially against 841 South Jackson, protecting these structures. This deck gun pumped 22,000 gallons in 30 minutes.

Hinsdale's Engine 341 supplied a single line taken between the two homes, numbers 835 and 841 South Jackson, to lend additional water coverage to protect these homes. This line pumped 2,000 gallons in 10 minutes.

Clarendon Hills laid a line from Route 83 to cover the house at 830 South Jackson. This line was wyed off into two smaller lines and they operated for about 20 minutes, using 4,000 gallons. Western Springs was kept in reserve and not used during the fire. Other departments responded, even though they were not called. The hose lines continued to wet down exposed homes until the gas company shut the main down—approximately one hour from the time they were notified of the break.

Relatively minor window breakage occurred from the exploding gases upon ignition in 848 South Jackson. Some water seeped in via the broken windows. Damage to shrubbery and lawns from the flooding by

FIGURE 157. *This is similar to Figure 156, but the jet of burning gas shoots straight up. Inject the dry powder at the base of the leak and this will carry the powder up and extinguish the flame.*

FIGURE 158. *This shows control of the vertical fire by the same technique used in Figure 157. Do not, however, extinguish the fire if leak cannot be shut down in a few seconds.*

the hose streams also was evident. This was compounded by the movement of people in the area (some spectators), causing depressions from foot marks in the soaked grounds.

Damage to the homes and lawns approximated $2,000. Damage to the bulldozer was considered total (about $40,000) and total to the two dump trucks (about $40,000). The gas company lost 1,000,000 cubic feet of gas at their cost of $300 and labor costs to repair the break at about $2,000. Total losses were about $84,500.

Some of the more acute problems associated with this operation were these:

1. Severe radiant heat emanating from the flame column. It was necessary to cover the firemen with a hose stream so they could hold their positions. They also used benches to partially deflect the heat waves. Men received burns from a distance of 200 feet.

2. The deafening roar of the escaping gas completely prevented hearing in the immediate area. It was difficult to hear even a block away. This cut radio transmission to

FIGURE 159. *This was a test to determine whether dry powder could achieve control of a fire which might occur if a tank truck crashed into the side of a house. The fire has begun to involve the siding of the house. The fire was started by igniting kerosene in a pit dug along the side of the house. The pit was 20 feet long and 12 inches deep — filled with kerosene.*

the point where it was necessary to actually visit each point of operation to transmit orders—frequently by sign language.

3. It was difficult to keep the curious watchers away. There was the ever-present danger of a rock rolling down into the small excavation and being blown up with the force of shrapnel by the escaping gas. (This points up sharply the need to wear helmets—whatever the operation.)

4. This possibility also exists: When the

bulldozer blade broke the pipe, it may also have caused cracks around the immediate break. If this were so, then the pressure could eventually tear out large pieces of cracked pipe. This would not only cause these pieces to shoot out with explosive speed, but increase the size of the fire. One pumper was kept in reserve for just such a contingency.

5. The complete lack of radio communication made it impossible to establish and maintain a command post whereby units and

234

FIGURE 160. *After a preburn period of 5 minutes the side of the house was completely involved. Three trained firemen then moved in with three* *20-pound dry chemical extinguishers using all-purpose dry powder.*

FIGURE 161. *Only seconds later the fire was under control.*

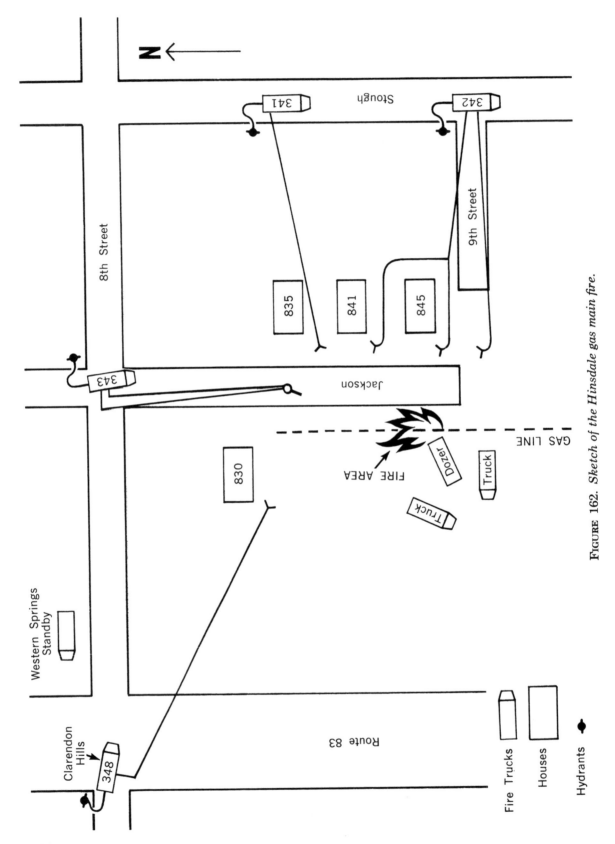

FIGURE 162. *Sketch of the Hinsdale gas main fire.*

orders could be centrally dispatched and co-ordinated. Thought must be given to going to the type of radio headset used at airports to communicate over the noise of jet engines.

Some minor problems manifested themselves:

1. Departments dispatched equipment not called for. They helped clog streets and disrupted some radio communications by the use of their radios which were on the same frequency.

2. The gas company could not state with any accuracy how long it would take to shut down the gas main feeding the fire.

As a followup we requested the gas company to send a representative to talk with us. There were a lot of questions which needed answering. The gas company co-operated fully and sent three qualified representatives who discussed the ramifications of the fire with us. The following are some of the questions and answers that came out of this discussion:

1. What pressure does the pipe line carry and do the pressures vary?

Answer: Pressures in this particular section of pipeline range from 145 to 160 psi.

2. Was there any danger of the fire being sucked back into the main as pressures were reduced during the fire?

Answer: No.

3. Was there a possibility of more pieces of main around the hole breaking away?

Answer: Yes.

4. Could we get immediate shutdown in the event of extreme emergency?

Answer: No. About one to 1½ hours can be considered good time to effect shutdown. The servicemen sometimes have to come from distances that require more than a half hours' travel. Then they have to consult maps and charts to determine which valves to close, bypasses to open, etc. In this case they had to control the leak from three shutoff areas.

5. How are valves closed?

Answer: Manually at the surrounding areas. There are no remote-control valves on this pipeline.

6. Can the gas company tell when there is a large leak because the pressure drops—

without prior notification? Can the gas company approximate the leak area without notification?

Answer: Yes, but they cannot pinpoint the break area.

7. Do high-pressure mains go through built-up areas?

Answer: Yes.

8. Does the gas company recommend that the fire department familiarize itself with the location of shutoff valves to use them in such emergencies?

Answer: Definitely not. Not even the regular gas company servicemen handle these valves. They use special teams for such cases. If an untrained man operated the wrong valve, he could increase the pressures.

The discussion concluded late in the evening with gas company representatives stating they were most appreciative of the part played by the fire department. They were generous in their praise, claiming the handling of the fire was exactly the way this kind of problem should be approached.

The gas company people considered this one of the really major breaks, and one individual stated that this was only the second fire of this magnitude he had seen in 22 years of service.

Operational guidelines

The following are some additional points to consider at breaks in natural gas mains. Your tactics will vary depending on whether the gas has been ignited.

Gas not ignited. If you are called to the scene of a major break and no ignition has taken place, do not attempt to light the gas—you may precipitate a violent explosion. Evacuate the area for 500 feet in all directions.

Don't be too quick to connect your pumpers to hydrants and lay out lines; because if for some freak reason the gas pockets and ignites, you may lose men, hose, and pumpers. When the area has been safely evacuated, keep your men out of the suspect areas until shutdown has been effected.

If you can make a hydrant connection upwind, it is safe to do so. If you suspect gas

FIGURE 163. *Acetylene cylinders can explode with tremendous force. This is the remains of an acetylene cylinder torn apart by an explosion.*

FIGURE 164. *Acetylene cylinders torching at the vents. Don't put this fire out unless the vent flame starts to pull back into the cylinder. If so, put the fire out immediately. Move the cylinder out into the open where it can leak harmlessly.*

FIGURE 165. *An explosion started this fire in a chemical plant. The railroad car at the siding is pumping ethylene oxide and feeding the fire. The* *objective is to cool the exposed tank car and shut the valves on top.*

FIGURE 166. *Firemen play stream on exposed railroad car of ethylene oxide to keep it cool.*

FIGURE 167. *Men (on tank car at left) move up onto car to effect shut-down.*

has pocketed (this is not likely), try dissipating the gas cloud with high-pressure fog streams.

Remember to operate with the wind at your back.

If gas has ignited. If you arrive at the scene and ignition has taken place, there is no longer danger of an explosion. You should still evacuate the general area in case the fire cannot be contained and begins to spread rapidly.

Don't attempt to shut valves on high-pressure pipe lines. You may make the situation worse by increasing rather than decreasing the pressure.

Don't take hydrants too close to the break. You may not be able to hold your position because of radiant heat.

Don't try to put the fire out—even if it starts to slow down when the gas company begins to close the valves.

Get hose lines covering the exposed face of the buildings as soon as possible. Don't waste the water in the form of curtain sprays. Radiant heat passes readily through drops of water. Keep wetting down the exposed buildings. This will protect them far better. Get men into these exposed buildings to do the following:

1. Close windows on exposed side.
2. Open windows on unexposed side.

FIGURE 168. *With shut-down completed firemen move down under cover of hose streams. The fire* in the chemical plant will now burn itself out harmlessly.

3. Move furniture away from exposed side.

4. Use salvage covers as needed if water is getting in via broken windows.

5. Shut off gas and electricity.

If water supplies are limited and it is doubtful whether you will be able to keep the building fronts wet, give thought to covering the building fronts with foam. Foam has an insulating value and may stick to the building until the gas company shuts the valves.

Be careful not to drive streams directly toward shingled roofs. The water will get under the shingles and leak into the house. Direct your water up and let it fall like rain. This will avoid damage.

Be careful that men don't get too close to the fire. In bright sunlight with almost complete combustion, the flames from natural gas are almost invisible.

Make sure men wear full protective gear because of the possibility of pieces of metal or rocks sliding into the break area and being hurled with explosive speed by the high pressures.

Communication will be almost nil because of the terrible roar of the escaping gas. You will have to rely on messengers to relay orders to operating units.

If heat is severe enough, have men on hose lines not only wet each other down, but use benches, large garbage pails, or any bulky object to deflect the heat waves.

Other flammable gases

Acetylene which is not dissolved in acetone is unstable and may explode under pressure or shock. Acetylene forms explosive compounds with silver, copper, and mercury. Don't allow any fire to play on an acetylene cylinder; the cylinder walls may weaken.

If fusible plugs have melted and are burning, allow them to do so, but do not allow this to go on too long. The expanding gas may cause a refrigerating effect in the cylinder. This will lower the internal pressure and may cause the vent flames to be drawn back into the cylinder. Extinguish the vent fire before this happens and move the cylinder (under cover of hose lines) outside the building where the gas can leak off harmlessly. If the flame is drawn back into the cylinder it will continue to burn there, breaking down the acetylene into hydrogen and carbon. The cylinder walls may heat, glow red, give off a frying, hissing sound. An explosion may be imminent. Set up a master stream or any device which can play water onto the cylinder without the need of manpower. Do this for as long as 10 hours or until the cylinder loses its red-hot appearance. Don't fight fires from inside a building if acetylene cylinders are involved in fire—unless you can direct the streams from behind a secure barrier. The same will hold true of other flammable gases in cylinders. (See Figures 163-164.)

Ethylene is a strong oxidizing agent and becomes spontaneously explosive in sunlight with chlorine.

Ammonia is extremely corrosive to body tissue. Water fog will neutralize great quantities of gas. Keep cylinders cool by use of water fog.

Hydrogen sulphide is highly toxic and dangerously reactive with nitric acid and oxidizing materials. It may be found in sewers and other areas where sulphur products undergo incomplete combustion.

Ethylene oxide is a dangerously reactive gas and can explode violently in contact with tin, aluminum, iron oxide. It is soluble in water but can continue burning even though diluted to a ratio of 22 parts water to 1 part ethylene oxide. (See Figures 165-168.)

Chapter 21

Lumberyard fires

LUMBERYARD FIRES are a triple threat. First, in many cases there is a large area of highly piled lumber that is readily susceptible to ignition. Second, lumberyards often have accessory sheds in which are stored specially processed lumber such as cabinets, doors, windows, plywoods, and hardwoods. These sheds often are open at one side, for ease in loading, are flimsily built, and serve only to keep rain water from the finished products. Ignition of these sheds is common. Third, factories which manufacture the finished products just mentioned are often found in the same lumberyard. If this is the case, we have not only the lumberyard storage itself but a large, very combustible factory, conducting a hazardous trade. (See Figure 169.)

If a lumberyard fire is well-involved, be careful about connecting pumpers to hydrants close to the fire area upon arrival. Lumberyard fires spread with incredible speed. Since there are no exterior walls or partitions of noncombustible construction, there is nothing to break the draft and slow the flames' progress. Firebrands and radiated heat may be so severe that it is impossible to continue operating. If you have two or three lines from the pumper covering exposures, the enforced shutdown may cause the loss of water. There

are cases on record where the flame spread so rapidly, it was necessary to cut hose lines with axes to free pumpers for evacuation of the area.

Don't underestimate the potential of these fires. Get help in early if you think you may need it. Lumberyard fires require large lines, ample water supplies, and the manpower to put them in use.

Consider nearby buildings even though they are not at first threatened. They may be exposed by sudden wind changes. If water supplies are low and streams inadequate for this type of fire, the smaller streams may be effective in keeping exposures wet down. If the limited amount of available water would not extinguish the fire, it would be wiser in this case to use it to protect the exposures and let the fire burn itself out. Large storages of lumber in unsprinklered sheds or highly piled in the open always present the potential of a serious, rapidly spreading fire. (See Figure 170.) Because the piles are at times so high, with narrow aisles between stacks, fire once started may be difficult to control even with large water supplies, adequate manpower, and equipment. Weather factors such as high wind or extreme air conditions may contribute to a fire's rapid spread.

FIGURE 169. *A fire destroyed nearly all the lumber stored in the open at this lumberyard fire. The fire was finally stopped at the large frame shed by heavy streams from ladder pipes and an elevating platform.*

FIGURE 170. *Even 2½-inch lines are not very effective in fighting fires of this type. Men cannot hold their positions because of the intense heat.* *Lumberyard fires require heavy streams from deluge guns, elevating platforms, and ladder pipes.*

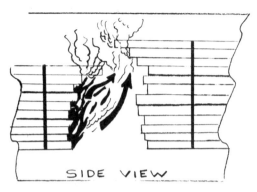

SIDE VIEW

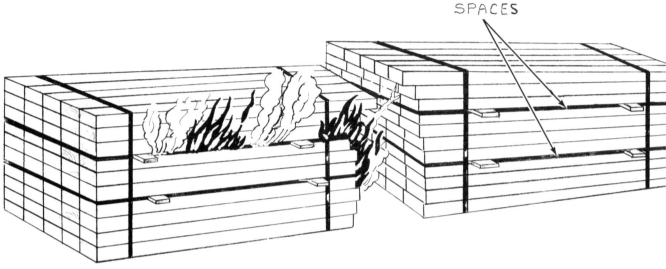

SPACES

FIGURE 171 (Above). *This drawing illustrates how fire will eat its way into the rear of lumber piles and how uneven pile ends tend to trap sparks and heat for easy ignition. The spaced method of lumber storage shown here allows fire to travel easily through the piles.*

FIGURE 171A (Right). *This photograph of a lumber pile shows how fire can burrow deep within the pile. As it burrows in, the piles begin to shift and topple. This opens the piles for further penetration of fire. This type of fire can be handled by inserting piercing nozzles into holes burned by the fire, by pushing garden hose into the openings, or by heavy streams directed against the face of the pile to drive water deep into the crevices.*

FIGURE 171B (Left). *Fire entered this lumber pile by burning into the openings provided by the spaced pile method of stacking lumber.*

FIGURE 172 (Below). *This lumber is stacked in the typical way with spaces between boards to provide air circulation. Fire burns into these spaces to easily involve interior of the piles.*

FIGURE 173 (Above). *At times the heat from a lumberyard fire is so intense that positions in the path of fire spread cannot be maintained — even though the position is crucial to the protection of exposed buildings. In such cases operate the stream from the sides. Play the stream alternately on exposed building and advancing fire.*

FIGURE 174 (Right). *The noise of exploding tires may cause firemen to fear storage of explosives in the yard. They may withdraw from crucial positions unnecessarily. It is true the explosions could be truck fuel tanks, but in such cases there will usually be a marked brightening and heightening of the flames.*

FIGURE 175. *These lines are crucial. They are preventing the fire from involving the homes behind the firemen. However, note the overhead power lines. These men are in a precarious position as the power lines could fall. In such cases the power lines should be cut by the electric utility company. Until this can be done, lines should be placed in a deluge gun with sufficient pres-sures to allow men to operate in less exposed positions. Another alternative is to set up the deluge gun with a wide angle fog pattern playing onto the fire without men having to remain in position to operate the stream. The stream should be kept under observation, however, to insure that the exposures are being protected.*

Lumberyards are often built near the city's edge, on the waterfront, or at railroad sidings, to cut down on shipping costs. When the yard is on a waterfront and the city has fireboats, they will be a great help in supplying the large quantities of water needed for such fires. If the yard is beside railroad tracks, access to the fire may be limited to approach from only one side. Line placement will be difficult because of the tracks, possible high-voltage overhead power lines, and the need to stop train traffic. Where possible, dig out the fill between the railroad ties and lay the hose lines under the tracks. A lumberyard must be designed to provide vehicular access to the stored piles of lumber. Thus the roadways through which trucks may be driven for loading purposes are fairly wide. The ends of the piles facing the roadways are usually flush, regardless of the length of the individual boards. This means the rear of such piles will be uneven if the board lengths are uneven. The longer lumber will project beyond the shorter pieces. These irregular lengths expose a maximum surface area and trap the fire. Here the fire burrows deep into the piles where it is unnoticed and where water penetration is difficult. (See Figures 171-171A.)

The smooth sides and ends of lumber piles are not as susceptible to fire burrowing into the depths of the pile. Generally the flame will burn and char visible ends. Water application will readily extinguish the fire.

Even where lumber is stored with flush faces at both the front and rear of the piles, fire may burrow within, because of the piling method. There are two methods of piling lumber. One is to stack the boards directly on top of one another. This is desirable from the fire department's viewpoint because it presents few spaces for fire to enter. The other method is used to provide air circulation between the boards. Furring strips are used as spacers every few boards. This allows fire to penetrate and burn deep within the pile. (See Figure 171B-172.)

Few fires present more rapid spread and greater exposure threat than lumberyards. Sparks and brands will fly for hundreds of feet. It will be vital to get heavy streams between the fire and the threatened structures. It is preferable to place such streams in the path of the wind to head the fire off. But the heat may render such positions untenable. If this happens, direct the streams from the side but operate them to head off the fire and keep the exposed piles and buildings thoroughly drenched. (See Figure 173.)

If you must make a choice between the burning piles and the exposures, ignore the burning piles. Use the streams to protect what is not yet burning but is directly exposed and in the path of the wind.

Because of the large areas and highly piled lumber, it is difficult to cover the fire area efficiently with hand lines or heavy streams at ground level. The lumberyard fire is one fire where streams from ladder pipes and elevating platform baskets will be invaluable. The heavy calibre stream from above can sweep the yard, extinguishing surface fire, protecting exposures, and cutting down on the flying brands. The water runoff from the tops of the piles will darken the fire at the sides and rear.

Once the rapid flaming combustion has been checked, the heavy streams may be shut down. Now move in with hand lines. Because of the need to maneuver in and around piles (particularly the rear), the use of 1½-inch lines is advisable. Men should be cautioned against the danger of falling from slippery tops of high piles and the chance that these piles might topple onto the men below.

Another hazard commonly found in lumberyard fires, particularly when the yard is closed, is the storage of trucks or propane-fueled fork lifts. Not only do you have the vehicle fire but the danger of exploding fuel tanks as well. Frequently firemen are driven out by what they fear to be exploding fuel tanks. In reality it is the blowing of vehicle tires from the fire. (See Figure 174.)

The following are some helpful operating techniques to keep in mind at lumberyard fires:

1. Organize a spark and brand patrol. Check the roofs of nearby buildings.

2. Avoid punishing firefighters by operating streams from opposite directions—toward each other.

3. Check for danger of falling electric wires. (See Figure 175.)

4. Get hose lines into exposed buildings.

5. If the yard is surrounded by a fence, open the gates and large doors for ready access. Where there are not enough of these gates, cut openings through the fence to avoid long hose stretches and to provide a ready retreat for men and equipment.

6. Provide good lighting for overhauling.

7. Wait for daylight to overhaul, if possible.

8. Keep a watch line for 24 hours.

For the techniques involved in overhauling lumberyards, see Chapter 17.

Chapter 22

Department store fires

THERE IS no clear definition of the term department store or mercantile building. In the small town a department store may be a one-story store of moderate area stocking goods of varying description. In a large city it may be a multistory building of tremendous area stocking anything and everything up to and including small yachts. Two examples will give an idea of the height and area of some of these large stores. The Neiman-Marcus store in Dallas is seven stories high with 35,000 square feet on each floor. Macy's in New York City is approximately the same height with about 60,000 square feet on each floor.

Hazards of department stores

These immense structures present almost every hazard one can think of. One unusual example is a department store fire in West Germany in 1963. Pressurized aerosol containers involved in the fire produced frightening pyrotechnic effects. The resulting panic took 22 lives. It was reported that the fire spread rapidly after 1,000 of the pressure-packaged containers with flammable contents exploded or were jet-propelled as "flaming torches."

Here are some of the hazards to be alert for:

1. There may be more than 1,000 people shopping at one time.

2. There is ample fire loading. These stores stock just about every flammable product: combustible cotton dresses, flammable paints, plastics, lumber, to name a few.

3. There is no fire alarm signal for alerting shoppers that they will understand. The public address system may be of no help. It is doubtful that it would be heard above the panic that would follow signs of smoke.

4. Most people are not familiar with the secondary paths of egress. They are not familiar with stairways since shoppers above the ground floor usually rely on elevators or escalators.

5. Floor areas are only rarely subdivided.

6. Aisle space is small. Temporary storage, display materials being rearranged, or furniture may block the aisle.

7. In the more progressive cities, stair shafts and elevator shafts are enclosed, but too often the self-closing doors to these stairways are blocked open.

8. Escalators expose all floors. The trend to the moving stairway negates the function of the enclosed stair and elevator shaft. It forms a vertical opening exposing all floors above any fire which starts near the escalator. Two methods are used to keep the convenience of escalators, yet cut down on the hazards of unprotected vertical openings: First are the deluge sprinkler heads which will send a shower of water around the es-

calator in case of fire. Second is an air curtain. The pressure near the escalator is greater than the surrounding atmosphere. This is supposed to keep the smoke and heat away from it to prevent involvement of other floors.

The efficiency of both these methods is open to question. Smoke can travel up the vertical opening without being hot enough to fuse the sprinkler heads. There is always the possibility of water being turned off at the time of the fire (this happened in the Neiman-Marcus fire in Dallas on December 19, 1964). In the case of the air curtain, it is possible the forced draft will intensify the fire, sparks, and smoke. Fire that gets by the air curtain will be forced up the open escalator by the pressure.

9. Many department stores have been built in smaller towns and suburban areas where building regulations are less stringent. In outlying municipalities, the water supplies may not be sufficient for large fires.

10. Sprinklers generally are installed, otherwise the insurance rates would be prohibitive. Building regulations, however, may not require standpipes. Without standpipes firefighting operations will require long ardous hose stretches. To further complicate matters, there may be a manpower shortage.

Study these department store fires

Fires in such structures as the typical department store can cause severe loss of life and untold monetary losses. Several examples will point up some of the problems of these buildings.

In 1947 a department store fire in New Zealand killed 41 people. The store consisted of eight interconnected buildings of ordinary construction. They were unsprinklered, with open stairs and elevators. The fire started in the basement during store hours. A delayed alarm to the fire department (the store phone operator spent 10 minutes trying to locate the store manager before sending the alarm) allowed the smoke and heat from the basement to sweep into the upper floors, cutting people off from the exits. The official investigation listed the following causes of fire spread and loss of life:

1. Large fire areas.
2. Unprotected vertical and horizontal areas.
3. Excessive fire-loading for the occupancy.
4. Delayed alarm.
5. Excessive use of combustible fibreboard in the building.

In December, 1958, a department store fire in Colombia took 83 lives. The fire took place in the first floor of a three-story building. It started in a creche made of flimsy combustible material. The creche was midway between the front and rear of the store. There was only one exit—at the front of the store. People between the front door and the fire got out. Those behind the fire died.

In Tokyo on August 22, 1963, a fire burned more than 110,000 square feet of the seventh and eighth stories of an eight-story, reinforced concrete building.* Seven persons were killed and 114 injured in this very smoky, hot fire. Damage was estimated at $6,475,000.

From the outside the store appeared to be a single, modern building. Actually, it was an unsprinklered group of additions behind a modern front. There were open stairs and escalators throughout.

The fire started in the seventh floor cafeteria while the store was closed to the public, but there were more than 340 employees in the store at the time. Workmen were fumigating the restaurant with a flammable insecticide (flashpoint 63° F.). During the lunch hour a workman dropped a match on the floor, igniting the insecticide. The fire spread rapidly, feeding on combustible merchandise, ceiling coverings, etc. The entire seventh floor became involved and the fire spread to the eighth floor via rear windows and open stairs, trapping people. Those who waited at the windows were eventually rescued by fire department ladders.

Firemen were limited in their approach to the fire because of railroad tracks. Ladder trucks were hampered by the tracks at the rear and by overhead trolley wires at the front. The mazelike layout of the store in-

---

*This report is from the Marine and Fire Insurance Association of Japan.

terior similarly slowed hose line placement. The fire was confined to the upper two stories in about three hours. It took the effort of more than 1,100 firemen with 70 vehicles.

The fire in the Neiman-Marcus store in Dallas, Tex., caused no loss of life, but damage was more than $5 million. The fire was reported at 3:42 A.M. after a delayed alarm of 30 minutes. Only the basement was fully sprinklered. The other floors had only water curtain sprinklers around the escalators. The fire started on the second floor and roared up to the fifth and sixth floors via these open escalators. Water to the sprinklers had been turned off and the fire department did not know about it until too late. The Dallas Fire Department moved in with hand lines, but the combination of terrific heat and smoke conditions was too much. The men were driven out.

The fire was finally darkened down by the use of two elevating platforms and aerial ladder pipes. Hand lines were then moved in to mop up.

A fire in a six-story and basement department store almost 200,000 square feet in area killed at least 325 persons on May 22, 1967, in Brussels, Belgium.* The property damage was estimated at more than $20 million. The store was protected by an ionization-type alarm device, but it did not cover the sales area where the fire started. There were no sprinklers and there were open stairways and light shafts.

The store had been built in three sections: Section I (about 70 years old) was of unprotected steel members and wooden floors. The center section was of steel frame protected by concrete. There was a large light well, open from the first floor to the roof and covered by a steel frame and glass dome. All floors opened into this huge light well. (This type of construction is found in United States department stores, also.) The third section was completed in several stages and was built with unprotected steel columns in the basement and first floor. The upper-floor columns were protected. The floors were concrete on protected steel.

*The discussion on this fire is based on information from the National Fire Association of Brussels.

There were numerous open stairs, elevators, and escalators throughout the building. There was a lack of horizontal, fire-resistant cutoffs. There was a store fire brigade and an alarm system direct to the fire department. The building was not sprinklered.

It was common to find several thousand shoppers in the store at one time, though only about 1,500 were shopping at the time of the fire.

The fire started near a large open stairway on the second floor at about 1:00 P.M. Fire and smoke spread so rapidly that most of the people on the second floor and above were trapped. The heat and smoke rose via the open stairs, escalators, and elevator shafts. People climbed out on window ledges, some jumped to the street.

Fire response was delayed by narrow streets and congested traffic. Within a short time the fire had involved the entire structure. Heat was so intense that firemen had to shut their lines down and move their trucks to a safer location. Fire spread to several woodworking and textile plants in the area. In less than one hour the section with unprotected steel framing collapsed.

Department store operating techniques

There is one factor that will greatly influence your handling of a fire in a department store, and that is whether the store is open for business and filled with shoppers or closed with no shoppers present.

Store not occupied by shoppers. Generally speaking, a fire in a large mercantile or department store, when it is closed to the public, presents much the same problem as any other combustible occupancy. If it is a one-story store, it is handled much the same as a supermarket fire. Operations at multistoried stores follow much the same techniques as at any tall building.

Every effort must be made to move hand lines in to the seat of the fire. Rely on standpipes and sprinklers. If the fire becomes too intense or the smoke and heat prove too punishing, the hand lines must be backed out. Then elevating platforms and ladder pipes will have to be used to darken down the fire.

People shopping in the building. Should the fire occur when the store is occupied, there is a severe threat to life. Shoppers unfamiliar with the emergency exits will try to get out the way they came in. If electric wires are involved, elevators and lights may become inoperative. Sprinkler and standpipe pumps may not function. (This is another reason why outside fire department connections to standpipes and sprinklers should be supplied by pumpers). People trapped in darkened buildings will panic and trample each other.

Engine company crews must lay in hose lines with the objective of heading off the fire. The lines should be operated to protect threatened means of egress. If necessary, direct the streams at the ceiling, over the heads of people. This is to deflect water down between the threatened shoppers to slow the advancing fire. Avoid bringing hose lines in through the same door that people are using as an exit. If the fire is on the second floor, or higher, get the lines up by means of ladders. Keep the exits free to let the people move out. Back up all lines that are crucial to the operation, or where the loss of water may trap firefighters.

If you are operating off a standpipe, bring the 2½-inch line up to the point where the smoke and heat buildup is not too heavy to still be able to see. This may be up to a fire door or some such point. If the fire requires large volumes of water, advance to the fire using the 2½-inch line. But where the volume of fire is not that heavy, wye off the 2½-inch line into two 1½-inch lines. It will be easier to traverse narrow aisles, passageways, and wind around partitions with the 1½-inch line. It is becoming extremely difficult with today's undermanned companies to manage the cumbersome, stiff, and unwieldy 2½-inch lines under these conditions. Where you will not operate off standpipes, bring the 2½-inch line to the building and as far in as you can move before the going gets rough. Here again, wye off into 1½-inch lines. Follow the same procedure on upper floors. That is, bring the 2½-inch line up to the floor on which you will operate before wying off to 1½-inch lines.

It is true that the 1½-inch line lacks the cooling capacity of the larger stream, but as a rule its lightness and maneuverability more than make up for the difference.

If the fire is in the basement, make every effort to hold it there until the shoppers have been able to vacate the store. It may be wise to avoid cutting the floor for cellar pipes or venting via the main floor until the people are out. If the smoke wells up, the shoppers may panic and refuse to exit through smoke.

Some additional operating hints

The following techniques may be helpful in department or mercantile store fires.

1. Operate as calmly as possible. Try to allay panic. If there are revolving doors, remember that they can be collapsed to provide free exit space. Some revolving doors are held open by small hooks and eyes on the bottom of the door. On others, all that is necessary is a push on two of the wings at the same time to collapse the doors. But you should study the door mechanism in advance.

2. Send laddermen to all floors to ventilate, search, and guide people to safe exits. Avoid ladder rescues unless absolutely necessary. Shout encouragement and instructions to the people on upper floors.

3. One stair can exit more people safely than a dozen aerial ladders.

4. Laddermen can operate house standpipe lines as needed.

5. If the exits are insufficient to get the people out quickly, break out front show windows (remove hanging pieces of glass) and move the people out this way.

6. It may only be necessary to bring people down to the floor below the fire to remove them from danger.

7. Search toilets, dressing and fitting rooms, locker rooms, first-aid stations, offices, small lunchrooms, and all such areas.

8. Remember the old trick of venting stores at street fronts. Use a 20-foot ladder to push in the plate-glass show window. Then push in and knock down the flimsy partition between the store proper and the show window space.

Chapter 23

Residential structure fires

RESIDENTIAL STRUCTURES, for the purposes of this chapter, will refer to all types of buildings where people live and sleep. Life safety is the dominating feature which guides the tactical operations in fires in these buildings. Life safety is critical where responding units are so short of manpower or equipment that it is impossible at the outset to conduct normal lifesaving and fire extinguishing operations.

Types of residential structures

There is a wide variation in the types and sizes of residential structures. Some are more of a fire hazard than others. But these dwellings may be categorized into the following broad sections as they relate to occupancy:

1. Private dwellings (one or two families).
2. Multiple dwellings (three or more families).
3. Hotels.
4. Motels.
5. Rooming houses.

Type of construction

The five types of residential structures all may be found in just about every type of construction—frame, ordinary construction, or fire-resistant construction. It is therefore important to understand their fundamental differences.

Frame construction. All structural members are of wood. The exterior also is of wood, unless the building exceeds 2,500 square feet in area and is less than 20 feet from other structures*. If this is the case, the exterior wall must have a two-hour fire-resistant rating, according to the National Building Code.

Ordinary construction. Exterior walls must be noncombustible with a two-hour minimum fire-resistant rating (National Building Code).

Fire-resistant construction. All structural members, including floors and roofs, are completely noncombustible (National Building Code).

These three broad categories of construction are not to be considered legally correct. The legal interpretation will vary depending upon the building code used. The terms are used here simply to distinguish broadly between the types. For example, ordinary construction can apply to everything from a fairly well-constructed building with heavy

---

*This compliance is rare. Most older cities have frame buildings closer than 20 feet.

timber construction, to a substandard building with brick exterior, wood-joisted floors, open wooden stairs, and unprotected light and vent shafts.*

Basic strategy for residential fires

Get hose lines to the seat of the fire. That is the fundamental rule. Basic fire strategy dictates that proper fire operational techniques require moving the hose line in to the seat of the fire rather than attempting extinguishment by line operation through windows or doorways. This fundamental strategy is particularly true in residential structure fires. Regardless of how punishing the fire may be, whether or not it is necessary to use breathing equipment, get the lines into the fire area. Do this and you will rarely fail to establish control of the situation.

The following pages will discuss each type of residential structure fire separately.

The private dwelling

Private dwellings are nearly always detached from nearby structures. There usually is a separation at front, back, and on both sides. In some cases, where the side distances are small (10 feet or less), there may be a fire extension hazard. But usually such hazard can be mitigated. The firefighting tactics will be similar, whether the dwellings have frame or masonry exteriors. But there is a difference. In the frame dwelling, fire can run the exterior walls. Should it become totally involved, the exposure problem will become acute if buildings are nearby. There also will be showers of sparks and flying brands, requiring more hose lines.

The typical private home is a two-story building with the bedrooms upstairs. Attics are often finished and used as bedrooms by younger members of the family. In larger homes you may find two inside stairways with one designated as the service stair. Both stairways will be open and the main stairway may have a skylight over it at the roof. Cellars can be large. Heating plants are

---

*For a more complete description and explanation of all types of construction categories see Volume 4 of the National Fire Codes of 1970-1971, NFPA Standard 220.

generally forced warm air systems with ducts running the walls. There will be only one entrance to the cellar from somewhere off the kitchen.

Ranch homes. The newer private homes are now often only one story high with no cellars. The firefighting problems here are minimized. Move in one hose line and you will usually extinguish the fire. Care must be taken to see that no fire spreads through the duct network. This feature may allow combustion products to involve the rest of the home. Particularly vulnerable is the hanging ceiling space.

Don't be unduly alarmed if smoke pours from the attic ventilators. This often prompts men to assume fire is in the attic, and they rush to cut the roof. This is rarely necessary in a one-story or even a two-story home. It only opens the roof to the elements after you leave the scene. Ventilate such buildings by power fans, doors, and windows.

Cellar fires. In the six to eight-room two-story home, cellar fires can be punishing. Again, if you can advance a hose line down the cellar stairs to the seat of the fire, you will normally extinguish it. Make sure there has been no vertical extension; examine the baseboards and feel the walls. If necessary, open the baseboards at the upper level for examination. Ventilate both the cellar and upper floors thoroughly. Use breathing equipment if necessary. Don't rush to cut the roof; this will only ventilate the attic and may pull the fire up the side walls. Make a thorough check of the duct system.

Fires in the bedrooms and attics will be punishing also, but get the hose line up to the fire and you will achieve control. Open windows from ladders; check the roof for involvement.

Large private homes. The large two- to three-story private residence presents a more serious firefighting problem than the smaller homes. Usually there are two interior stairways. Be careful on this point. Undue concentration on the one avenue of communication may allow fire to extend up a rear stairway. The stairs in these older large homes are wide. They are open from the first floor to the top, and are all wood. There will be hot-air ducts throughout the home running from large, compartmented cellars. Attics frequently store a great deal of old furniture, but sometimes they serve as servants' quarters.

A fire at night in one of these older large homes presents a serious life hazard. The immediate needs are to force entrance, ventilate, search for people overcome, ladder the building, and advance the lines. You might need up to three companies of five men each. It would be wise to get help in early. It is imperative in this kind of fire to get all hands on the first hose line to try and advance it upstairs as rapidly as possible. In addition, move other lines up by the rear stairs or by ladder.

As a rule, there will be sufficient separation between homes to avoid a severe exposure hazard, but sparks and brands may fly several blocks. If the vicinity has wood-shingled roofs, other fires may start. Have the area patrolled for such a possibility.

The following are some of the problems to anticipate at private dwelling fires:

1. Some of these homes may be 40 feet high. Usually they are set far back from the street behind large trees. This prevents effective use of aerial ladders or elevating platforms to reach roofs and upper floors.

2. The trees and heavy shrubs may also prevent efficient placement of portable ladders or use of exterior streams should they become necessary.

3. Long winding driveways. Houses are at times 300 feet from the street—don't stretch short!

4. Roofs may be large and steep. Wooden shingles often complicate the problem.

5. Expect to find a great deal of furniture inside.

6. There may be servants' quarters in the attic.

7. Air-conditioning plants (ductwork) can spread the fire.

Multiple dwellings

The buildings under the category of multiple dwellings include tenements, apartment buildings, and flats. The very old multiple dwellings vary considerably in size, style, and design from city to city. They may be from three to six stories high and from 25 to 50 feet wide. Fire escapes are common. They are found in both the front and rear. Often the front fire escape ends at the top row of windows while the rear fire escape continues to the roof via a gooseneck-type straight ladder. Occupancies range from four families per floor in the old buildings to about eight families per floor in the more recent buildings. The very old buildings are often completely frame or substandard ordinary construction. If seriously involved, these buildings burn rapidly.

It is impossible in a book this size to discuss each type of multiple dwelling in every city, but the same general construction features will be found in most areas. Even though there may be some variation from city to city, the firefighting tactics will be pretty much the same. In other words, the problems involving fires in these structures can be classified and standard firefighting tactics may be used to control and extinguish the fire. This is not to minimize the problem. A fire in these old dwellings during the night, when people are asleep, presents a serious life hazard. It would be bad enough if the building were isolated and efforts could be devoted to the single structure. But unfortunately hazards to both life and the building are compounded because multiple dwellings are often built in rows.

Here are some of the hazards and problems these dwellings present to the fire department:

1. Entrance to the cellars is gained by a thin flimsy wooden door at the rear of the first floor hallway under the first flight of stairs to the upper floors. Such flimsy doors will burn through in minutes, exposing the interior wooden stairs and all floors above.

2. Individual apartment doors also are of thin wood—often with glass panels and glass transoms.

3. Partitions are of wood lath and plaster.

4. There may be wooden wainscoating on stairs and halls.

5. There may be open rear wood stairs for use as fire escapes.

6. Air and light shafts present vertical flues inside the structure to carry fire to the upper floors.

7. The buildings often have common hanging ceiling spaces which allow rapid lateral movement of fire to adjoining buildings.

8. Common party walls allow cellar ceiling joists to butt each other on the dividing wall, creating a horizontal flue to adjoining cellars.

9. In very poor sections there may be no central heating plant. Such areas use kerosene stoves—either fixed or portable. Floors and stairways become oil-soaked and burn like tinder if ignited. Storage of fuel oil in cellars is common.

10. The stoves themselves commonly explode, causing a scattered flammable liquid fire in the apartment.

Cellar fires. Fires often start in the cellar of these buildings. Cellar fires are particularly hazardous because the entire structure and its occupants are above and exposed to the combustion products. The smoke and heat rise rapidly throughout the structure, permeating stair shafts and apartments. The cellars in these buildings are depositories for anything from 55-gallon kerosene drums to lumber, furniture, and paint. It is common to assign a small storage bin to each tenant for storing his excess furnishings. These bins are flimsily framed out with wood. For security reasons, they often are covered with slats or wire mesh. There is absolutely nothing to prevent fire from involving all these storage bins. There is no question about it: there is more than sufficient fire loading to provide a hot, fast-moving, serious fire.

Gas meters are another serious problem. When fire melts the lead seals on the meters—and this usually happens—the leaking gas ignites. This not only adds to the flames, it also presents the possibility of explosion. If the stream operation is blind (as with a cellar nozzle) there is a good chance you may extinguish the gas flame. If this is so and there is no gas main shutoff in the street, chances are you will have an explosion. Although the fire may have been almost extinguished, until overhauling is completed there will be some smoldering embers. The leaking gas will accumulate until it reaches the ignition source and will then explode. This is another reason why every attempt must be made to enter the cellar with hose lines—to eliminate the potential of accidentally extinguishing such a gas flame before the gas is shut off.

In such cellar fires, the first line should move down by way of the inside stairway. Stretch a second line to cover the floor above.

If the first line finds it impossible to advance down the cellar stairs because of smoke and heat, back it out. Close the door to the cellar but keep this line in the hall in case the fire starts to burn through the door or moves up by the stairs, partitions, or shafts. If there is an outside entrance to the cellar from the street or rear yard, send the second line down this way. Keep the door to the cellar closed until the people above have gotten out, then open it intermittenly to ventilate the cellar. Send a third line to cover the upper floors. Start to get a cellar pipe ready but don't cut yet!

If excess heat and smoke prevent you from moving the second line down the front or rear, send a fourth line to work abreast with the second line. Try to advance together, driving the smoke and heat ahead. If the two lines can't make it, back them out. Put one line into the cellar nozzle over the hot spot in the floor. Send the other line to help cover the floors above.

As soon as fire conditions have abated somewhat, try again to get the inside line down the inside stairs. However, if such an attempt is to be made, the cellar nozzle and front or rear lines should be shut down. If the gas meters are burning, keep a stream above the flame to prevent the fire from burning into the ceilings. *Do not extinguish the gas flame!* There will be a shutoff valve at the point where the gas line enters the building. Close this valve.

Whenever possible, avoid having lines operate so that they drive the combustion products toward the opposing crew. Neither company will be able to advance and the chances are that both will be driven out. Then the fire will continue to burn and move up through the flooring, shafts, or partitions. If this movement is suspected, open these vertical arteries and direct streams to stop this vertical fire extension. If fire is traveling up a shaft, direct the stream up into the shaft so the water reaches as high as possible. Don't worry about the fire in the lower part of the shaft. The water that falls back down will take care of this.

Fires on the other floors, with the exception of top floors, should be handled by two lines without much trouble.

Generally, one line is required at the fire apartment and the second line is used to cover the floor above. These fires are usually confined to a single apartment with superficial extension to the floor above by way of partitions and ceilings.

If the apartment is large or fully involved, bring the second line to back up the first. Send a third line to cover the floor above. Where there is a fire escape, send another line up it. This line may succeed in darkening down the fire enough to let the inside line move in. It can also cover any internal exposure to the floors above. It can keep the fire escape tenable for people who may try to get down this way. There is no hard and fast rule as to whether the second or third line should go to the floor above now, or to back up the first line. This is a priority which must be determined at the scene by the officer in charge. Don't overlook the possibility of shafts that may allow the fire to involve the floors above or the building across the shaft by way of the windows.

If fire involves one or two apartments on a floor and a stair shaft, it will be necessary for the first line to quickly knock down the fire in the apartments and then proceed immediately up the stairs to cut the fire off before it gets to the floors above. People on the upper floors will be in terrible danger. Where such conditions are found, direct the stream

up the well hole* as soon as water reaches the nozzle. In this way the water will reach the top floor, and cool down and protect the upper floors momentarily until the line can be advanced to the fire floor.

This procedure also will help prevent the fire from getting into the hanging ceiling. But back up this first line immediately with a second line to completely extinguish the lower-floor fire. If this precaution is neglected, the men advancing up the stairs will find themselves in a dangerous position—with fire behind and above them. If the roof skylight is opened at this point, the tendency would be to pull the fire below them up the stairs, surrounding them with fire.

In such fires 1½-inch hose is satisfactory. Its light weight and mobility make it ideal for fires involving apartments, shafts, and stairways—anyplace where you have to move around sharp corners, in and out. In these situations, lines have to be advanced rapidly. If the fire proves to be too much for the 1½-inch hose, back it up with a 2½-inch line (always a good practice anyway if you have the manpower). Don't use a large stream as a substitute for moving the smaller line into the seat of the fire. If the apartment or hall is fully involved in fire, use the ceiling as a deflector for the hose stream. It will serve as a giant sprinkler and give far greater coverage over the fire area.

The reason for concern about fire extending into the hanging ceiling space is that once fire enters here it can spread rapidly and involve not only the entire space but the buildings on each side as well. If this is a possibility, then lines must be laid to the top floors and the roofs of the buildings on each side. Don't open the ceilings until water is available at the nozzle. The roof can be opened immediately, however, because if fire was in the hanging ceiling space, such an opening tends to draw the fire toward it, lessening the potential for lateral involvement.

If people are trapped by fire advancing behind them or if fire is billowing out the win-

---

*The well hole is the narrow space between the stair banister and the landing. Looking down from the top floor, you can see all the way down to the lowest floor. This space through which you can see all the way is the well hole.

dows and threatening the floors above, use the deluge gun or heavy exterior street stream to achieve a quick knockdown or to drive the fire back from the endangered people. But don't delay advancing the line and moving in by way of the inside stairway. This must be advanced as rapidly as possible. Make sure that the exterior stream is shut down or directed over the roof as soon as the inside line has reached the fire floor. This will be evident by the lowering of the volume of fire or steam or spray coming from the windows.

Railroad flats. One type of multiple residence is called a railroad flat because each room is in line with the next and you have to go through one to reach the other. There is a fire escape at either the front or the rear. Should there be a fire between the occupants and the fire escape, they will be trapped. If they are cut off from escape via the front fire escape and door, they will rush to the rear, screaming for help. If conditions are serious, it is easy to concentrate on the front and totally forget that people may be trapped at the rear. Rescue at the front is possible by portable ladders to windows, aerial ladders, elevating platforms, fire escapes, and life nets. The rear generally is not accessible. There may be no exterior access to yards or courts there. There may be no rear alleys. Rescue here will be difficult. You will have to bring portable ladders out the rear first-floor windows and raise them to the trapped victims, or have men descend from above on ropes, or use life nets.

Standard operations at these fires call for ladder companies to raise ladders as needed for either rescue or advancement of lines to upper floors. They should gain access to the roof for examination or ventilation by going up the inside stairs of the adjoining buildings. Failing other safer means of roof access, they would use the aerial ladder or elevating platform. After completing the roof assignment, men would move down the fire escapes, ventilating the floors by windows from the fire escapes and examining each floor for people overcome or for fire extension. These duties are covered in detail in the chapters on ventilation and ladder company operations.

Some of the more recently constructed of these old buildings are not as hazardous as the oldest ones, because there were changes in the construction of multiple dwellings as time passed. Frame multiple dwellings were no longer allowed. Hall toilets were moved into individual apartments, ending one vertical shaft in the hallways. More rigid requirements were instituted as to fire retarding the shafts, the under side of the stairs, and doors to individual apartments.

An important change came around 1900 when the cellar was cut off from the upper floors by fire-resistant construction. And there was no longer an entrance to the cellar from inside the building. The only way into the cellar was through an outside street level door, reached through a court or alley. This major improvement coupled with the fire-resistant cellar ceiling allowed fires to be more readily confined to the cellars. Generally, too, these buildings are more fire-resistant and it is easier to hold fires to the individual apartments.

With newer buildings, there is no longer the urgency in getting lines to the floors above if the cellar is burning. Lines are brought to bear on the fire from the doorway and moved in as soon as possible. Because these buildings are considerably larger, there were windows to the cellar on every street front and at times facing on inner courts. Lines can be directed to darken down the fire from the windows until the doorway line can move in. The cellars also can be ventilated via these windows.

Because the buildings are much larger, with as many as 12 families per floor, the cellar storage is larger. With this additional storage it is possible to get serious fires in these cellars. In such fires, lay additional lines into the cellar. Move other lines to upper floors also, if extension via shafts, pipe conduits, or ducts is possible. As a rule, fires are confined to the cellar with superficial extension upward to the floor sleepers*, baseboards,

---

*Sleepers are the wood nailing strips embedded in the concrete to which the hardwood floors are nailed.

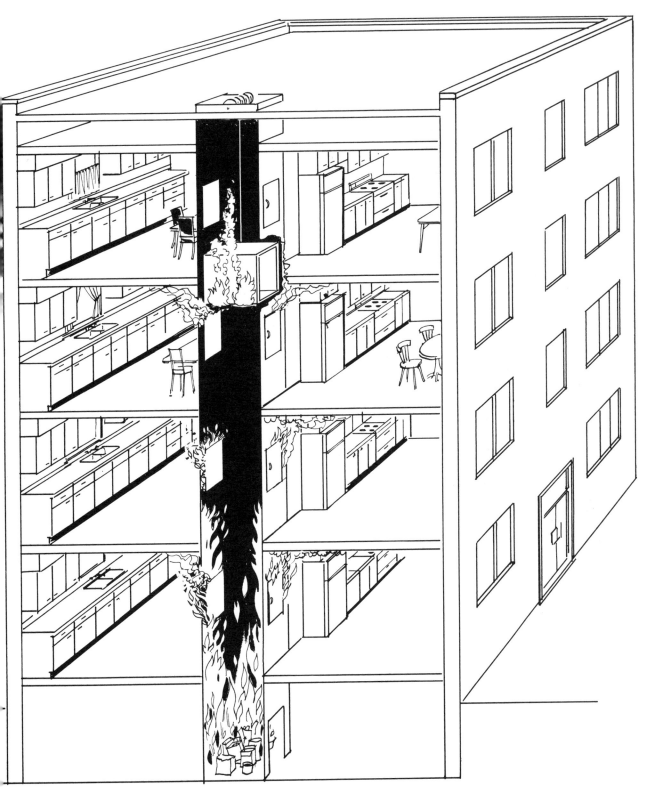

FIGURE 175A. *This is a typical dumbwaiter shaft serving two apartments on each floor. If fire starts (or enters) this shaft it can enter the kitchens of the apartments on floors above the original fire. In a similar way it may involve the hanging ceil-* *ing space and fan out over the entire structure. It is important in such cases to examine each apartment on the course of the shaft — particularly hanging ceilings.*

and flooring. But travel by pipe chase is a possibility.

Fires in the individual apartments are generally handled by moving a hand line into the fire apartment and, in larger apartments, another line up the fire escape. A precautionary line is taken to the apartment above the fire if several rooms are involved. Examination of the ceiling and side walls determines the need for additional line placement.

These buildings have dumbwaiter shafts—sometimes in the hall and sometimes in the individual apartments. If in the apartment, the same dumbwaiter usually serves two apartments on each floor. Be careful. Fire in the shaft will involve both of these apartments. And the fire may involve more apartments on the course of the shaft. (See Figure 175A.) The hanging ceiling space in particular must be examined for involvement because these shafts were commonly used by repairman to run additional electric cables, gas lines, or pipes to the apartments. These lines enter the apartments through a hole from the shaft into the ceiling space of the apartment. If a fire occurs in the shaft, it can easily follow a pipe or conduit right into the ceiling space of the apartments. In similar fashion, fires can get into the hanging ceiling spaces.

If you suspect this condition, lay lines to head off the fire. Open ceilings and side walls to expose hidden fire travel. (See hanging ceiling fires in the chapter on Concealed Fires.)

This type of multiple dwelling frequently has commercial occupancies (usually stores) on the street floor. The ceiling joists of the stores are on the same level with the ceiling joists of the first-floor apartments. Fire can run the store partition and get into the ceiling space or enter the ceiling space by heat conduction through the usual metal ceiling from a fire in the store. Then the fire can run laterally through the joists to involve the apartments. It can also extend to the apartments above the store by burning through from the store below. Therefore, if there is a serious fire in one of these stores, not only should you check for other store involvement, but it is important to check the apartments above and on each side of the store on the floor above the fire.

Large multiple dwellings. The most recent type of multiple dwelling of ordinary construction is the six- or seven-story building built in the shape of the letter H. They cover a large area and are more fire-resistant. There is a large open garden in the center with walks to the individual wings. While the parts of the "H" are supposedly separate buildings, there is one common hanging ceiling over the entire structure. The dividing walls between these wings terminate at the ceiling of the top floor. Fire can extend to these hanging ceilings by partitions, poorly fire-stopped columns, soil pipe recesses in bathrooms, vent shafts in kitchens, poorly constructed dumbwaiter shafts, and incinerator flues.

Cellar fires and fires in the apartments are handled in the same way as fires in the multiple dwelling where there is a fire-resistant cutoff from the cellar to the floor above.

The major problem in these large apartment buildings is the hanging ceiling space. If fire extends to this space, it can fan out over the entire complex. Any fire in a shaft in such structures should be treated with caution. If you suspect fire may have entered the hanging ceiling, bring hose lines to the top floors of each separate building on either side of the suspected area. Get a line to the roof and cut to try and draw the fire up and out of the hanging ceiling. Open the ceilings of the apartment surrounding the dumbwaiter shaft as soon as you have water to the nozzles. Don't open the ceilings until you have the water; the fire may drive you off the floor and involve the apartment.

Because fires in so many of these structures have caused the loss of the entire top floor, buildings of this type of more recent construction have dividing walls up through the roof which end in a parapet wall. This eliminates the fire spread in the hanging ceiling space from one building to the next. It still requires checking, but as a rule the fire will not pass the wall below the roof.

Fires still enter the one hanging ceiling space and burn through the roof. If no precautionary lines are taken to adjoining roofs, they can become involved from the other fire.

High-rises. The fire-resistant multiple dwelling may go to skyscraper height. Witness the Marina Towers in Chicago. These twin structures reach a height of 520 feet. The more recent Hancock Building in Chicago is 100 stories high, with apartments in the upper half of the building and business offices in the lower half.

Tall apartment buildings usually have frontages ranging from 100 to 200 feet and depths of more than 150 feet. They have enclosed stairways and elevator shafts and are protected by standpipe systems.

Fires in individual apartments are usually confined to the apartments. There are cases, however, of serious fire spread down corridors or by way of exterior windows into floors above.

The principal hazard in such buildings is the storage of such materials as paints, flammable liquids, or lumber in the cellar. Fires in these cellars usually are confined to the point of origin, unless fire enters air-conditioning ducts or pipe shafts. Fires in cellars are handled by moving in hand lines to the seat of the fire. Self-contained breathing equipment will probably be required because there will be few or no windows for ventilation.

Fires in the individual apartments can be hot and serious. In large buildings, it may be advisable to check the layout of the apartment on the floor below before entering the fire apartment. For operational techniques in these buildings, see Chapter 14 on high-rise fires.

For those who have never experienced the difficulty of "making a long hall," let me explain. Often the company makes its way to the fire apartment without difficulty. The good, tight, fire-resistant construction keeps the heat and smoke inside. If the door is hot to the touch, you can be sure the inside will be like an oven. If the apartment is large, there may be a long hall (possibly 50 feet long) to traverse before reaching the room or area on fire. The fire may be off the long

hall. You cannot get a shot at it until you reach the bedroom with the nozzle. Then you have to make a sharp turn to reach in and apply water to the fire. There is no other way to put out such fires. Men will have to endure a great deal of punishment.

It was much easier in the old flimsy tenement house with fire escapes. Lines could be moved up this way after seeing the fire from the fire escape. Ventilation was simple. Just open the windows from the fire escape. But there are no exterior fire escapes on modern fire-resistant dwellings. The men must realize that they will be in for a rough few seconds.

Before opening the door to the fire apartment, pull up your surplus hose, folded so that it will not kink. When you open the door, you can move in fast without having to call for more hose to reach the fire. The faster you move in, the sooner you will extinguish the fire—and the less punishment you will take.

An even more serious situation may occur. This is where the fire has gotten out of the apartment and the heat wave is traveling down the hall corridor, feeding on combustible carpeting, paint, and the wooden faces on apartment doors. Firemen will find they face smoke and heat as soon as they open the fire door of the stair shaft. They will again suffer brutal punishment, but the hose line must be advanced to the fire apartment and moved in to extinguish.

One final factor should be noted in fires involving older multiple-dwelling residential structures: News stories frequently report a serious fire in such a residential structure where there was almost complete burnout on the top floor. The roof may be completely gone; yet there was little or no loss of life. Other fires of less magnitude cause the deaths of many people.

The reason for the difference is nearly always the location of the fire. While the fire on the top floor may be more serious, people who are alerted have to get down only one floor to comparative safety. Once below the fire, they no longer are in danger. The fire will continue to burn and destroy the top floor, but there is ample time to evacuate the premises.

FIGURE 176. *This is a skylight in a cheap hotel. The hotel has open wooden stairs leading to upper floors and guest rooms. In case of fire involving either the stairs or corridors it is vital to open this skylight to pull the combustion products up and out. This is also an excellent place to examine the hanging ceiling space for involvement. Simply break open the side wall just under the skylight.*

On the other hand, if a fire starts on a lower floor or in the cellar, it exposes all floors above (unless the stairs and elevators are enclosed). By the time people are alerted, they may find it impossible to get down the stairs or even the fire escapes. Frequently they are asphyxiated in their beds.

A top-floor fire is simpler for the fire department (if within range of their ladders or if the building is equipped with a standpipe). Firemen move up to the fire, not encountering the heat and smoke, until they enter the fire floor. This is quite the reverse of moving down into a cellar in the face of the rising heat and smoke.

It is true a fire on the top floor can partially fill a building with smoke if the roof or

windows are not opened. The smoke eventually would back down to the floors below. But if the smoke began to build heavily below, it would tend to slow the fire above by depriving it of oxygen.

Hotel fires

Hotels come in every type of construction. But common to most of them, tending to aggravate an already serious fire problem, are these factors:

1. The people employed are not always of the highest calibre. Frequently they cannot read English, and thus are unable to comprehend precautionary signs and instructions.

2. Hotel managers are reluctant to call the

fire department unless it is absolutely necessary. They often attempt extinguishment with the hotel staff. This results in a delayed alarm and an attendant spread of fire.

3. Convention guests frequently are less than alert at bedtime. Excess food and drink have dulled the normal precautionary senses; they may not wake readily in the event of danger.

4. Even well built fire-resistant hotels can and do introduce hazards that cause disastrous fires. It makes little difference whether a structure is built of masonry if the interior is filled with highly combustible materials. For example, this situation is not unusual: Corridor walls or lobbies are lined with thin wood paneling, ceilings are finished with combustible tile fastened in place with flammable mastic. Now add to this open stairways and no sprinklers. One can expect a holocaust in any such hotel, regardless of its structural stability.

5. Guests are transients. They are totally unfamiliar with any exit other than the elevators. In case of fire, there would be a mass rush of panicky guests to use the elevators, tying them up and depriving the fire department of their use. Should a fire involve an interior stairway or smoke render it impossible to use, there probably would be a loss of life.

Now we will discuss each of the three main types of construction and the fire problems associated with them.

Hotels of frame construction. This type of hotel is rapidly disappearing. But they are still found on the outskirts of cities and in resort areas. As a rule, they are not more than three stories high. Remodeling operations over the years preclude any valid generalization as to features. It is common to find wide-open, carpeted, wooden stairs which lead from an ornately furnished lobby to the top floor. Doors to apartments are wood panel with glass transoms. Wood paneling is to be found in the stair shaft and main corridors leading to the guest rooms.

Fire escapes are usually found at the corridor ends, while the main stairs are at the center of the building. There is usually a large attic topped by a sharply pitched roof. Such hotels should be completely sprinklered or the life hazard in the event of fire is severe. Where such hotels are sprinklered, make sure to lay in a line to the fire department siamese connection.

If a fire involves the cellar or lobby, move hand lines in onto the lobby floor immediately to prevent the fire from involving the stairs. Should the stairs become involved while people are still in their rooms or trying to get out, there will probably be a loss of life—unless you can get hose lines up the stairs to cut off the fire. The object here is to prevent the fire from involving the corridors and guest rooms. Get another line in to back up the first line. Send additional lines up the fire escapes or ladders and move in on the threatened floors. It is common to have skylights over the stairs in flat roof construction. But in these buildings don't expect to ventilate through the skylights because of the pitched roof. There is no good way to ventilate the stair shafts. Cutting the roof may not help to ventilate the stair shaft or the corridors because the opening will only ventilate the attic unless it is possible to push down the top-floor ceiling. If this can be done, it will ventilate the stairs and corridors. If there are windows in the stair shaft, break them out quickly. Attics may be ventilated by cutting roofs and opening windows or louvers at the gable ends.

Fires in individual guest rooms are readily handled by 1½-inch lines which must be moved in to the fire area. Should the fire get out into the corridor, it could spread laterally to involve other rooms, cutting off the occupants from escaping either down the stairs or on fire escapes. If this occurs, get another line to back up the first line quickly. Do not forget to check for attic involvement.

Ladder company personnel should get ladders to windows where people are trapped. Even when no people are visible, ladders should be raised. Firemen should move onto floors to examine guest rooms for people overcome. Self-contained breathing masks will probably be needed for search because the floor above the fire in many cases is untenable without them.

FIGURE 177. *This is a narrow corridor in an old hotel. Fire in one guest room could quickly cut off escape for people in other rooms who could not get by the fire. Firemen should move hose lines down the corridor as rapidly as possible to reach the fire area. If there are fire escapes, send a second line up the fire escape. Cover the floor above with a third hose line.*

In this kind of fire, life nets may be necessary. Don't forget to check the rear of the building because there may be people waiting at the windows for rescue.

Nonfire-resistant hotels of ordinary construction. These are the older hotels. They usually range from two to six stories in height. They frequently have open wooden stairways. If there are elevators, they are enclosed in open iron grillwork. Both stairway and elevators open onto a long corridor with guest rooms on each side. The rooms have plain wooden doors and often glass transoms. Interior partitions are of wood lath and plaster. (See Figures 176-178.)

There may be interior light and vent shafts. Fires from guest rooms can extend into these shafts and get into guest rooms on the other side of the shafts or extend to rooms above.

FIGURE 178. *There is no central heating in guest rooms of this second rate hotel. The lobby and corridors are heated, but guest rooms receive their heat through open transoms to each room. (The wire mesh over the transom at left is for security.) Fire in any room of this hotel would seriously jeopardize the people in other rooms because of these transoms. Firemen must move in with hose lines and search for victims.*

These older hotels are replete with hazards ranging from storage rooms on each floor with mattress, sheets, and insecticide, to the upholstered furniture in the lobby (which opens directly to the stairs above). There may be a restaurant in the lobby with the exhaust ducts running through the upper floors enclosed in nonfire-resistant partitions.

Cellar fires in these old hotels are hot and smoky. The cellars contain a great deal of combustible storage, such as old lumber, furniture, screens, awnings, mattresses, chairs, paints, and insecticides. These fires are handled much like cellar fires in old nonfire-resistant tenements, except that there is an even greater urgency because of the potential loss of life. Make every effort to hold the fire in the cellar—at least until the guests have been evacuated. Get lines into the lobby and try to get down the inside stairway to the cellar. Check to see if there is a rear stair and if so get lines down there too. If there is an outside street entrance to the cellar, try this route should the other lines be unable to penetrate the cellar.

Make sure a manned hose line is left in the lobby to keep any fire from coming up the inside stairs to involve the lobby and upper stairs. Get ready for cellar nozzles, but don't cut until the people are out. The smoke will render the lobby stairs untenable. Make sure the fire is not moving up by way of shafts, partitions, or ducts. If you suspect this, move hand lines to the upper-floors. Avoid stairs being used by guests. Get the line to the upper floors by ladders, elevating platforms, or fire escapes.

If the fire originates in the lobby, whether in the restaurant portion or in upholstered furniture, one or two lines should control the situation. The danger of a fire in this area is the possibility of extension via the open stairway and elevator shafts to the upper floors. Even where the fire itself does not spread, the heat and smoke will penetrate the floors above, endangering the people on them. Men should be sent to ventilate the building and search for people overcome. If needed, move hand lines to the upper floors.

Fires may originate in upholstered furniture stored on individual floor lobbies (usually directly outside the elevators). This was the cause of the Conrad Hilton Hotel fire in Chicago in the winter of 1970. A fire here immediately exposes all the corridors and, indirectly, the guest rooms by way of open transoms and poorly fitting plain wooden doors. Such a fire is handled in the same manner as a fire extending from a guest room into the corridor. Fires in individual guest rooms (usually caused by a combination of tobacco and alcohol) are readily controlled by one hose line. Examination should always be made of the floor above and rooms on each side, if it is a sizable fire.

Fires get out of guest rooms into corridors because the guest awakens and, seeing the fire, runs out into the hall for safety. He seldom stops to close the door to his room. Also a fire in the room may burn its way through the door into the hall. If this occurs,

get help in early—you probably will need it. Move two hand lines into the corridor. If there is a standpipe, use it. But remember, do not take the elevator to the fire floor. You may step out into a raging inferno.

Sweep the corridor with the stream to hold the fire back. Keep moving until you reach the seat of the fire and extinguish it. The second line follows the first, putting out the fire passed up by line number one, and covers the other guest rooms. Move a third line to the floor above to check on upward extension. Move additional lines up fire escapes and rear stairs to cover the fire floor and floor above. As firemen move into position, they ventilate by opening windows off the fire escape or guest rooms.

These fires will be extremely difficult. Men moving into long corridors, working their way toward the fire area, must be prepared to take punishment. They will be met by a pall of heat and smoke as soon as they enter the fire floor and open the door to the hall. If they fail to move in, the people trapped on the floor may die.

Check on the possibility of fire extending by way of shafts. Direct a stream up into the shaft to kill any rising fire in these vertical arteries. Where fire is extending into other rooms because of windows facing on a common shaft, get lines into these exposed points to prevent the extension and also drive streams toward the fire.

If people are trapped in guest rooms and in danger, try to get them out by stairways, ladders, aerial platforms, or by rope from above. It may be possible to get them to the roof and over to an adjoining roof of equal height. Where there is no adjoining roof, give thought to bridging the roof with portable ladders and getting them out this way. The same method may be employed by bridging ladders across narrow shafts. Remember that the people in most trouble may be those with rooms at the rear facing inner courts. Engine men should carry forcible entry tools to be able to force doors to rooms while they are advancing lines along corridors.

In fire operations at these hotels, if there is any question of the fire being promptly contained, evacuate the hotel.

Where evacuation is decided upon, use the interior alarm in the hotel and have the switchboard operator phone all guest rooms. Put extra people to work at this task if they are available. Make use of hailers and public address systems on apparatus.

In hose line operations, wherever the hotel has a standpipe use it. By using this appliance, line placement will be simpler and operations measurably speeded.

Fire-resistant hotels. These hotels range up to skyscraper height with large frontages of up to 250 feet. They are constructed of reinforced concrete or protected steel frame. All vertical arteries are enclosed with fire-safe materials and standpipe systems are provided.

These are hazards which contribute to fires and their spread:

1. Central air-conditioning and the problems associated with the ducts.

2. Repair areas which store large quantities of lumber, paint, and furniture. These areas generally are in the basement and provide ample fuel for a serious fire.

3. Storage rooms on each floor with daily supplies of linen, mattresses, chairs, and insecticides.

4. Public-assembly areas such as ballrooms, dining rooms, and meeting rooms.

The problem of transient guests is the same in any hotel. They are unfamiliar with the hotel layout and its exits.

Cellar fires rarely affect the guests, although there may be some superficial smoke extension via the ventilating ducts.

Fires in individual guest rooms as a rule are not serious. They may present a problem if there is delayed discovery or if the employees try to extinguish it themselves, then run away, leaving the doors open to the corridor. Fire then may spread to the corridors, cutting off access to the stairways from some rooms. Though perfectly safe in their rooms, guests often become panicky. Try to shout instructions to calm them.

Fires in these hotels are nearly always confined to the area of origin. Spread may occur if fire enters the elevator shaft and feeds upon grease on the rails and cables or wood in the elevator car. In such cases, smoke can rise to great heights and seep out of the shaft doors. The elevator machinery room at the top of the shaft may become involved and damaged; the elevator system may become inoperative.

Direct a stream up into the shaft to extinguish this fire. Vent the corridors and examine guest rooms if smoke involvement is heavy.

A more likely source of heat, smoke, and fire extension to upper floors would be by way of pipe chases. This was one of the serious contributing causes in the Jacksonville, Fla., hotel fire on December 29, 1963, in which 22 people died.

As with fires in the older nonfire-resistant hotels and in high-rise structures, when fire gets into the corridor, it may move down the corridor and into rooms where doors were left open by fleeing guests. The fire will move by feeding on wall finishes, carpeting, or wood trim. The entire length of a hallway soon becomes a terribly smoky oven. Because of inability to properly ventilate by way of the stair shafts, conditions in this hotel may be worse than in the nonfire-resistant type.

Since there may be no way to know just where on the floor the fire is, lines are sent up each stairway (connecting to the standpipes on the floor below). They then advance toward the fire area. Men will undergo terrible punishment in such situations because they are moving in toward the heat and smoke. No water should be used until the fire is met. Every effort should be made to avoid lines operating against each other.

Smoke may penetrate floors above by way of ducts, pipe recesses, or elevator shafts, but generally such penetration will be minor. Fire will not extend except by exterior windows or pipe chases, as explained in the chapter on high-rise fires.

If guests remain in their rooms and use damp towels and bedclothes to seal off the cracks in the door, open the windows, and keep their heads outside for air, they will be perfectly safe.

Operating procedures for all hotel fires

There are some general operating procedures which apply to hotels of all types. They should follow this pattern:

1. Do not alert the occupants if you are sure the fire is a simple one and can be handled easily. This is so you won't have a horde of panicky guests stampeding down, restricting operations, falling, and injuring themselves.

2. Do alert the occupants if the fire is serious or promises to become serious. This can be done by using the interior fire alarm system (with which the guests probably will not be familiar), using the telephones from the hotel switchboard to the individual rooms, or using the bells and sirens of the apparatus to awaken the people. Use hailers or public-address systems, too, and shout instructions to the awakened guests.

3. Make use of the knowledge and help of the hotel staff.

Engine companies. The general guidelines for engine company operations at hotel fires are these:

1. Start to supply the sprinkler system (if available) by the fire department siamese connection. Immediately move hand lines to the fire area through the inside stairs. If the building has standpipes, use them. If the inside stairway route is not usable, use fire escapes, ladders, or the elevating platforms.

2. Use hose lines to keep the fire from getting in and running up shafts. If fire has entered such shafts, direct hose streams into them. Aim the stream upward. Try to ventilate the shaft at the roof.

3. Move 1½-inch hand lines along hallways and corridors to prevent fire from involving other guest rooms.

4. Unless the volume of fire rules out its use, 1½-inch hose is ideal for speed and mobility in such fires. This is particularly true if you are short of manpower.

Ladder companies. There are three general guidelines for ladder companies to follow at hotel fires:

1. Use portable ladders, aerial ladders, or elevating platforms to reach trapped occupants and to move in hose lines.

2. Force entrance for engine company crews, ventilate, search, and remove those overcome.

3. Use standpipe fire hose as needed.

For specific firefighting techniques in hotels, see other sections of this book as follows: Cellar fires, see the section in this chapter on fire-resistant multiple dwellings; Guest rooms, see section in this chapter on fire-resistant and nonfire-resistant hotels and the chapter on high-rise fires; Pipe chases, see the chapter on concealed fires.

Motel fires

This section will discuss the typical one- or two-story motel with individual guest rooms branching out horizontally. While many modern multistory buildings are called motels, they really are hotels and should be handled as such under fire conditions.

There have been large property losses and some deaths in motel fires. The cause is usually a delayed alarm or lack of water supply.

Most motels are built with common hanging ceiling spaces ranging undivided over wide areas. There is a preponderence of combustible wall finishes, and sprinklers are rare. Major losses usually result when fire from individual guest rooms or the kitchen gets into the hanging ceiling space and spreads laterally to involve the entire roof space. This causes the ceilings to drop and expose the rooms below to the fire. (See Figure 179.)

In this type of fire situation, bring lines to the rooms on each side of the fire, pull the ceilings to expose the fire and extinguish it. Usually guest room fires can be readily extinguished by one 1½-inch line and ventilation. Don't forget to examine for involvement of the hanging ceiling space.

Sometimes motels are heated and cooled by individual units in the rooms. In such cases, there is no problem of spread by way of duct systems. But usually motels are served by an extensive forced-air duct network which can spread the sparks, heat, and smoke throughout areas interconnected by ducts. All such areas will have to be thoroughly checked for involvement.

FIGURE 179. *If this building were built in one straight section, rather than a U shape, it would be nearly 200 feet long. There are no fire stops in the entire attic — even between the main section and the extension wings. Fire from any guest room getting into the attic could rapidly fan out* *through the entire roof space. Eventually the fire would drop through ceilings to involve other guest rooms. In such a building, send lines to each side of the suspected areas and pull the ceilings to expose hidden fire travel.*

Rooming houses

Whether they are called rooming houses, furnished rooms, or boardinghouses, these single-room occupancies present a severe loss of life potential. Originally the buildings were large private dwellings in good neighborhoods. With economic changes and shifts in population, these areas became vast slums. The once-private homes are partitioned off into many small single rooms and rented to either individuals or small families. Where

originally there was one family of perhaps five people in the building, there now might be up to 40 people occupying the same space.

The buildings are old, poorly maintained, and range up to three or four stories in height. There may be a cellar below the basement. The main entrance is by way of a front stoop anywhere from three to six feet high. There is usually a basement entrance under the front stairs.

Inside there is an open wooden stairway from the main floor to the top floor, and a stairway to the basement and a narrow sub-standard stairway from the basement to the cellar. Sometimes there is a skylight over the main interior stairs.

Access to the individual rooms is from the corridor by way of a thin paneled wooden door with a glass transom. In the very cheap rooming house, there may be no heat in the individual rooms. They rely on the heat from the halls to warm the rooms through the open transoms. Any fire in the hall immediately fills the other rooms with smoke and heat by way of these open transoms. There may be no means of egress, or at best an improper secondary exit. Often this secondary means of egress is through another guest room which may be locked. This is not at all unusual and such conditions may be found even in large cities.

It is common to find unprotected vertical openings such as dumbwaiter shafts, air shafts, light shafts, or unused hot-air heating ducts running behind the closets.

Cellar fires are difficult to fight. The narrow inside stairway provides the only way down. There are no windows for ventilation. The old coal chute, which may provide one method of ventilation, is usually found on the sidewalk directly in front of the building.

Open all windows on floors above; open the roof over the stairs. Move a hose line down into the cellar by way of the inside stairs. Have a second line cover the basement floor. If the fire appears to be of serious proportions, place a third line in on the main floor to protect the inside stairs and prevent fire from involving the upper floors. Get cellar nozzles ready, but don't cut the floor yet.

Give the men operating the hose lines a chance to try to make the cellar. Premature operation of cellar nozzles may drive the men back out before they have had a reasonable chance of success. While these fires often turn out to be mask jobs, it is true (as it is in many fires) that if the first hose line pushes in very rapidly it may extinguish the fire quickly. If the firemen stop to put on self-contained breathing equipment, the time required may allow the heat and smoke to build

to the point where it will be impossible to operate on the floor above the fire—even with breathing apparatus.

The more practical method is to proceed as explained above, but have additional incoming units don their masks. They will be ready to take over the line operation from the first team if they are in difficulty. There will be a rapid advance of the line by the first crew without taking time to don masks, but incoming units with masks will be available if needed.

Where such buildings are built in rows, there may be parapeted division walls. If this is so, there will be less likelihood of fire getting into the hanging ceiling space and involving similar structures alongside. However, don't rely completely on this. Sometimes repairs, settling, or the deterioration of mortar joints may provide an opening for fire to pass through. The prudent officer will check for such possible spread. If there is any indication that fire may involve the roof, place protective hose lines on the roofs of the buildings on each side. If you don't do this, fire burning through may involve the adjoining roof surfaces.

People on upper floors and in the rear may be in desperate trouble. It is imperative to advance hose lines rapidly to these areas and not only attempt to extinguish the fire but search for and remove those overcome.

Be careful of interior light and air shafts. These may allow fire to pass from one floor to the next or to an adjacent building where people not yet involved may be seriously endangered later. If such a possibility exists, evacuate buildings on each side.

Cellar fires in these structures are handled in the same manner as those in old nonfire-resistant multiple dwellings (discussed in this chapter). Fire operations on upper floors parallel those on upper floors of the old non-fire-resistant hotels discussed in this chapter. But make sure to check on fire extension to adjoining buildings by way of defective party walls, ceiling joists in the cellar, and hanging ceiling spaces.

Chapter 24

Supermarkets—shopping centers

MOST SUPERMARKET fires start for the same reason fires start in other buildings: faulty heating equipment, electrical defects, or careless smoking. But because of construction defects a small fire easily grows to become a major-loss fire. Such defects as the lack of sprinklers and automatic fire-detection devices contribute to this. Other factors are the huge undivided shopping areas, large open hanging ceiling spaces, and an enormous amount of combustible stock. More than 75 percent of these fires start in the service area.

To give a more thorough understanding of the problem, let us examine the origin and development of the supermarket. Supermarkets are the result of a natural growth of the larger type grocery or delicatessen of the past. When one of these stores was erected in a neighborhood, other establishments were forced to compete or go out of business.

Store owners began to take advantage of the "captive customers." Shoppers were in the store to purchase groceries, then why not include other items the shopper needs or wants? This soon became profitable. Such additional stocks were offered for sale as pots and pans, books, hardware, clothing, and drugs.

As the stores continued to grow in size and scope, there was a need for expansion. In the congested urban areas there was not always space for expansion. In addition, land and buildings costs were high. Help was not available at low cost because of heavy unionization. Code restrictions placed severe limitations on building construction. But more important than all this was the automobile. New stores needed parking areas. With the supermarket, people could drive to do their shopping. Here they were assured of sufficient choice and variety of goods.

The tremendous migration to the suburbs and the large mushrooming growth of these areas showed a ready market for the store operators. The supermarket was the answer to the problems of both the shopper and the store owner.

But while the supermarket answered most of the needs of the consumer and the businessman, it created a headache for the average small fire departments in the areas selected for these shopping centers. They lacked the experience and expertise to handle this kind of situation. Other problems became apparent:

1. These small fire departments were unfamiliar with the salient construction features which cause these shopping centers to burn down.

2. The inspection process, from the blueprint stage to occupancy, was less than adequate.

3. The small department lacked the man-

power and equipment for large fires. Mutual aid might have to come from a great distance with resultant long delays. Even when distance was not a factor, many mutual aid operations possess a common number of ills which add up to poorly co-ordinated firefighting operations.

4. The combination of a lack of street fire-alarm boxes and little vehicular or pedestrian traffic late at night almost insures delayed fire alarms. If a fire does start, it may achieve considerable headway before it is discovered. Even then, the passing motorist would have difficulty in notifying the fire department.

5. The lack of effective crowd control allows motorists to park anywhere to watch the fire, frequently blocking the fire apparatus approach.

Construction features

Large open space. The modern supermarket is a one-story (without cellar) structure ranging in area from 10,000 square feet on up. Because of the large unbroken floor area and combustible stock, there is ample fuel and oxygen to feed a fire. Once started, there is nothing to block the progress of the flames. Fires in such large open areas gain great headway, rapidly creating large drafts. These in turn help fan the fire to even greater proportions. The entire area is subjected to the effects of heat, smoke, and gases. Firemen trying to move in from the front may have to travel over 150 feet to reach the seat of the fire. In most cases they are driven back by a tremendous pall of heat and smoke. They then resort to the use of exterior streams which in all too many cases are not very effective because they do not reach the seat of the fire.

The average hand line shifted to an outside position is nearly always too small for effective penetration in fires of such proportions. Exterior streams should be of large calibre. Large-capacity nozzles should be well supplied by an ample number of large hose lines to cut down on friction losses which rob the nozzles of effective pressures. This does not preclude the use of large capacity fog guns, provided they can deliver the water to

the point of operations—namely, the heart of the fire and not just the smoke.

Generally speaking, once tactics have shifted from an interior attack to an outside operation, the fight to save the store is lost.

Height of store. Single-story structures are an advantage to the fire department because it is easy to get to the roof. Such ready access is important in order to examine, ventilate, or use cellar nozzles through holes cut in the roof. Be extremely careful of low-hanging electric wires—usually in the rear. In the dark, men could be electrocuted by ladders contacting charged wires. (See Figure 180.)

Exterior walls. The front is all show window and the main exits are usually at one side. Such construction requires the use of long steel girders supported by Lally columns. To hide the steel structural members from view, the builder "boxes" in with light wood. Framing these support members leaves large hollow spaces where fire can enter and travel beyond ready sight. (See Figure 181.) While these steel beams are covered from sight, they must be considered as unprotected from the viewpoint of resisting the effects of fire. Frequently one sees an ornamental wall built above and resting on the steel girder at the front. If the steel girder gives way, it may cause this ornamental wall (which is not tied in, but simply rests in place) to come down on the men below. There are no windows in side walls or rear walls.

Construction materials. Materials commonly found are brick veneer over cinder block, plain cinder block, or occasionally solid brick. If the store is part of a group of other stores, the side walls are of cinder block which serves as a common party division wall.

Usually the only openings, other than at the front, will be one or two service doors at the rear which are usually heavily barred when the store is closed. These service doors double as a secondary means of egress from the interior of the store when it is open to the buying public. In addition to the rear service doors, you may find small windows.

FIGURE 180. *This is a common sight at the rear of a supermarket. While the transformers and wires are clearly visible in the daylight, under heavy smoke conditions at night the wires may not be seen.*

They will be for toilets. Such windows are usually heavily barred from the inside. You may also notice large louvered openings, some of which run as large as eight to 10 feet square. Don't leap at this as a ready way to force access or to ventilate the store when it is closed. Such louvers are probably for the refrigeration machinery room and there will be large fans just behind the louvers. This refrigeration machinery room

will have a substantial door heavily barred on the store side. The lack of a ready means to ventilate these buildings is a serious problem because when you cannot ventilate to rid the building of heat, smoke, and gases, you do not, as a rule, advance hose lines readily. (See Figures 182-183.)

Roof features. This type of occupancy calls for a large undivided floor area which auto-

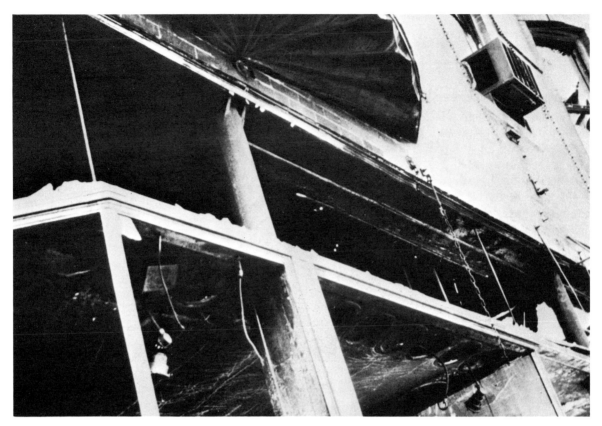

FIGURE 181. *This open space is typical of those found over the front show window of many* *stores. Fire can get in here and attack the unprotected steel girder.*

matically dictates truss construction to avoid columns or supporting partitions. However, if the span is excessive, even the truss construction will require supporting girders and columns. The truss may be built of wood or steel; both are commonly used. Because of the size of the roof span, the truss is often more than six feet high at its center point. This is the reason for the high hanging ceiling space prevalent in this kind of construction.

Where wood is used for the truss, the construction members must be of far greater size than a steel member to carry the same weight. But while steel is less bulky and stronger in weight-carrying capacity, it resists fire less than heavy wooden members. Unprotected steel in a fire will gain strength up to about 400° F. Beyond that temperature it weakens rapidly. Once temperatures reach about 1,100° F., collapse must be expected.

Another factor must be considered with unprotected steel structural members. This is expansion, which can be enough to push walls out to the point of collapse. The walls may also be pushed out far enough so that, as the steel cools and shrinks back to its normal length, there is no longer sufficient bearing on the side walls to support the roof. Collapse occurs. When steel, highly heated by the fire, is hit by cold hose streams, an uneven cooling takes place. This can cause twisting and bowing, which may precipitate roof collapse. If supporting metal columns are unprotected, they may fail, too.

Whether trusses are of wood or steel, they are only as strong as their individual members. If several of these burn through or fail, the entire truss may fail.

Steel bar-joist construction is in common use today for roof supports. Gypsum concrete is generally used for the roof covering. The

FIGURE 182. *A typical solid masonry wall with no windows. There is no easy way to ventilate the store through this wall.*

construction method is to lay solid insulating boards across the bar joists. Thin-gauge wire mesh is laid over these boards, on top of which is poured about three inches of gypsum. The gypsum is then waterproofed by the usual felt and tar covering.

On the inside, the bar joist supports metal hangers which in turn hold the finished ceiling squares. Older stores use wooden furring strips which are nailed to the underside of the bar joist. These furring strips were then used as nailing supports for metal ceilings or combustible fibre ceiling squares commonly called Celotex.

It is true that the metal ceiling itself is not combustible. But it will conduct heat very rapidly and allow the nails to burn loose from the wooden furring strip. Then the ceiling will drop. The sharp metal edges can cut severely. The combustible fibre ceiling squares also will burn and drop to expose the hanging ceiling to the fire below. Neither ceiling is desirable.

Ceilings can be installed with adequate fire-resistant ratings at no added labor cost, though the materials may be more expensive. Installation methods are about the same for both types of ceilings. But this is not the whole solution. Supermarkets with rated ceiling assemblies are still being destroyed by fire. Once the fire gets into the hanging ceiling space, the heat quickly buckles the light steel framing and supporting wires. If this happens, the ceiling tiles drop and the bare steel joists quickly fail. (See Figures 184-187.)

There is danger to unwary firemen in the gypsum roof. The gypsum roof covering is light, strong, and will not burn. It can be cut or chopped open readily for either ventilation or the use of cellar nozzles. The very nature of its superior fire-resistance and insulating characteristics may present a grave hazard to men sent to work on the roof during a fire.

FIGURE 183. *The rear wall of a supermarket usually has several service doors which are heavily barred except when being used for delivery. This photo illustrates how delivery trucks can block fire department access to the rear. Be careful of placing fire apparatus in these narrow alleys at the rear. Walls may collapse onto apparatus before they can be removed. There are several ways to open such buildings: (1) breech walls, (2) cut doors with torches or power saws, or (3) cut a small hole in the center of a door, drop T-iron attached to heavy steel chain through the hole and attach other end of the chain to apparatus. Pull frame and door out. But remember, these operations should not delay the advancement of hose lines through the front of the store. Windows at the front of the store should be opened for ventilation.*

Well-trained men know what to look for on conventional wood-sheathed roofs: (1) melting or bubbling tar, (2) dry spots on a wet roof, (3) snow melting in one area, and (4) hot spots. One or more of these signs would indicate to firemen where the fire was in the hanging ceiling space. But these signs would not be evident in a well-constructed gypsum roof. With the wood-sheathed roof, fire often vents itself by burning through. Fire will not do this with the gypsum roof. If the heat cannot readily dissipate, then it is obviously building up in the hanging ceiling space and may be seriously weakening the roof supporting members. This condition may be sufficiently severe to cause sudden collapse before men on the roof can sense trouble. The same lack of burning through

FIGURE 184. *In this building fire entered the hanging ceiling space from a fire below. The ceiling squares have been removed to examine the hanging ceiling spaces. Note the light framing which holds the ceiling squares in place. Once fire gets into this space it quickly warps the light metal framing. The ceiling squares drop and the store and roof space are exposed to the fire.*

and venting will delay the discovery of fire at night by passing motorists. The result is extensive fire spread because of delayed alarm.

Some shopping centers have done away with the conventional roof construction and employ the huge laminated arch, which does not rest on the side walls, but rather on a concrete bulkhead at the sides of the store near ground level. The arch is ornamental in appearance and is used as part of the open-finished ceiling. Since this type of construction is usually sprinklered and there is no concealed hanging ceiling space with unprotected metal members, one may expect superior fire-resistance and less chance of collapse at fires.

Where stores are built in rows, the divid-ing walls are commonly cinder blocks of substantial construction. This makes a solid fire stop, preventing passage of fire from one store to another. But there are two features which may lessen this advantage:

1. Communicating openings between stores. Such openings should be protected by automatic fire doors but often they are not.

2. The hanging ceiling space. This is why it is so important to open the roof early. It will allow the fire to vent upward and prevent later involvement. The bar joists of adjoining stores rest on the common party wall. If the builder carried this wall up and through the roof, ending in a parapet about two feet above the roof covering, one can be reasonably sure no fire will pass through. But even with such construction, if the area where the

FIGURE 185 (Above). *In this building, fire got into the roof space causing ceiling tiles to drop. There is complete destruction. For evidence that fire traveled in the hanging ceiling space, note the lack of burn marks on the counter at bottom of picture.*

FIGURE 186 (Right). *This photo reveals other evidence that fire traveled in the hanging ceiling space. The light stainless steel railing at right in photo is not even marked. If fire had traveled below it would have shown on this railing and counters.*

FIGURE 187. *In this photo you are looking down into a burned out hanging ceiling space. Note* *how the top of the ceiling joists are burned, indicating that fire traveled in this space.*

joists rest on the wall is not well sealed with masonry, or openings are later made or allowed for heating pipes or ducts, the fire stop is negated. In serious fires with twisting and shifting of steel roof supports, there may be enough movement to crack or dislodge the blocks around the metal members. If this occurs, an opening may be provided through which fire will pass from one ceiling space to another. (See Figures 188-190.)

It is important in such fires to bring hose lines to protect the roofs on each side of the fire should fire burn through the roof or should collapse occur. Such fires can involve adjoining combustible roof coverings even with parapet walls in place. Another precaution must be taken below in the stores on each side of the fire. If you suspect that fire may have entered the ceilings, make small openings in the ceiling alongside the wall dividing the two stores. A small opening later

found not to have been necessary is a small price to pay compared to taking a chance and losing a whole row of stores.

Neighborhoods at times dictate architectural style. The author is familiar with one area where truss roofs were frowned upon for their lack of esthetic balance. Therefore, this roof was altered in appearance by the addition of a false gable at the front and sides of the supermarket and the adjoining row of stores. This created a hollow space at the front of the stores that was common to the entire row of stores. There was a parapet wall between the supermarket and the other stores. But the catch was that where the party wall met the false front gable, it did not seal off the space completely. (See Figure 191.)

Store layout—design. The interior of these stores pretty well follows a standard pat-

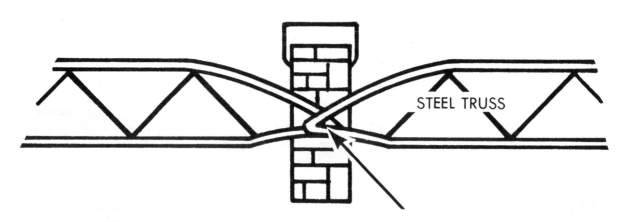

FIGURE 188. *This is typical steel truss construction with bar joists resting on a common party* wall. *The arrow shows the point where fire may pass through from one store to the other.*

FIGURE 189. *Part of a wooden bow-string truss was anchored in this dividing party wall, cre-* ating *a space where the fire could easily pass from one store to the store alongside.*

FIGURE 190. *Here, a girder rests on a common dividing wall. Note the large opening which allowed fire to pass into the other store. This open-* *ing may not have been this large originally. Shifting girders probably dislodged more bricks than were left out during the building's construction.*

tern: A large undivided floor area separated from the utility and storage areas by a partition which often is not solid all the way to the ceiling. Fire in the utility or storage areas easily exposes the main body of the store to heat and smoke. If supermarkets had standard fire walls or partitions between the service and sales area, that would in most cases prevent the spread of fire into the sales areas. This would minimize the danger to the shoppers and reduce possible damage to merchandise.

Partitions which are not all the way to the ceiling form an obstruction to hose line penetration, particularly in smoky conditions. As the firemen begin to move in from the front, they see a dull glow in the rear of the store and open up the line. The water hits the partition and never reaches the fire. This is a case where fog lines may cause excessive

water damage and eventually drive the firemen out of the store because the fog lines do not have sufficient reach to do the job.

The experienced nozzleman will switch to a straight stream, direct the line toward the ceiling, and sweep the stream from side to side. In so doing he may get the water over the partition and deflect the water off the ceiling onto the fire. This way, he may put the fire out in a very short time and with little water damage. Contrast this with the blind operation of a fog stream which lacks reach.

This may sound like heresy, but there are times when the straight stream does a better job. To illustrate this point, assume a mattress fire in a bedroom at the end of a long hall. All the fog in the world won't put it out. Advance the line until you reach the bedroom doorway. Use a short burst with a straight

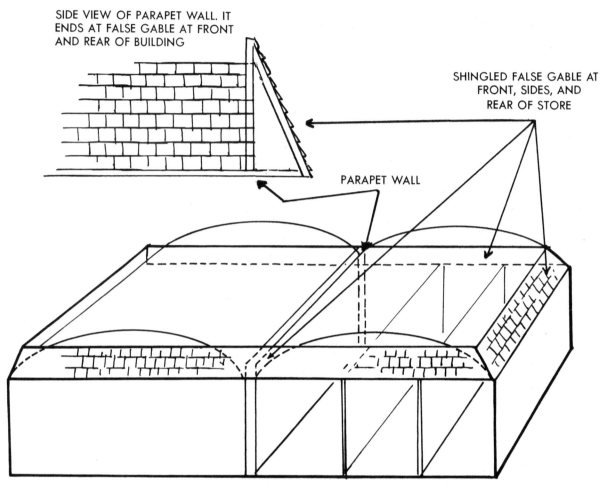

SIDE VIEW OF PARAPET WALL. IT ENDS AT FALSE GABLE AT FRONT AND REAR OF BUILDING

SHINGLED FALSE GABLE AT FRONT, SIDES, AND REAR OF STORE

PARAPET WALL

FIGURE 191. *Even though the parapet wall separates the main sections of this row of stores at the roof, the false gable at the front may not be fire-stopped. The parapet wall may end at the false gable as shown in the side view above. Fire can easily travel through these open spaces.*

stream and the fire is out. If the operation is properly done, there won't be enough water on the floor to mop up.

The older supermarkets

The older supermarkets, those predating the modern shopping center type of construction, are much smaller in area and do not present as serious a fire problem as the new stores, but they present other difficulties. These buildings usually have cellars or dwelling occupancies above the store. Some have both cellars and apartments. Often there are multiple-dwelling occupancies on either side of the store.

Cellar fires are common to these stores, and one may spread to the floor above by running partitions, side walls, burning through wood flooring, by way of old floor heating registers, and by open interior stairs. If there are two inside stairways to the cellar, the chances are that one of them will be permanently blocked by a conveyor mechanism used to bring goods up from the cellar. When there is no conveyor, wide planks are sometimes used to form a slide to carry goods up and down. Under smoky conditions with poor visibility, this is a danger that firemen must be prepared to encounter.

If there are dwellings above the store, remove the people early in the fight. Fire can extend readily and rapidly to such dwelling occupancies by running the side walls. Usually, entrance to the upstairs is by way of a hall and stairs just at the side of the store. If fire enters this partition wall, it may cut off the stairs. Often there will be a secondary egress at the rear of the dwelling units which leads to a wooden open stairway across the roof of the supermarket. Should fire go through the roof of the store, it will cut off the means of egress.

In such fires, hose lines should be laid to the floor above the store. A line should be laid to protect the rear stairs. Check the partition between the store and hall to be sure no fire is traveling up by this means.

If the store is part of a group of stores with common party walls, a cellar fire can extend to cellars on each side by openings in these walls. Often the floor joists run across the party walls into the adjoining cellar, forming a horizontal flue for fire to travel through.

In such cellar fires it is important to have the adjoining cellars checked by opening the ceiling (if covered) and placing protective hose lines in the exposed cellars.

In the very old stores you will find a main center wooden girder supported by wooden columns (sometimes old tree trunks). Check this feature as soon as you can. Such columns are often out of plumb and so rotten at the floor level that they provide practically no support for the girder. Such buildings can collapse.

Firefighting operations in old stores. Generally, fire operations in these older stores are quite standard.

In cellar fires bring in two lines—one to cover each stairway. Get one line down to the cellar to extinguish visible fire. If the cellar stairway is too hot to move down, keep the lines covering the stairs and lay a third line to a cellar nozzle over the hot spot. Don't forget to check and cover the upstairs should the fire run partitions.

For fires inside the store, lay two 2½-inch lines—one to back up the other. Lay a line to cover the upstairs and another to cover the rear exit.

Ventilate the store and cellar, as well as the upstairs.

Except for its size, the inside of the older stores resembles that of the new supermarkets. They have been remodeled to present a modern appearance.

Exit facilities

A characteristic to be found in both the older stores and the new supermarkets is poor exit facilities. Usually there are two doors at one end of the store, one opening inward and the other opening outward. The "out" door is powered to open automatically as the person passes through. In some stores both doors are powered to open automatically. The shopper entering the store often must go through a one-way turnstile device which does not allow him to return as he came in.

The powered doors are operated by air pressure generated by a compressor which is driven by an electric motor. If the power fails, as it might in a fire, the door can still be pushed open because there will still be some air pressure in the compression tank and lines. But after about five openings the air will be used up. Then it requires considerable effort to push the door open. A child could not open the door under these circumstances and the chances are a woman would also find it difficult. Imagine this possibility: A woman tries to open the "out" door. When she encounters difficulty, she may think the door is inoperative and seek another way out. She finds she cannot open the other door, either. Remember, the other door opens in, and there is usually no grasp handle on the inside. Now she may panic and push against the door that opens in. Other people see her trying to get out and try to get out this way, too. They pile up in a heap against the door and prevent its being opened from the outside by rescuers.

But the doors aren't the only problem. Shoppers will encounter difficulties in making a safe exit even before they reach the exit. Panicky shoppers can be funneled out only through the checkout counters. This will slow them considerably even if they don't trip over a long line of shopping carts usually stored between the checkout counters and the front show windows.

What about the rear emergency exits? This is the next recourse for shoppers who cannot exit through the front. Taking the rear exit means going through the service or utility areas. Have you ever examined one of these service areas? It is always blocked by stock, carts, or rubbish. Even if the people should find their way to the doors, they may find them locked.

Considering these poor exit facilities and a serious fire in the store which may flash over paper displays, hanging signs, or combustible stock, the potential for a large loss of life is obvious. (See Figure 192.)

Supermarket firefighting operations

Firefighting tactics and operations at a supermarket fire depend on several variables. Important factors to consider are whether it is daylight or nighttime and whether the store is open for business.

Daylight hours. The chief in charge will encounter these major problems during daytime hours:

1. A peak load of shoppers on busy days. Parking lots will be filled with cars that block hydrants and access to the store, impeding apparatus movement.

2. Life hazard to shoppers will be severe with possible panic conditions.

3. There will be difficulty in getting hose lines into the store. The only route available will be occupied by people leaving the store. Should fire occur at the rear of the store, it will propel the shoppers toward the front exits. These exits will have to be kept open and clear to allow the people to escape safely. It would be a serious tactical error to lay lines through the same exits being used by people escaping. In fact, you may not have enough time to get them all out anyway. In such cases direct streams toward the ceiling, over the heads of the people. The ceiling can deflect the stream to form a water curtain between the people and the fire.

4. Any line operation from the rear to attack the fire in the service area and protect the people should be directed so as not to drive the smoke and heat toward the occupants. This may be done by directing the stream at the ceiling over the general fire area.

5. A very real danger is the potential spread of fire to adjoining stores via doors, pipe conduits, ducts, common dividing walls, or the hanging ceiling. Heat conduction through walls may ignite combustible stock on the exposed side.

6. Be alert for the danger of fire spread to concealed spaces, side walls, ducts, and hanging ceilings.

7. Watch for the buckling of unprotected metal structural members and collapse.

Because of the great number of occupants, it will be wise to call immediately for extra companies, medical aid, and ambulances. Also set up an emergency depot for treatment of the injured and get additional supplies of blankets, etc.

Night. The following are the major problems the chief in charge will encounter during the night if the store is open for business:

1. Operations will be much the same as for daytime fires, with the exception of possible loss of electric power. If the store is plunged into darkness, loss of life must be expected. Every effort must be made to move in with lines and hand lights to help evacuate people.

2. If you set up powerful lighting devices from the trucks, avoid directing the lights so they blind people and firemen trying to get out. Aim the lights high enough to prevent this from happening.

Engine company operations. Your engine company operations also will depend on the time of day. In general, follow these rules:

Daytime operations for engine companies:

1. Don't bring a hose line into an entrance being used by evacuating shoppers.

2. Break out show windows cleanly and advance into the store this way.

3. Direct streams over the heads of people so as to place a protective curtain of water between the fire and threatened shoppers.

4. Don't advance line if it may become an

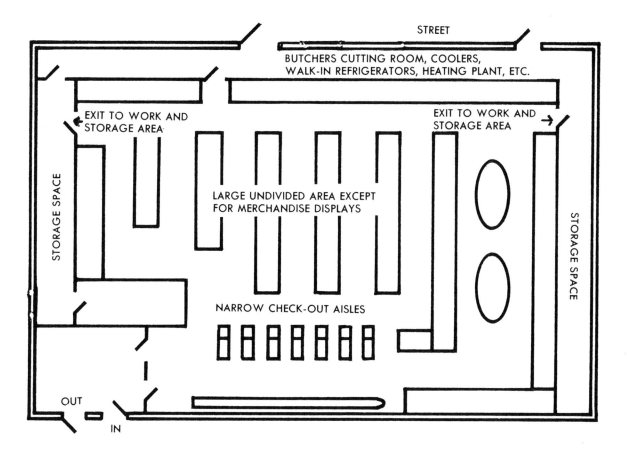

FIGURE 192. *This is the interior layout of a typical supermarket. Note the numerous features that hamper rapid exit of customers and deter firefighting operations: narrow check-out aisles, small doorways to enter and exit often with a turnstyle inside, and the large undivided interior.*

impediment to panicky shoppers or cause them to trip and fall.

5. When the store is clear of shoppers, advance the line toward the fire.

6. Place hose lines to cover threatened exposures. Because of the threat to life, line placement should cover the endangered people before exposures are covered.

7. Whenever fire conditions are heavy or wherever a company is operating in a precarious position, back them up with a second line.

8. Remember, higher buildings are exposed if fire seriously threatens or breaks through the roof. This will require lines for protection.

9. Sparks and brands landing on other roofs may cause other fires. Assign spark and brand patrol.

Engine company operations during night fires (no occupants):

1. Advance a line via main entrance toward the fire.

2. All other points from six through nine (under day fires above) remain the same (except for need to cover occupants).

Ladder companies operations. In general at supermarket fires, follow these guidelines for ladder company operations:

Daytime operations for ladder companies:

1. Help evacuate store—search for people overcome and remove them.

2. Ventilate. Remove show windows if necessary.

3. Ladder the building.

4. Pull ceilings under fire.

FIGURE 193. *In this type of supermarket construction a three-foot girder runs the perimeter of the store. It is covered with light metal sheathing. In case of a hanging ceiling fire (when access to the interior of the store is difficult), remove this metal sheathing and sweep the hanging ceiling space with streams from the outside.*

5. Examine adjoining stores for fire extension.

6. Open the roof for ventilation and insertion of cellar nozzles.

Nighttime operations for ladder companies:

1. Force entrance front and rear. Be careful in forcing entrance to a store when the show windows are hot to the touch. Forcing entrance may allow air to rush in, mix with the hot gases inside, and precipitate a smoke explosion. The roof should be opened first to allow the heated gases to escape harmlessly upward. Now direct a hose stream from the side (never directly in front) onto the hot show window. They may break from the action of cold water on hot glass. Wait a moment or two to see if the interior lights up, then move in. In this way you will not be trapped directly in the face of a smoke explosion.

2. Ventilate the building.

3. Ladder the building.

4. Pull ceiling under fire.

5. Check for extension on each side of building.

6. Open the roof for ventilation and insertion of cellar nozzles.

(The numbering sequence does not mean these steps are carried out in the order given. Many of these functions are performed simultaneously by different men.)

Some don'ts. In general, avoid the following practices in fighting supermarket fires:

1. Don't allow lines to operate toward each other.

2. Don't ventilate where it will cause an exposure hazard until the exposure is covered by hose lines.

3. Don't open side walls or windows if the show windows are hot to the touch—you may precipitate a smoke explosion.

4. Don't expose men to excessive punishment from fire and smoke—use self-contained breathing masks.

Some do's. In general, do the four following things at a supermarket fire:

1. Call for help early.

2. Consider the possibility of early roof collapse.

3. Lay out and prepare heavy stream appliance well-supplied with large lines if it appears you will have to resort to an outside fight. It is much better to lay out the heavy artillery and not need it than to find suddenly that you do need it and then frantically try to set up and do a poor job of it.

4. Place your hose lines at all times so that you head the fire off. In other words, try to anticipate where the fire is going and have a line there before it shows up. If you wait until it does show to get a line in position, it may be too late. (See Figure 193.)

Chapter 25

Warehouse fires

BECAUSE THERE is no set pattern of construction and occupancy, it is difficult to generalize about warehouse fires. But there are some characteristics of occupancy and building construction that are quite typical and therefore important to understand.

Most warehouses have large open areas. In many cases these buildings are four or five stories high. When they are more than one story high they will have large freight elevators with the problems of the vertical shaft. Stairways are usually open to compound the fire problem.

You can expect to find almost anything in a warehouse. It may be piled high with furniture awaiting delivery or you might find huge rolls of paper.

The furniture storage warehouses operated by household moving and storage firms are found in most communities. In these warehouses you will find the contents of entire apartments stored—usually temporarily. Each floor is divided into small cubicles with wooden slatting or wire forming the partitions. The partitions separate and safeguard the household goods and furniture of the individual customer.

Except for these flimsy partitions, the floor is one large area. While the partitions will not hold back the fire, smoke, and heat, they do obstruct the penetration of hose streams. Aisles and corridors are usually narrow and poorly lighted. Even with fire-resistant warehouses, losses are high because of the flammable contents.

Some of these older buildings present all the problems of the modern windowless buildings. In effect, some of them are windowless. Because many of them are located in slum areas, burglary is a problem so windows often are either bricked in solidly or heavily barred. Sometimes they are protected by steel shutters.

Another problem in these buildings is the absence of personnel. Usually the only personnel present will be the few people in the office on the street floor during business hours. Since there is no human occupancy on the upper floors, any small fire easily develops into a fire of serious consequences before discovery.

Exits are frequently inadequate and blocked with storages.

Firefighting operations

Every effort should be made to try and move hand lines into the interior to reach the seat of the fire. If there are standpipes, use them, and if there are sprinklers make sure to pump into the outside fire department connection. This also holds true with the standpipe. While each floor may be divided into relatively small compartments by combustible partitions, the fact that these partitions are

FIGURE 194. *Windows in this warehouse on both floors were boarded up, creating a difficult ventilation problem. When you cannot ventilate a building, you cannot move in hand lines. Failing penetration with exterior streams the fire will eventually burn on up and through the roof. Get ready to protect exposures.*

FIGURE 195. *This is the same fire shown in Figure 194. The fire department succeeded in opening several of the boarded up windows. By this time the heat had built up to the point where mixture with the needed oxygen caused the entire interior to ignite. The building became totally involved in minutes. In such fires, heavy* streams should be readied in anticipation of such a condition. Exposures must be protected in advance. If there is a water shortage, use the available water to cut down on heat radiation, knock down flying brands, and keep exposures soaked. Prepare for possible wall failure. Remove men and apparatus from exposed areas.

FIGURE 196. *Walls begin to fall. Apparatus and men were removed from danger area well in advance. Brick walls will usually fall outward about 1/3 of their height. In this case the building was 30 feet high. The wall fell out to about 12 feet, but some bricks hit the ground and bounced much further out. Be alert for overhead wires which also may fall.*

FIGURE 197. *These are rolls of roofing paper weighing over 1500 pounds each. Fire burns on the surface as well as burrowing into the interior of the rolls. It is impossible to adequately overhaul a high pile of these rolls unless power equipment is brought in to separate the piles. Heavy streams are necessary not only to knock the fire down, but to protect the roof structure from collapsing onto the rolls. If this happens, the fire will smolder for weeks unless the roof is combustible and burns away.*

FIGURE 198. *There are several unique dangers to fire in rolled paper or roofing paper. (1) If the high rolls begin to shift they will roll rapidly and may crush firemen. (2) The tremendous weight of a shifting pile pushing against walls will cause the collapse of upper floors or roofs onto men be-* *low. (3) If stock is piled tightly with little aisle space, the water absorption may cause expansion of the rolls of paper. This may push the walls out and cause the roof or upper floors to collapse. (4) The absorption of water may overload floors to the point of collapse.*

open and often do not reach all the way to the ceiling may allow you to get water onto the fire. If conditions are as described, switch to a straight stream for range. Aim for the ceiling to deflect the water down. Operating in this manner may get water onto the fire even where the burning area is behind obstructions.

Where lines cannot advance into the interior, it may be feasible to set up deluge guns to operate from protected doorways. With large nozzles and adequate pressures, sufficient range may be obtained to reach the fire. Where windows do exist and outside streams have to be used, their penetration is limited because of the compartments and other stock blocking the windows. Even where stream penetration is possible, excessive areas without dividing fire walls will nullify the effect of any exterior streams. Streams operated via windows or from doorways can reach only so far, depending on size, pressure, etc. If the warehouse is so large that streams from the exterior or doorways cannot hit the fire, and they cannot advance into the interior, then it is obvious the fire will burn on until it destroys most of the interior. After the roof has collapsed, you may be able to move the lines in, but the collapsed roof deck resting on the burning material will make water penetration more difficult or ineffective.

Be cautious when stored materials can absorb water. If water-absorbent materials are stored with little clearance from each other and little clearance along the side of the building, a dangerous situation may be created. First, the added weight of the absorbed water may overload an already weakened floor. Second, if there is no room for the material that absorbed the water to expand, it may push the side walls out and collapse the building. Don't forget that the weight added by a heavy stream can mount enormously if the water does not run off or is not evaporated by the heat of the fire.

Ventilation. In addition to all these difficulties, ventilating a warehouse is at times impossible. Windows are not necessary to warehousing operations. At best they represent a loss of wall space. If there are windows, the chances are stock will completely close off any access to them. Roof ventilation, while very desirable, may be too dangerous to attempt with a serious fire below. In a multistory warehouse, where it may be impossible because of smoke and heat to hold positions on the fire floor, the floor above may be tenable with the use of masks and ventilation. If so, try cellar nozzles from the floor above onto the fire below. Where there is an open stair shaft it should be opened at the roof.

Should inside stream operation become dangerous or impossible, you must resort to exterior streams from elevating platforms, ladder pipes, adjoining buildings, or fire escapes. If there are no window openings in the fire buildings or if they are so located as to preclude good stream penetration, fire spread to upper floors and roof must be expected. You can expect collapse to follow unless the building is of massive protected steel and concrete construction.

In some instances, it may be possible to breech side walls to get streams operating onto the fire. The problem, however, is with upper floors. There is no platform from which men can operate. If there are adjoining buildings, it is possible to have men try to work off their roofs.

Firemen formerly attempted to work off short ladders, from adjacent roofs, or from fire escapes which were still in place even though all the windows had been bricked up. These were difficult operations. Any success took a long time which generally allowed the fire to spread beyond the point of control. Two innovations now may prove to be more successful. The elevating platform basket not only will provide the platform from which to operate, it can easily carry all the tools and equipment needed right to the point of operation. The increasing rise and versatility of shaped, packaged explosive charges may give us the ability to open side walls as needed and thereby assure stream penetration. (See Figures 194-198.)

Solving
firefighting problems

Chapter 26

Pointers on solving problems

THIS SECTION deals with various kinds of fire problems. Some of them are theoretical, others are based on actual fires. A description will be given of each building involved, usually accompanied by a sketch. The student can compare his methods of fire attack with the author's. This will not only give him practice in solving problems but will help prepare him for writing examinations for promotion and generally test his skill.

Assumptions must be made

Unless the description of the buildings, the fire involving them, and the accompanying sketch are completely detailed, the student, basing his judgment on sound reasoning and standard tactics, will have to make certain assumptions and proceed from there.

When we institute a search for people, for example, we assume there may be someone trapped in the fire building. Similarly, placing a hose line on the floor above the fire assumes a possible involvement there. When we call for help, we assume that certain conditions exist inside the burning building that may require it.

But how does one know if he is reasonably correct in his handling of a fire situation? The answer to that question must necessarily be given in generalities. First, one's assumptions must be reasonable. It would be foolish, for instance, to credit a person with proper tactical ability if he assumes there could be no explosion in a tank of burning flammable liquids. Nor could he expect high marks if, given a lumberyard fire with a strong wind blowing toward houses directly in the path of the flames, he failed to place heavy streams between the threatened homes and the flames. On the other hand, if he calls for a great deal of help for a small fire which obviously could be contained, he again shows a lack of understanding of basic tenets.

The proper way to handle a problem of this kind on an examination is to state the assumptions you will make and upon which you will base your answer. This may be done at the beginning of your answer or during the sizeup of the fire.

Need uniform language

In working with problems such as these, one must have a method of discussing the engine and ladder company operations in a way that all departments, large or small, can relate to. Large cities with well-manned departments are organized into company units and operate as such. If a chief wants two lines laid, for example, he tells the officer of the incoming company and it is a valid assumption that the lines will be laid. A properly manned engine company can lay two 2½-inch lines.

Smaller departments have less manpower, and in all-volunteer units company operations, as an integral unit, almost disappear. It can no longer be said that a company can lay two lines. Sometimes manpower in the initial response is so limited it may be difficult to get one 2½-inch line into operation.

Therefore, in discussing fire problems we will not assign specific lines to specific companies. Rather, we will itemize the positions to be covered in order of importance and designate them as Line 1, Line 2, etc. The orders would be carried out as rapidly as men were able to respond and comply.

The same reasoning applies to ladder companies. Large city departments assign five to six men to busy ladder companies. It is obvious such a unit could do double the work of a three-man unit. In some small cities—even those with all-paid departments—it is not uncommon for the ladder truck or elevating platform to respond with only a driver.

It obviously, then, is not practical for this text to assign related ladder company functions at fires to specific ladder companies as integral units. We have no way of knowing how many men will respond with a unit, so we cannot assume the amount of work they can do. As with the engine companies, we will designate the work to be done and the priorities. Properly manned companies that do function as integral units still will be able to compare their operations at fires for examinations purposes.

The sample answers by the author will, in the case of ladder company operations, indicate assignments by "ladder company number or available units" indicating about what one could expect per normally manned (4- to 5-man) ladder company.

Sample exercises start with line placement and follow with ladder company procedures. That does not mean that the assignments will always be carried out in this order. Frequently, where several companies report in simultaneously, a number of assignments are given at the same time to such companies. If, for instance, a ladder company reports in first, it naturally would be told what to do. Such orders would not be held up pending the arrival of the engine company.

Writing a sizeup

If a student contemplates taking a promotion examination, he should become familiar with the mechanics of writing a sizeup, or evaluation, of the fire problem. This information will also help him learn how to handle actual fire problems because it gives him a "key" to follow. Here are the key items we will use:

Life	Auxiliary Appliances
Time	Water Supply
Height	Weather, Wind
Area	Apparatus on Hand
Construction	Communications
Occupancy	Salvage
Location & Extent	Special Matters
Exposures	

When answering such problems, if a sketch is not provided, the student should:

1. Make a quick rough sketch of the fire building and those immediately exposed, listing the essential information on the sketch.

2. Using the sizeup key, fill in the appropriate information.

3. After this is done, check to see if the pertinent details were accurately recorded on the sketch.

4. Now go ahead and answer the questions. Making up your own quick sketch if none was provided, or adding essential details in the proper places, eliminates the need of continually referring back to the detailed written description. You will have a visual aid which is much easier to understand than a complicated written explanation. It shows graphically where the fire is, where the exposures are, etc. If the description gave the water main sizes, the hydrant locations, or essential construction details, this information should also be shown on the sketch.

Chapter 27

How conditions affect your tactics

IN AN EARLIER chapter on "Theory of Hose Line Placement" and in other parts of this book, we laid down some guidelines for hose line placement by fire companies. These are general rules, but many men seek more positive assurance that once a rule is established it will hold true in all fire situations. Unfortunately, this cannot be the case.

It is entirely feasible for conditions to exist where the first engine company will operate correctly in the main hall or the first floor; at another fire in the same building, this engine company might properly be placed in an adjoining building. It might even be perfectly proper in the same structure to assign the first engine company to operate from a window directly to the rear of the fire.

In other words, the placement of engine companies will vary depending on specific conditions when the companies arrive.

To illustrate what we have said and provide some practice situations, we will analyze briefly six fires in the same building but under different conditions. Each situation requires the hose lines to be placed in a different position. To place them correctly, you should be guided by five determining factors that really are a form of condensed sizeup for quick evaluation and action. We also are assuming that elevating platform and aerial

ladder pipes are available if needed on initial response.

Here are the five determining factors:

1. Wind direction and its force.
2. Extent of fire by the time water is applied; is the fire localized or spreading?
3. Is life in danger? If so, how will the application of water best protect life?
4. The size, construction, and occupancy of the fire building.
5. Are there auxiliary fire appliances which can be used?

Here is a description of the building we will use for all six examples. It is 75x100 feet in area, six stories high of ordinary construction (brick exterior with wood joists and floors). The building is occupied throughout by light manufacturers of various mercantile products, all flammable. There is an open, interior wooden stairs at the front and an elevator enclosed in open iron grillwork next to it. The secondary means of egress is by way of an iron outside fire escape on the rear.

The fire building fronts on a wide (100 foot) street and to the right there is a building of similar type and height. On the left there is a 12-story fire-resistant factory, 100x100 feet in area, that is used for light manufacturing. It is equipped with a conventional standpipe and sprinkler system.

There is no window protection in the part

of the factory above the roof of the fire building. Directly across the street are 12-story factories all equipped with standpipe and sprinkler systems. In the rear of the fire building is a seven-story old brick building of ordinary construction, 200x100 feet in area with the largest dimension facing the street front. There are no built-in fire appliances in this large structure. There are iron shutters protecting the windows of this building, but from experience the fire officers in the area know they are not closed at night. There is only a 15-foot separation between the rears of the buildings. The entire neighborhood is protected by an excellent high-pressure looped water system.

Six fires, six problems

The following six fire problems all are based on the foregoing situation. All six fires occur in this same structure. In each situation, place the first four hose lines and give your reasons. Compare your placement with the answers given at the end of the six fire situations.

First Fire: A fire starts on the third floor during business hours. By the time firemen arrive the fire has possession of that floor. The weather is hot, there is no wind.

Second Fire: The conditions are the same as at the first fire except that this occurs at night and the building is vacant.

Third Fire: The conditions are the same as at the first fire except that the fire occurs at night with a 60-mile gale blowing against the front of the building.

Fourth Fire: Again, this is a night fire with no life hazard. The fire starts on the top floor and by the time firemen arrive the entire top floor is burning and fire is showing through the roof. There is a 50-mile wind blowing against the windows of the 12-story building alongside. The wind also is blowing flames against the rear windows of the building directly behind the fire building.

Fifth Fire: Fire originates in the cellar during business hours, roars up the elevator shaft, and mushrooms on the top floor. The fire has evidently entered other floors, as evi-

denced by smoke showing at all front windows. There is heavy flame on the top floor, with dense smoke coming from all the cellar openings. Several persons have already jumped from the front windows. When the firemen arrive, girls are still coming out the front entrance.

Sixth Fire: This fire also takes place in the cellar during business hours. There is no fire above the cellar but smoke has permeated the building. There is no wind. The employees are still in the building when the firemen arrive.

Here are the answers

These are the answers to the six fire situations above with respect to placing the first four hose lines and the reasons for the assignment. All hand lines will be 2½-inch with combination nozzles.

First Fire:

Line 1. To an elevating platform or ladder pipe in the front of the fire building, directing the stream in on the third floor to darken down the fire and prevent its spread to the floor above by fire burning through ceilings or lapping out of windows into the floor above.

Line 2. Up the inside stairs to the third floor and move in to extinguish fire and protect life. This line also will serve to prevent the fire from cutting off the stairway for use by people getting out of the building.

Line 3. Up the rear fire escape to the third floor to darken down fire and prevent extension to upper floors by way of rear windows, negating use of fire escapes for people trying to get down.

Line 4. Up the inside stairs to the third floor to back up the first line. Insure enough hose in the stretch to be able to move up to the floor above if it becomes necessary.

Reasons for actions

There is a serious life hazard here. People above the fire may be unable to get down because the inside stairs, elevator, and fire escape may be untenable. Line placement here is designed not only to reduce the intensity of the fire but to keep the stairs and fire escape from becoming involved in order to safeguard these vertical arteries so they can be used to get the people out.

Second Fire:

Line 1. Into an elevating platform or ladder pipe in the front, directing the stream in on the third floor to darken down the fire and prevent extension to the floor above by fire burning through the ceilings or lapping out of the windows into the floor above.

Line 2. Go around the block and lay a line into the third floor of the rear building. Operate out of the rear window onto the fire to keep it from crossing the 15-foot court.

Line 3. Up the inside stair to the third floor and move in on fire floor as soon as elevating platform has darkened down the bulk of the fire. Elevating platform would be shut down as hand line moves in.

Line 4. To back up Line 3 and then move to fourth floor if it becomes necessary.

Reason for actions

Since there is no life hazard involved, line placement is directed to cutting off the fire from extension to the building at the rear, and to cover any possible extension to the fourth floor.

Third Fire:

Line 1. Go around to the rear building and lay a line to the third floor. Operate out the rear window onto the fire to keep it from crossing court.

Line 2. Same as Line 1 but to the fourth floor and operate in similar manner.

Line 3. Into an elevating platform or ladder pipe at the front of the fire building and direct the stream in onto the third floor to darken down the fire and protect upper floors by auto exposure via front windows.

Line 4. Move a line up the inside stairs to the third floor and operate in on the floor to extinguish fire. This line also will prevent the fire from spreading and involving the inside stairs.

Reasons for actions

There is no life hazard involved, therefore operations are directed toward preventing rear building involvement and extension to the fourth floor. Because of the gale-like wind blowing through the fire floor via the broken windows, the rear building is seriously exposed so it is imperative to get hose lines in as soon as possible.

Fourth Fire:

Line 1. Connect a 3-inch line to the standpipe siamese of the 12-story building adjacent to fire building. Get into this building with rolled-up lengths of hose and operate from standpipe connections on seventh and eighth floors out the windows onto the fire below.

Line 2. Connect a 3-inch line into and supply the sprinkler siamese of the above exposed building, then go around to the rear building and operate line out of the rear sixth floor window onto the fire.

Line 3. Go around to the rear building and operate line from the roof to keep fire from crossing the court and involving this exposed roof.

Line 4. Into an elevating platform or ladder pipe in the front, directing the stream in on the sixth floor to darken down fire.

Reasons for actions

There is no life hazard. Lines are placed and operated to keep the fire from involving the building alongside and at the rear. Notice that when lines are placed to cover a floor or roof, the lower floor is covered first.

This is done so that men above will not be cut off by fire extending below them, as might be the case if higher floors or roofs are covered first.

Fifth Fire:

Line 1. Move into the inside hall and direct a stream up the stair and elevator shaft to kill any fire involving these vertical arteries. Then move down the cellar stairs to prevent any further involvement of the shafts.

Line 2. Move up the inside stairs as rapidly as possible, darkening down fire as you proceed. This line is vital; if it cannot make the top floor the people trapped will die.

Line 3. Go up the fire escape, darkening fire from the windows as you move up to the top floor to operate in onto the fire floor.

Line 4. Up the inside stair in manner similar to Line 2.

Reasons for actions

There is a severe life hazard at this fire, and the lines are directed to prevent the inside stairs and fire escape from becoming involved and to keep the fire confined to the cellar, as much as possible, until the people are out.

Sixth Fire:

Line 1. Move a line down the inside stairs to the cellar to extinguish the fire and prevent the stairs to the floors above from becoming involved.

Line 2. Move down exterior entrance to cellar and try to darken fire down from this point. Avoid streams operating against each other. If the inside line is "making" the fire, shut down the second line.

Line 3. Put this into a cellar nozzle should the inside lines be unsuccessful in holding the fire. If the first line had to back out, it would remain in the hallway of the first floor to hold any fire extension via partitions, burning through cellar door, etc.

Line 4. This should move up to the second floor to be ready for any extension.

Reasons for actions

It is important to make every effort to keep the fire from extending up and involving the inside stairs. This would prevent the people from getting out. The line placement here, while not necessarily completing extinguishment, will hold the fire in check until the people do get out.

Chapter 28

Seven firefighting problems to solve

FOLLOWING are some trial examples which the student should study to see if he understands the technique.

Example 1
Shoe Store

A fire occurs in a one-story shoe repair shop at 22 Adams Street. To the east of the shoe store is a one-story department store (No. 24) and on the corner of Adams and Roe Street is No. 26 Adams, an empty one-story store. On the west of the shoe repair store is No. 20 Adams, a one-story drugstore, and west of the drugstore is a very old three-story frame dance hall. There are five buildings fronting on Jones Street—No. 12, an old four-story multiple dwelling; No. 14, a one-story dress shop; No. 16, a one-story empty paint store; No. 18, also empty; and No. 20, a movie theater. Directly behind Nos. 14, 15, and 18 Jones Street is an inside court backing up to Nos. 20, 22, 24 Adams Street. East of Adams Street is Roe Street and west of Adams is Smith Street.

You are a captain in charge of an engine company and are first to arrive at this fire, which takes place at 9 P.M. on a hot summer night. The fire has completely involved the shoe store and is showing at front show windows. There is a strong wind blowing from the north.

Based on the foregoing description, write a sizeup of this fire, making up your own sketch. When it is completed, compare your sketch and your answer with the sample sketch (Sketch A) and sizeup that follow.

Sizeup example 1: shoe store

Life: None in the fire building—some danger always exists for the operating forces. There is a chance of the fire's extending via the rear court to the multiple dwelling on 12 Jones Street (though not likely) and some smoke involvement of the theater (also not likely).

Time: 9 P.M. indicates the stores are closed for the night and will require forcible entry for examination. There probably was a delayed alarm because the stores were closed. The hot summer night means windows in dwellings and dance hall, if in use, will be open and susceptible to smoke involvement and flying brands, should the fire go through the roof of the shoe store.

Height: Presents no problem because it is easily within reach of fire department ladders and hose streams. The dance hall with windows overlooking the drugstore would be a serious higher exposure if fire were to involve the drugstore.

Area: Not mentioned—such stores usually are not more than 40 to 50 feet wide and perhaps the same deep. Therefore the areas are not large and are readily subject to control.

Construction: Not mentioned—general construction of rows of stores is to have common hanging ceilings; roofs are generally flat; wood sheathed over wood ceiling joists; partitions between rows of older stores may be wood lath and plaster. I assume such to be the case here. I would expect windows at the rear of the store facing on the inside court. There may be flimsy division walls in the cellars between stores. Fire extension is possible via rear court, hanging ceiling space, and common party walls in cellars.

Occupancy: A shoe store with little hazard. There may be storage of flammable rubber cements; highly polished heels on ladies' shoes may be made of pyroxylin plastic which, in burning, gives off poisonous oxides of nitrogen. Advise men to use self-contained breathing apparatus if smoke is reddish brown in color (oxides of nitrogen). If fire involves drugstore there is additional hazard of chemical fumes.

Location and extent: Fire is clearly defined and in full possession of store, with possible extension to stores each side and to rear of stores on Jones Street. Assumption here is that no such extension has taken place yet and shouldn't with proper attack.

Exposures:

North—Rear of stores on Jones Street via windows facing on court.

South—By way of direct flame blowing out of the store and breaking into other stores alongside by front plate glass windows. This is not too likely if companies operate quickly since wind is blowing directly south.

West—The drugstore in similar manner to the department store to the east.

East—The department store by way of common hanging ceiling and flimsy partition walls.

If the fire burns through the roof of the shoe store it will expose the roofs of the stores each side and the three-story dance hall by flying brands. (Again, this is not too likely because of the favorable strong wind direction). If the fire burns through the roof and begins to involve the department store, the theater may require evacuation.

Auxiliary Appliances: None in the fire building—there may be sprinklers in the department store. I assume there is. There may be a standpipe in the theater. I assume there is. The department store sprinkler siamese should be supplied in case fire did involve the store.

Water supply. Not stated—I assume it is adequate.

Weather—wind: Hot summer night—windows may be open, creating susceptible conditions for flying brands, smoke involvement. The strong wind is favorable in that it is blowing the fire, smoke, and sparks away from the exposed areas. Hot weather exhausts men quickly if fire duty is severe and prolonged.

Apparatus on hand: Question states I arrived first with engine company. Implication is that more companies are enroute. Help certainly is needed for this fire; my rough estimate is that I will need up to six 2½-inch hose lines as well as men to perform necessary related ladder company functions. Such help would be called immediately.

Communications: Would be by mobile and portable radios—not a major factor in this fire.

Salvage: This would be started as soon as fire was under control—particular emphasis would be placed on covering stock in the department store if need showed.

Special Matters: There may be panic in the theater but this is unlikely.

SKETCH A—Shoe store

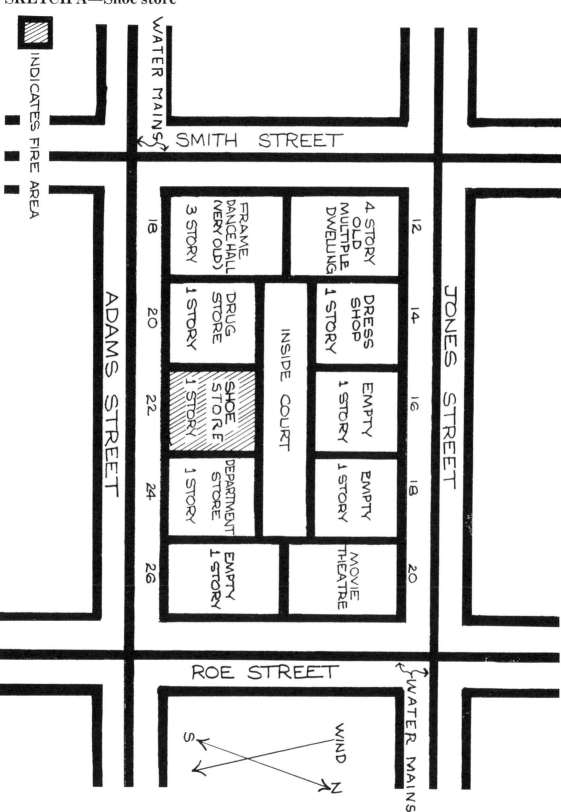

Example 2
Mattress Factory

Following is a description of a fire problem with a sketch (Sketch B) much as the candidate would find it.

No. 160 Henry Street is an old three-story brick-exterior, wood-joisted mattress factory built in 1890. The five-story school was built around the same time; it has open wooden stairs and windows overlooking the mattress factory. The auto repair shop at No. 170 Henry Street is a modern structure with unpierced walls and a gypsum roof over standard open-bar joist construction. Nos. 85 and 89 Watt Avenue were originally one building but were subdivided in 1920. No. 89 was used as a candy factory but has been empty for years. No. 93 Watt Avenue is of similar age and design to No. 160 Henry Street, but is used to make bed springs. The office building is a modern structure with standpipes and windows overlooking the factories to the west. The tenement houses on Watt Avenue are all frame construction, those on Henry Street are fairly modern having been built in 1960. The northeast corner of First and Henry Street is occupied by a used-car lot, as is the southeast corner of First Street and Watt Avenue. The east side of First Street between Henry and Watt is a public playground. The buildings on the west side of Second Street are all one-story stores. There are hydrants on the corners of all intersections fed by a looped 10-inch main on Watt Avenue, an 8-inch main on Henry Street, and a 6-inch main on First and Second Streets.

On January 2 at 3 A.M. on a clear cold night, a passer-by noticed a red glow at the front of the first floor of 160 Henry Street and turned in the alarm. By the time the fire department arrived, fire had full possession of the first floor of 160 and heavy smoke build-up was evident on the upper floors. There was a 20-mile per hour wind blowing from the south. The normal response to this area is two engine companies, one ladder company, and a battalion chief.

Based on the foregoing information, mark up the sketch with what you think should be added. Then write a sizeup of the fire. Compare your answers with Sketch C (showing the author's additions) and the sizeup of this fire written by the author.

Sizeup example 2: mattress factory

Life: Nil except to fire forces. There should be no trouble keeping the fire from involving the tenements on Henry Street.

Time: 3 A.M. indicates probable delayed alarm; though factory is closed, there may be a watchman on the premises; if fire has been burning for a long time, there is the possibility of a smoke explosion if vented improperly.

Height: Except for the 20-story building, which should prove little problem, every building is within easy reach of all fire department equipment (ladders, hose streams). Exterior streams will be effective at such low heights.

Area: Sketch shows Henry and Watt to be 250 feet long, so the fire building probably is no more than 60 feet wide by about 80 feet deep. Except for the school and office building, areas are well within reach of streams and should not constitute a severe problem.

Construction: Fire building is very old, presumably brick and joist. Such buildings afford little protection against the spread of fire. On the contrary, the building material itself, being combustible, will add fuel to increase the intensity of the fire. These old buildings are major problems once they become seriously involved. Age dries out and warps wooden structural members. There are unprotected vertical arteries in such buildings. The shaft between the two factories constitutes a serious threat to the exposed factory on Watt Avenue. A common construction feature in old factories was unprotected cast-iron columns, which have a bad record in fires. If the columns are superimposed one on top of another, one column failure may cause entire building collapse. If such fires involve more than one floor and burn out of control for more than 20 minutes, back out

SKETCH B—Mattress factory

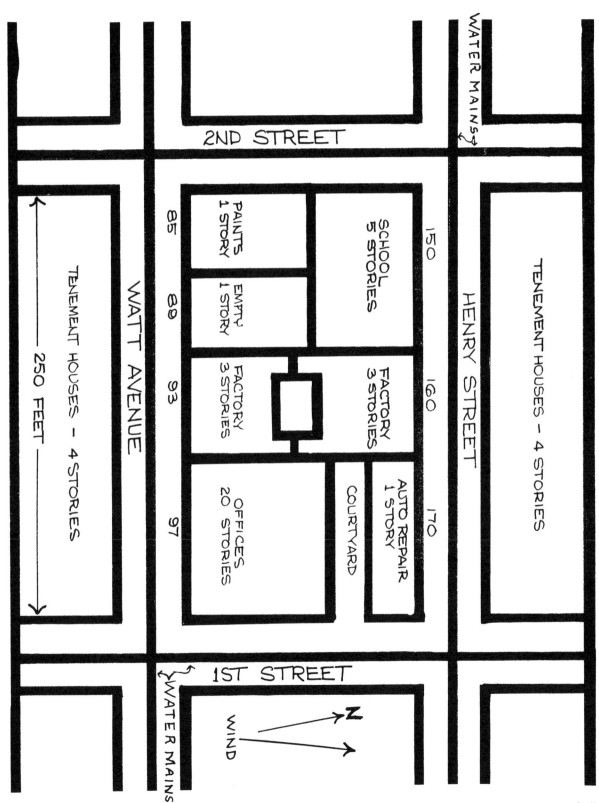

all interior hose lines and resort to heavy exterior streams.

Occupancy: Mattress factories generate large amounts of smoke and make hot fires. The other occupancies which may be a factor in this fire are:

A. The old school which has windows overlooking the mattress factory and if involved will create serious problems for the fire department.

B. The factory on Watt Avenue, which may become involved via the inside rear shaft. If involved, the weight of metal used in fabrication and flammable finishes poses a threat to the stability of the building and the safety of firemen.

C. The 20-story office building could become involved via windows but this could be coped with readily.

Location and extent of fire: The first floor of No. 160 Henry Street is completely involved, and involvement of the upper floors is probably imminent. Heavy exterior streams will be required in front of the fire building to drive back the fire and darken it down to give hose lines a chance to advance. The complete involvement of the floor indicates it may be blowing out of the rear shaft and threatening No. 93 Watt Avenue. Collapse of such structures must be anticipated if the fire is not quickly contained.

Exposures: All floors of 160 Henry Street above fire as well as:

North—the tenements across Henry Street constitute a mild exposure because in spite of the wind the exterior streams should be able to drive back the fire blowing out of 160 Henry Street. Should the fire go through the roof of the fire building, the tenements would be threatened. This, too, could be protected by anticipating such possibility and setting up an additional appliance such as an elevating platform or ladder pipe.

South—the factory at 93 Watt Avenue is a serious exposure on all three floors if the fire in 160 Henry Street blows out the shaft in the rear. This has to be anticipated and guarded against by placing hose lines on first and second floors and on the roof of 93 Watt Avenue and directing streams out rear

windows to prevent fire crossing the shaft.

West—the old school could readily become involved if fire goes through the roof of the fire building via the windows overlooking it. This, too, has to be anticipated and guarded against. If interior lines are withdrawn from the fire building, such spread must be expected and hose lines placed on the fourth and fifth floors to protect against this. Frequent examinations of all roofs not protected by hose lines would be made in the event flying brands land on combustible roofs. The former candy factory could be exposed if fire seriously involved 93 Watt Avenue. This is not a serious threat.

East—the auto repair shop is not really exposed because of solid walls and gypsum roof. If the fire building becomes completely involved and collapses, it could fall onto the repair shop. In anticipation of this, a line should be laid to this roof. The 20-story building is exposed at the northwest corner where it overlooks the fire building and would be exposed via windows if the fire were to go through the roof or completely involve the factory at 93 Watt Avenue. Because of superior construction and standpipes in the office building, it will be easy to keep fire from involving it. Men should be stationed on the fourth, fifth, sixth and seventh floors, and instructed to use hose lines from the standpipes onto fire coming from fire buildings below, if such did develop. It also would be essential then to pump into the fire department connection to insure an adequate water supply to the standpipe.

Auxiliary Appliances: Standpipes as mentioned would be used as specified under "Exposures." Since no mention is made of sprinklers, the assumption is that there are none. If there were sprinklers in the fire building, one of the first hose lines would be used to augment the sprinkler supply.

Water Supply: No mention is made of pressures in the mains, but based on the 10-inch and 8-inch mains looped by 6-inch mains on First and Second Streets, I would judge there is an adequate water supply for this fire.

SKETCH C—Mattress factory sizeup

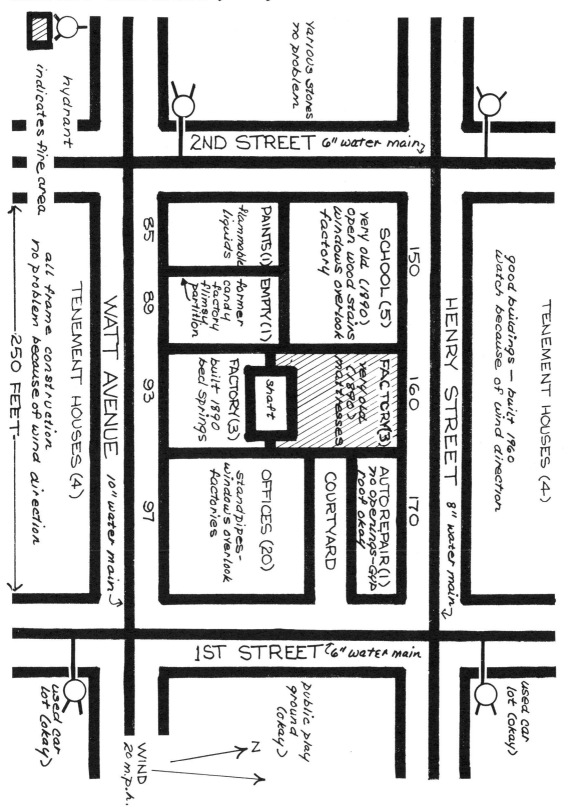

SKETCH C—Mattress factory sizeup

hydrant
indicates fire area

250 FEET

all frame construction
no problem because of wind direction

WATT AVENUE   10" water main

TENEMENT HOUSES (4)

85   89   93   97

PAINTS (1)
flammable
liquids

EMPTY (1)
former
candy
factory
flimsy
partition

FACTORY (3)
built 1890
bed springs

OFFICES (20)
standpipes-
windows overlook
factories

COURTYARD

Shaft

FACTORY (3)
very old
(1890)
mattresses

AUTO REPAIR (1)
no openings—GYP
roof okay

SCHOOL (5)
very old (1890)
open wood stairs
windows overlook
factory

150   160   170

HENRY STREET   8" water main

2ND STREET   6" water main

various stones
no problem

good buildings — built 1960
watch because of wind direction

TENEMENT HOUSES (4)

NUMBERS IN ( ) INDICATE HEIGHT IN STORIES

1ST STREET   6" water main

used car
lot (okay)

public play
ground
(okay)

WIND
20 m.p.h.

N

used car
lot (okay)

317

Weather: Clear, cold night in January indicates that there is some danger of frozen hydrants. The operations will be hampered by spray turning into ice, making treacherous footing on ladders, fire escapes, and streets, all of which will retard operations. Men will be encumbered by heavy clothing; ventilation of the fire building will be more effective because of the lack of humidity; the 20-mile wind, while creating a mild exposure for the tenements on Henry Street, is helpful in that it will not blow fire against school and office building if fire goes through the roof of the fire building.

Apparatus on hand: Two engine companies and one ladder company are completely inadequate for this fire. Assuming each engine company could lay one 2½-inch line, I would need additional manpower and pumping equipment to lay at least six more 2½-inch lines and 10 more ladder company men to do the necessary work of forcible entry, laddering, venting, and examining for fire spread if fire did not begin to involve exposures mentioned earlier.

Communications: Use of radios on the apparatus and portables would be sufficient to co-ordinate operations at this fire.

Salvage: Would be started as soon as fire was under control.

Special Matters: Need to call public utilities to shut gas and electricity in affected buildings.

Now we will progress to where the student should attempt a sizeup and handle the fire situation as well.

Example 3
Cellar Fire

You respond to a cellar well-involved in fire in the early morning hours of New Year's Day in a three-story residential structure at 21 Polk Street. The building is of ordinary construction built in 1929 in what was then a respectable middle-class neighborhood. Throughout the years conditions changed to where the entire area is now considered a slum and designated for urban renewal.

The only entrance to the cellar is by an inside stair in the hall. There originally were two families per floor but because of economic conditions many such structures have been remodeled to either single-room occupancies or split up to house additional families.

You will be in charge of this fire. You have a normal response of two engine companies, each with a 1,000-gallon pumper and one ladder company. The engine companies respond with three men each; the ladder company with four men.

Discuss this fire from the viewpoints of hazards involved, peculiar problems you see, and your techniques of extinguishment. In your discussion state clearly where and why you place hose lines and what you expect each hose line to do. Treat the ladder assignments in similar descriptive manner. Refer to Sketch D as needed.

This fire problem really requires a sizeup in order to answer the question of hazards, techniques, and extinguishment intelligently.

Sizeup example 3: cellar fire

Life: The threat to life here is severe because there will be dozens of people sleeping off New Year party effects in a building not designed to resist fire. All floors above are subject to heavy smoke and heat involvement. People at the rear are cut off from rescue by ladder.

There may be extension to adjoining cellars of Nos. 19 and 23 Polk Street, with smoke and heat permeating the two structures and presenting a threat to life.

SKETCH D—Cellar fire

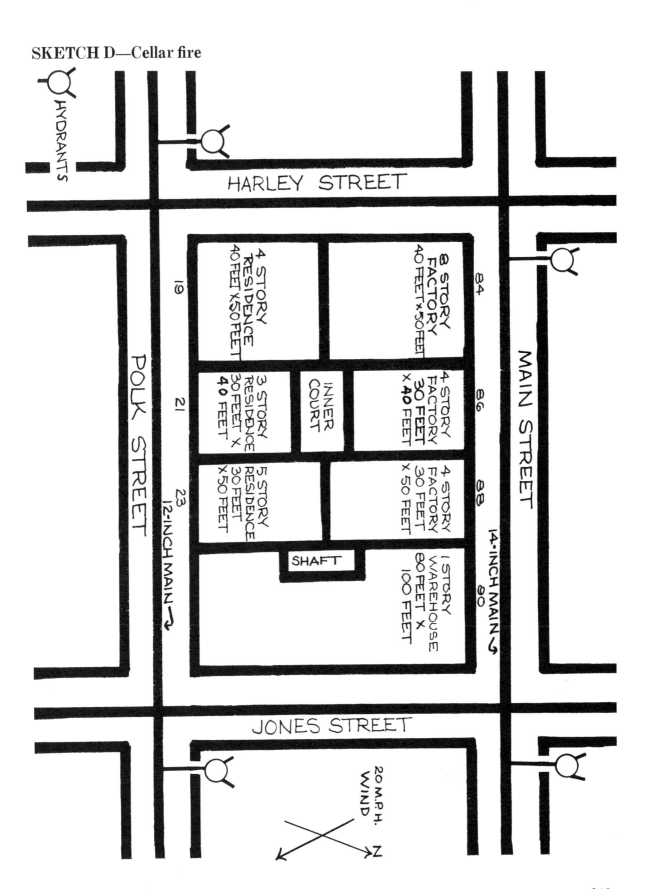

319

Lastly, there always is a hazard to the operating forces, particularly in cellar fires. Masks probably will be needed.

Time: The early morning hours on New Year's Day indicate delayed discovery. No one would be on the street on a holiday morning to see and turn in the alarm. New Year's indicates cold weather, so responses will be slowed by need for firemen to bundle up. Men operate less efficiently in extremely frigid weather. The streets may be icy, hydrants may be frozen. Forcible entry will be required not only for the fire building but for all buildings requiring examination and ventilation.

Height of fire building: While there are three stories above the fire to consider, it is well within the height of ladders and streams. Even if upper floors become involved, it is only still two flights up. If the stairs remain tenable, most people can be readily removed by this method. The fact that the fire building is lower than the buildings alongside indicates a potential exposure to Nos. 19 and 23 Polk Street, particularly if fire goes through the roof. Most probably there are windows in the side walls of these two buildings overlooking the fire building.

Area of fire: 30x40-foot area presents no unusual problem.

Construction: Ordinary construction more than 50 years old indicates brick exterior with wooden joists, floors and wood lath and plaster partitions on upper floors. This makes for potentially rapid involvement and fire may run sidewalls as well as interior open wooden stairs. There is an inner court at the rear which could cause involvement of the buildings alongside and in rear.

Doors to the individual apartments are plain wood, most probably with glass transoms. If fire does involve the stairs, spread to the apartments is a distinct and grave possibility.

Cellars in such buildings are compartmented, with excessive storage of old lumber, furniture, carriages, etc. There is enough of a fire load to make a hot, fast-moving fire.

Ceiling joists probably rest on common party walls and fire may get from this cellar to buildings on each side in this manner. Usually, there are no ceilings in such cellars, and examination for such extension is simply by going to the cellars for visual checks. If there are ceilings, they should be opened at the side walls.

Occupancy: There may well be more occupants than the structure was designed to house. Because the neighborhood is rundown and rents have been reduced, owners took larger apartments and subdivided them. In some cases they converted to single-room occupancies, allowing housekeeping privileges. This all adds up to many more smaller individual areas to be examined and searched for fire extension and people overcome. Some of the converted rooms may have no access to fire escapes. People will be trapped with no way out.

Location and extent: The fire has involved the cellar and apparently is extensive. It will subject the entire building to smoke and heat. Generally, the entrance to such a cellar is by a wood door at the rear of the hall under the stairs leading to the upper floors. There is serious question of involving the stairs to the upper floors. If this does occur, there may be a loss of life. It is of paramount importance to confine this fire to the cellar.

Exposures: All floors above the cellar of 21 Polk Street are exposed, as well as:

North—Nos. 84, 86, 88 Main Street by windows facing on inner court.

South—None.

West—No. 19 Polk Street by common party wall in cellars, and windows facing on inner court at rear, as well as any windows overlooking the fire building if fire goes through the roof of 21 Polk Street.

East—23 Polk Street in similar manner as 19 Polk Street.

Auxiliary appliances: They are not a factor since there would be none in the fire building and the residential structures alongside. There may be standpipes and sprinklers in the factories along Main Street. If so, standpipe lines could be used to operate into the inner court should fire threaten the factories by this route.

Water supply: The water supply and hydrant spacing are good, as indicated by a 12-inch main on Polk Street and a 14-inch main on Main Street. If hydrants are not frozen, there is ample water for this fire.

Weather-wind: Since there is no mention of adverse weather conditions, the assumption is that other than the cold there is no unusual problem. Caution will be required so engines do not freeze, water extinguishers will have to be placed in closed cabs, nozzles will be kept flowing slightly so as not to freeze water in hose lines.

There is a possibility of water freezing on ladders, roofs, and fire escapes, making such operations hazardous.

The high winds would not be a factor in this fire unless it broke out into the open. Then it would badly expose adjoining structures if the wind were blowing toward them. In this case, the wind is blowing toward Polk Street and away from the potential exposures.

Apparatus on hand: The two engines and one ladder company would be insufficient for this fire even if they were not so short on manpower. Help will be needed.

Communications: Will be maintained by portable handie talkies.

Salvage: Would be instituted as soon as fire was under control.

Special Matters: None.

Extinguishing Process: Example 3: Cellar Fire.

The actual extinguishment process would require calling additional help immediately. The two engine companies on the initial response could barely lay one 2½-inch hose line each and the ladder company with four men could not perform the needed tasks for a fire problem such as this. Additional help would be required to lay three more 2½-inch hose lines and sufficient manpower to do necessary related ladder company function as spelled out later. The assignments listed will be given and carried out simultaneously or as fast as help arrives.

Line No. 1: Lay a 2½-inch line and try to get down inside the cellar stairs. There is a dual purpose to this strategy. First, it is the shortest and most direct attack on the fire. You have to move the line in and down to extinguish; it is the most efficient method, though punishing on the men. Second, you will be protecting the stairs to the floors above. If this line were not placed so, the fire would soon burn through the door to the cellar and involve the stair shaft. Once it did so, the use of the stairs for rescue, search, and advancement of lines is negated.

Line No. 2: Lay a 2½-inch line wyed off into two 1½-inch lines. Take one 1½-inch line into the inside hall of the fire building to prevent fire coming up partitions. The second 1½-inch line is available for incoming companies to use to cover the floors above, should this be necessary.

Line No. 3: Lay a 2½-inch line to the cellar of 19 Polk Street to check and contain any fire from coming across common party walls by running the floor joists.

Line No. 4: Lay a 2½-inch line to the cellar of 23 Polk Street and operate in similar fashion to Line No. 3.

One unit is kept on reserve, to be instantly available to lay a line as needed should fire break out of cellar and move up at any area. This might occur at the inner court behind the fire building. If the fire were to start to blow out into this inner court, it would be necessary to lay a 2½-inch hose line through 86 Main Street and operate out the rear windows to drive back any fire showing and threatening to involve the buildings exposed along the course of this court.

If the firemen cannot hold their position in the cellar of the fire building, they will back their line out, closing the door to the cellar. This line will be put into a cellar nozzle to attack the fire from the first floor over the hot spots. If this is not sufficient to darken down the fire, then use another 2½-inch line into another cellar nozzle to give you the additional cooling effect. This still leaves the 1½-inch lines to cover any extension to the floors above. The reason 1½-inch lines are used for the latter purpose is the mobility of the lighter line.

Unless the entire structure were to become involved, 1½-inch hose is perfectly suitable for residential fires above the cellar.

Ladder company assignments:

First ladder company (should be able to perform these four functions):

1. Ladder building if people are showing at windows and remove them.

2. Send one man to roof to vent over all vertical arteries.

3. Roofman then goes down the fire escape to help search for people overcome, venting by way of windows as he proceeds.

4. Send one man with engine company to force entrance as needed.

Second ladder company or available unit would:

1. Assist first ladder in ventilation, search and removal of people overcome or in need of assistance.

2. Send one man each to cellars of Nos. 19 and 23 Polk Street to open ceilings to check on possible extension of fire to these areas, then these men move up to vent and check upper floors.

3. Cut floor for cellar pipes, if needed, in No. 21 Polk Street.

Third ladder company or available unit would:

1. Assist second ladder company in ventilating 19 and 21 Polk Street.

2. If fire involves inner court and line placement is necessary via 86 Main Street, force entrance for engine company.

3. Check for possible extension to Nos. 84, 86, 88 Main Street.

As soon as fire is under control, ladder companies would begin overhauling. They would open ceilings and sidewalls of suspect areas for fire spread.

Engine companies would reduce the 2½-inch lines to 1½-inch for ease of movement. All units would co-operate in setting up emergency lighting, exhaust fans, picking up surplus hose, getting units back into service.

Investigation would be made for fire cause before starting salvage so as not to clear away any possible evidence.

Example 4
Factory — Nitrocellulose

Referring to Sketch E, building "A" is used for the manufacture of various small nitrocellulose plastic articles such as combs, handles for knives and spoons, etc. At 2 P.M. on a weekday, fire starts on the first floor and by the time you arrive has spread rapidly to the second floor and elevator shaft. Fire building "A" was built in 1920.

You have present at the time of your arrival three engine companies. You are in charge.

1. Size up this fire.

2. How would you handle this fire?

You may make any assumptions that are consistent with good standard operating procedures, but these assumptions must be clearly stated in your answer.

Assumptions:

1. Wind and weather normal and no problem. Assume fire takes place in warm weather.

2. Fire building is probably of older construction than surrounding buildings because of lesser height.

3. Area evidently is a well-built-up section and congested. (Notice size and area of other buildings.) This would indicate to me a rather large municipality and a more or less adequate building code. On this basis, since building "A" is a plastics concern (nitrocellulose) and six stories high, in all probability there is a sprinkler system. The rapid spread of fire indicates a strong possibility that the sprinkler may not be functioning, may have supply valve shutdown, etc.

4. I would expect window protection on the exposures to south, east, and west; the 18-story building probably would be protected only to about 50 feet above the roof of fire building "A."

5. I would expect fire drills to be required, so most probably all occupants of fire building "A" have gotten out safely, but I would search for people overcome regardless.

6. I assume because of their height that

SKETCH E—Factory—Nitrocellulose

323

the two eight-story factories, the 10-story factory, and the 18-story office building have standpipes.

7. Fire building "A" would have fire escapes front or rear only. Due to evident lack of egress from rear court, I expect the fire escapes on the front.

Sizeup: Example 4—Factory—Nitrocellulose

Life: Severe to occupants of building "A" if not previously evacuated from premises by orderly fire drills. Severe to operating forces due to toxic gases from fire, possibility of smoke and/or dust explosions, possibility of collapse of fire building. Sudden explosion may shatter windows of all buildings in immediate area; need to evacuate people from windows of all buildings facing building "A."

Time: 2 P.M. on a working day means an occupied factory of substandard construction. Probability is no delayed alarm because fire would be discovered quickly.

Height: Six stories; within reach of aerial ladders and exterior streams; upper stories not accessible to street streams, beyond reach of portable ladders. No way to ladder rear of building effectively for upper stories; must use aerial ladder or elevating platform to vent roof.

Area: About 4,000 square feet, probably one open area each floor. Strong drafts will intensify fire; may need heavy streams. Streams from fire escape and ladder pipes will reach rear of building.

Construction: Old ordinary brick and joist construction with open stairs and shaft makes for rapid involvement. Contents as well as structure are flammable, all adding to an intense, hot, smoky fire which will require heavy exterior streams and manpower. Sixty-foot width indicates need for girders supported by columns. These are usually of unprotected steel. If columns are cast iron, danger of collapse is greater.

Occupancy: Plastics of nitrocellulose base make for explosively rapid spread; toxic fumes of oxides of nitrogen; danger of explosion if not promptly vented. Need for self-contained masks to protect men from gases. Nitrocellulose can burn with sufficient intensity to seriously endanger structural stability of building (cast-iron unprotected columns). Storage of flammable solvents; grinding operations on plastic novelties make a dust explosion a hazard here.

Location and extent: Originated first floor, spread to second floor and elevator shaft. Indicates heavy body of fire, probable extension via open stair and elevator shaft, partitions, other vertical arteries. Need of getting lines into position to cut off further spread and to keep possession of stair shaft.

Exposures:

North—Constitutes a weak threat to buildings across Fourth Street but lines from deluge gun and elevating platform operating in front of fire building "A" should minimize this condition. Windows open in buildings to north plus workmen watching from these windows do present a problem. Have to vacate front of such buildings and close windows.

South—Eight- and 10-story factories exposed via inner court, particularly 10-story factory. Need to close windows of exposed floors and use lines from standpipes to operate onto fire from rear. Need to supply such standpipe lines by pumpers. If buildings are sprinklered, supply fire department connections by pumper.

West—Eight-story factory severely exposed, particularly by narrow shaft. Need to close windows, get lines into operation from standpipe to cover, check to see if fire is extending by way of overlapping floor joists of common party walls (very unlikely) and/or openings from fire building to this factory— (if sprinklered, supply if necessary).

Figures 199-202 illustrate how easily fire can spread by way of shaft openings.

East—18-story building will be of fire resistant construction but contents of same would be exposed if fire were to go through roof of building "A." There also is part of this 18-story building that is exposed by the

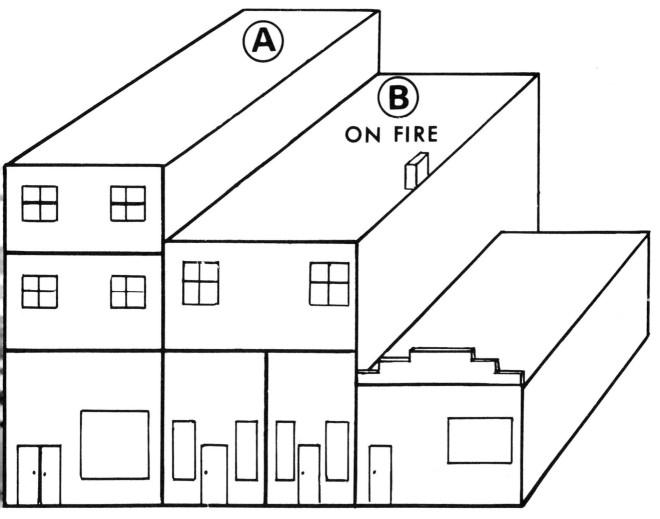

FIGURE 199. *This is a common type of construction found in most areas. Buildings appear to be separated only by division walls (no space), particularly when the smoke of a fire obscures vision. The reasoning then may be that there is no open-ing for fire to pass from one building to the next one. Thus the assumption is that there is no need to protect the adjoining structure. Such assumptions may be a prelude to disastrous spread. (See Figures 200-202).*

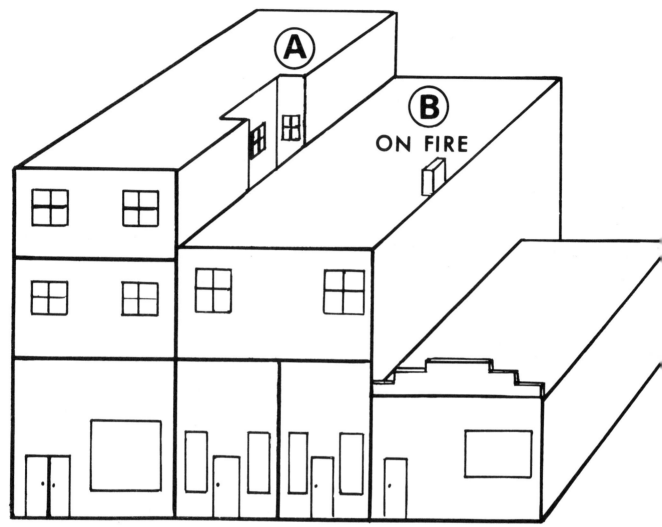

FIGURE 200. *This illustration shows why it is wise to send a man to the roof of the higher exposed building. Here he can examine for exposure to the roof as well as the shaft which may be clearly visible from his position. There may be no serious exposure problem here since the shaft is only in the exposed structure (Building A). There may be no openings into the shaft from* Building B. *If there are no such openings, the most likely danger is the burning through of the roof of Building B. Then fire could expose the roof of Building A or could get into the top floor of Building A through the windows. If either or both of the buildings are wood sheathed, the exposure potential is far more serious.*

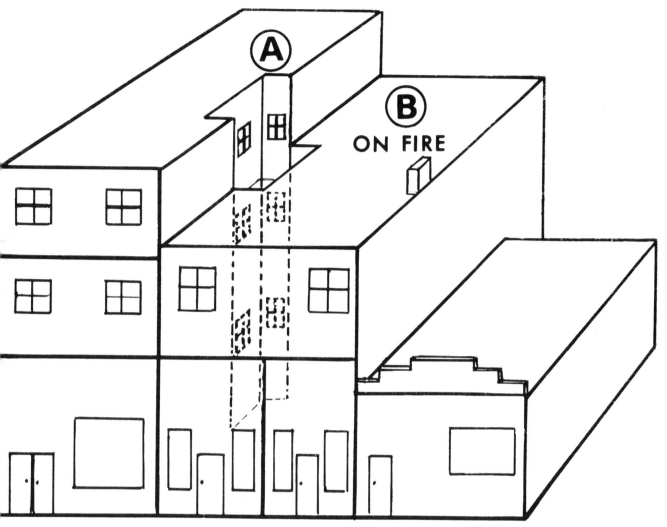

FIGURE 201. *In this drawing the shaft is common to both buildings. Now it is evident that fire can readily involve all floors of both buildings as well as the roofs. In some fires the smoke buildup is so dense it is impossible to see the shaft — even from the roof. In such cases, sending men to the interior of the exposed structure will reveal the hazard. Windows facing on such exposed shafts should be promptly closed to prevent the entrance of smoke, heat, and eventually fire. Hose lines must be brought onto such exposed floors, not only to prevent fire from entering, but to direct water onto the fire in the fire building from these vantage points. Pending the placement of such interior streams, exterior streams (if available and in proper position) should drench the exposed windows to prevent them from breaking because of heat. Do not direct the full force of the exterior stream against the exposed windows; this will only break them and allow fire to enter.*

FIGURE 202. *This photograph was taken after the fire in which the preceding drawings (Figures 199-201) are based. You are looking into the shaft from Building B, toward Building A. Build-* *ing B was heavily damaged by fire. Fire did not get into Building A, although it was seriously threatened. Note the superficial charring on the window frames of Building A.*

part that faces on the inner court at the rear of building "A." Fire from building "A" could get into the 18-story building by way of open windows. Most probably will not occur but need to check this building to see if any such spread occurs. Need to close windows on exposed side, open on unexposed side. Good vantage point for standpipe lines if fire goes through roof of building "A."

Auxiliary appliances: As mentioned, standpipes in buildings may be utilized; will save long stretches and conserve manpower; sprinklers in fire building "A" may be able to be placed in operation. Portable extinguishers in exposed buildings may be used to check incipient fires started by sparks and brands. Possibility of fire brigades in these buildings could be used to check various floors.

Water supply: Five hydrants in immediate vicinity indicate that hydrants in the area are ample in number. Mains are only 6-inch diameter but all are cross-connected except the one on Fifth Avenue. Only put one 1,000 GPM pumper or two 750 GPM pumpers on this main to avoid over-taxing it. Standpipes in buildings supplied by gravity tanks can supply lines for quite a few minutes, if need be, until supplied by pumpers through fire department siamese connections.

Weather, wind: No wind assumed, hence no bearing on fire. Weather is warm so must anticipate windows are open, creating greater danger of spread. Many people watching fire, crowds in street. Firemen may suffer from heat exhaustion due to exertion.

Apparatus on hand: Definitely not enough for this fire. Send for help. Fires such as this with its serious exposures could call for 15 hose lines or more. There will be a need for rescue units, medical aid, additional police for fire lines, public utilities.

Communications: Set up command post and communications unit, all companies operating in exposed and fire buildings to communicate with command post via portable radios.

Salvage: Started as soon as fire is under control and men are available.

Special Matters: Some danger of explosion in nitrocellulose occupancies. Do not underestimate the potential for rapid involvement of entire building "A" and spread to exposed buildings by shafts.

In calling for help, one must keep in mind conditions existing in his department and the normal manpower response to fires. In a large metropolitan department, the normal response to such areas would be three engine companies, each with the capacity to lay and operate two lines; two ladder companies, two battalion chiefs, and a deputy chief. Each additional alarm would bring another three to four engine companies and one ladder company plus squad and/or rescue units.

Based on such responses, this fire would call for a third alarm. But since this book is written for all departments, it would be misleading as well as confusing to call for such assignments in areas where each call for help may bring only one engine company. In some departments, a second alarm brings only one engine company and a third alarm a third company. It is for this reason—as explained at the beginning of this chapter—that in calling for help we will indicate such help by line numbers and ladder company work as ladder company (or available unit or manpower).

By so doing we will outline the necessary functions and the individual can adapt the situation to his own department. If, for instance, we call for 10 additional lines and in your city each engine crew can lay only one line, and three engine companies respond to each alarm, you then will call for a fourth alarm. Not only may we use up to 15 hose lines, there will also be the need for at least the manpower and equipment that four ladder companies would provide (or about 20 men) for the related firefighting functions that complement engine company work.

Extinguishing process

Because of the volume of fire on the first floor and its spread to the second floor, coupled with an extremely flammable occupancy, this fire must be attacked quickly. Inside line operation will be attempted, but if it is unsuccessful in slowing down the fire in 20 minutes, all hand lines should be withdrawn and reliance placed on heavy exterior streams until the fire is controlled.

Notify the dispatcher for the required help; also request ambulances, rescue squad, searchlight unit, public utilities, extra police to handle traffic and crowds.

Line 1. Three-inch line into elevating platform at front of fire building set back at opposite curb so as to leave street clear for incoming apparatus. There will be need to use aerial ladder here for roof ventilation. This line will drive in on first, second and third floors, darken fire, and help prevent extension via front windows. It also will be directed to top windows of elevator shaft to kill fire rising in the shaft. It should cool fire down and give the lines which will move up the stairs a chance to make the floor.

Line 2. Three-inch line to sprinkler siamese connection of fire building and start to supply same from pumper.

Line 3. Two-and-a-half-inch hand line to front entrance of fire building. Work in on first floor trying to protect stairs and preventing further involvement of second floor.

Line 4. Two-and-a-half-inch hand line to back up Line 3. Operate in on fire floor and move up to second floor as soon as fire darkens on first floor.

It is important for hand lines 3 and 4 to advance in on the fire floors not only to extinguish the fire, but also to protect the means of egress for any occupants who may be trapped.

Line 5. Three-inch line into siamese connection of standpipe of eight-story factory building west of building "A." Take four rolled-up lengths of 2½-inch hose, nozzles and forcible entry tools into this building and proceed as follows:

Operate a 2½-inch hose line from the standpipe on the first floor, directing the stream out the window up into the shaft to kill any flames rising in the shaft; also direct this stream across shaft into the first and second floor windows of the fire building. Spare hose would be used if it became necessary to direct streams from above the first floor. (This would be necessary if fire showed on third or higher floors of building "A.")

Line 6. Three-inch line into siamese connection of standpipe of ten-story factory to the south of building "A." Take same hose and equipment as specified for Line 5 into this ten-story factory. Direct stream from standpipe out of first floor rear window and operate in similar manner to Line 5.

Line 7. Three-inch line into siamese connection of standpipe of eight-story factory to south of building "A." Take same hose and equipment as specified for Line 5 into this eight-story building. Direct stream from standpipe out of first floor rear window and operate in similar manner to Line 5.

Line 8. Two-and-a-half-inch hand line up front fire escape of building "A" and move in on second floor to extinguish fire.

Line 9. Two-and-a-half-inch hand line up front fire escape of building "A" to third floor and move in on third floor to extinguish any fire showing.

Line 10. Fill in second 3-inch line to sprinkler siamese connection of building "A."

Line 11. Fill in second 3-inch line to elevating platform, if needed.

Line 12. Three-inch line into siamese connection of standpipe of 18-story office building. Take same hose and equipment as specified for Line 5 into this 18-story office building. Connect hose to seventh floor standpipe valve and be prepared to operate out of windows overlooking fire building "A." This line is simply placed here as a precaution should fire go through the roof of building "A." Meanwhile, spare men while waiting would be dispatched to make sure all window protective devices were closed.

Two engine companies would be kept in reserve and mobile, should it become necessary to lay additional lines at any point.

As soon as it is evident that companies are "making" the floors, the heavy exterior streams from the elevating platform should be shut down. The protective streams being operated from the surrounding exposures onto the fire will similarly be curtailed so as not to drive the smoke and heat back at the men moving in on the fire floors of building "A." By shutting down these streams operating into the windows, the natural path of ventilation will be restored. The smoke and heat will vent via these windows, making it easier for the inside lines to advance.

Ladder company assignments:

First ladder company (or available unit)

1. Ladder front of fire building and remove people showing.

2. Unless aerial is needed for No. 1 above, extend aerial to roof of fire building.

3. Send men to roof via aerial to vent over stairs, elevator shaft. (Cut roof, if needed, to increase vent area).

4. These men would come down the front fire escape venting by way of windows.

5. They would search for people overcome, and examine for fire extension on floors above.

The ladder company personnel would not be in conflict with the hand lines moving up the front fire escape because their assignments would be completed long before this line placement.

Second ladder company (or available unit)

1. Assist first ladder crew in search of fire building, paying particular attention to rear.

2. If people are trapped at the rear, you may be able to get them by taking extension ladders out into the inner court by going through adjoining buildings. Another possibility is by men coming down ropes from the top of the fire building, or life nets taken to inner court in same manner as ladders.

3. Men to go into adjoining eight-story

building to examine for fire extension on all floors. Close windows on exposed side, open them on unexposed side. Remove combustible stock from exposed windows. Use house lines from standpipe if needed, or use portable extinguishers for incipient fires.

Third ladder company (or available unit)

1. Assigned to cover the other eight- and ten-story factory buildings, performing the same functions as second ladder company crew did in the eight-story factory alongside fire building "A."

Fourth ladder company (or available unit)

1. Assigned to 18-story building to operate in similar manner, performing the same functions as second ladder company crews did in the eight-story factory building alongside fire building "A."

Rescue Company:

To use additional masks for search and examination of fire buildings; to use inhalators on people overcome. Use specialized equipment as needed.

Police:

1. Establish fire lines to keep people at safe distance.

2. Remove people at windows watching fire from buildings across street in case of explosion.

3. Clear traffic and keep streets clear for incoming apparatus.

Utility Companies:

1. Shut gas and electricity for fire building in street (Note: necessary to keep electricity on in exposed buildings for use of elevators, standpipes, fire pumps).

Ambulances:

1. Set up first-aid station in protected building or store nearby. With these forces, this fire should be controlled within an hour. Engine companies in exposed buildings would be on the alert to move up to other floors, as needed. Ladder company men, as soon as possible, would start to open ceilings and sidewalls to expose any hidden fire in building "A."

Examination would be made of cellar of fire building to determine whether fire had dropped down elevator shaft. If so, lines from reserve engine companies would be placed here.

One of the reserve engine companies would be used for a spark and brand patrol. If this fire completely involved the second floor and was not under control within 20 minutes, all inside forces would be withdrawn and the fire would be fought from the outside with heavy stream appliances.

Additional alarms would be transmitted so as to adequately cover exposed buildings on all floors exposed by spreading fire.

Constant check would be made on the fire building to assure building stability. (Would check for exterior walls cracked or leaking water through mortar joints, walls out of plumb, distortion or deflection of beams, front and rear walls bulging at any points).

As junior chief officers reported in, they would be assigned to supervise operations in exposed buildings and the progress of units inside fire building. They would be instructed to keep the command post advised of changing conditions.

We showed 12 hose lines laid, which would not be an unusual condition for this kind of fire. Should the fire in building "A" involve the entire structure, many more lines would have to be laid. An additional heavy stream appliance would be required at the front of building "A." Additional hand lines would be required in the exposed buildings and on roofs. We might well add another 10 lines in such case.

What should be kept in mind is that many of these hose lays are comparatively short (those feeding the siamese connections to standpipes and sprinklers) and require no manpower to continue in operation. The hose lines operating from the standpipe connections on the various floors will be even shorter. Therefore, the job is not as difficult as one might judge upon seeing a fire problem requiring more than 20 hose lines. In actual practice, too, not all the lines are operated continually. The hose lines off the standpipes might be used for only five minutes to darken down fire extending up the shaft, then shut

down and be used intermittently as needed. Many lines are crucial at the early stages of a fire in order to check a serious extension hazard. Such line may accomplish its purpose in minutes and thereafter revert to a holding or a standby operation where the hose line is there if needed.

If all lines were to be used simultaneously for a prolonged period at this fire, there would be a serious water shortage problem because of the 6-inch mains, even though they are well looped.

The same reasoning prevails with ladder company assignments. At the beginning of the fire there might be need for more than the number of men designated to perform related ladder company work. It might be that their functions would be accomplished within 20 minutes; then until the fire was under complete control laddermen would be assigned to assist engine company men in handling or laying additional hose lines. Fires such as this require a great number of men and equipment at the initial stages, but once control is established the Chief starts to relieve men and equipment as rapidly as possible.

Frequently, in discussions with members of small departments, they object that large cities can supply the men and equipment to lay the number of lines used in this fire problem, but that such strategy is inapplicable to small departments that at best cannot lay even one quarter of the lines. Therefore the argument goes that planning on this scale is futile and of no help to such small departments.

There is validity to the claim small departments cannot supply the number of lines and equipment this fire called for. This is a built-in limitation beyond the author's control. But it should not be used as an argument that because the department in question could not supply the needed strength, other tactics will handle the situation.

If a building is large enough, and because of its occupancy and/or construction is vulnerable to fire; and if the building constitutes serious exposure threats to similar large occupancies, then there are but two alternatives:

1. Either the department has the needed strength to cover the essential areas and will contain the fire (always assuming the strategy is correct).

2. If the department hasn't the needed strength, the fire building and exposures will burn down.

Now, faced with such serious fire potential, there is much the smaller department can do. If they cannot purchase and man the needed equipment (usually budgetary suicide for the small community), they must band together and plan for large-scale mutual aid. In their planning, account should be taken of the maximum number of men and equipment that may be needed. Then arrangements should be made with neighboring communities to supply the men and equipment when and if the need arises.

There are built-in limitations to massive mutual aid, but failing the ability to be self-sufficient, there is nothing else the small community can do. Failing to plan on such mutual aid under the aforesaid conditions is sheer neglect.

Example 5
Supermarket

In handling this supermarket fire we will try to show the difference in techniques under certain conditions; why an action may be correct when the store is closed but a serious error when it is open.

This fire occurs on a clear hot summer night at 2 A.M. in the Osco Drug Store which is part of a shopping complex of 800 feet of unbroken frontage by 200 feet in depth. The shopping center was built in 1960 and is of standard construction. The exterior side and rear walls are of concrete block. The fronts are all show windows with brick facing between stores. The roofs of the supermarket and drugstore are of steel truss construction and are not parapeted. The only parapet wall is between the drugstore and the furniture store. The other stores have conventional flat, wood-sheathed, tar, and gravel roofs.

There are no cellars in any of the stores. The rear utility areas of the drugstore and supermarket are sprinklered by a connection to the city water main. There is a two-way fire department connection for the sprinkler at the rear of the supermarket.

By the time the fire companies arrive there is a heavy volume of smoke inside the supermarket and the drugstore. At times a dull glow can be seen towards the rear of the drugstore.

When the chief arrives, he finds the two engine companies and one ladder company at the rear. The ladder company is cutting the rear steel door of the drugstore with a torch. One engine company has laid a 2½-inch line to the sprinkler siamese and is starting to pump in. The other engine company is trying to force the rear door to the supermarket. (See Sketch F.)

Questions:

1. In your opinion, were any of the companies operating properly at the time of the chief's arrival?

2. State the hazards and problems existing at this fire.

3. State how you would handle this fire. Refer to the sketch "F" as needed.

Answers:

1. The only proper action was by the engine company feeding the sprinkler siamese, and this company should have laid two additional hose lines to the front of the fire building.

2. To detail the hazards and problems really requires a sizeup.

All the details from the written description of this supermarket fire have been added to Sketch F. The altered sketch will now be referred to as sketch "G."

Sizeup example 5: supermarket

Life: None to any but members of the Fire Department.

Time: 2 A.M. indicates probable delayed discovery. There will be need for forcible entry. Delayed discovery may mean fire already has involved hanging ceiling. There may be a possibility of a smoke explosion.

Height: A one-story structure is an advantage in that it is easily within range of all fire department portable equipment. Access to the roof for examination, ventilation, cutting of roof, use of cellar nozzles through roof presents no problem because all stores are about the same height and there is ready access to all the roofs without additional laddering. One disadvantage of low height is that the overhead electric wire lines come to the rear of the complex quite low from the ground, making it easy in the dark or under heavy smoke conditions to hit them with ladders.

Area: The entire complex is 160,000 square feet in area. The description of the fire problem states the only parapet wall is between the drugstore and furniture store. In all probability, then, the stores to the east of the drugstore have a common hanging ceiling (about 100,000 square feet) and the remaining stores similarly will have a common hanging ceiling space of about 60,000 square feet.

The shopping area of the drugstore and supermarket is excessive. The size of these stores will provide ample fuel, both structural and contents. Drafts created by large unbroken areas serve to intensify the fire and aid in rapid spread. Heat conditions will make it difficult to advance lines to the seat of the fire. There will be need for large streams to assure adequate throw and penetration; smaller streams lack cooling capacity and will not reach the seat of the fire. Men will be driven out. Minimum streams in such fires should be 2½-inch.

Construction: The front wall is all show window with the main exits usually to one end of the store. This construction requires long steel I Beams supported on columns in the centers and on the block exterior walls. There is much wood framing and there are concealed spaces around the front structural members. The exterior side and rear walls, except for service doors, are unpierced and if locked present a difficult access problem. The truss roof generally has a fire-rated ceiling, but if fire does get into the hanging ceiling spaces (by ducts—openings around pipes, passing from one ceiling space to another by way of overlapping joists in common party walls) then the rated ceiling will quickly drop, exposing the unprotected steel to the fire below. Collapse must then be anticipated.

Occupancy: This type of drugstore is actually a department store and uses the counter checkout and one-way turnstile system which makes for poor exit facilities when store is occupied. Generally, there is a rear utility area and according to the sketch there is a large communicating opening from the drugstore to the supermarket. Because the supermarket is heavily involved with smoke, the rolling fire door which usually separates the two sections is either inoperative or blocked open. This means the fire, if not promptly checked, will involve the supermarket quickly. Between the supermarket, with its high fire loading, and the drugstore one must expect a major fire in a short time. When such stores are closed and fire has been burning for a long time, as is evident here, one must be

SKETCH F—Supermarket

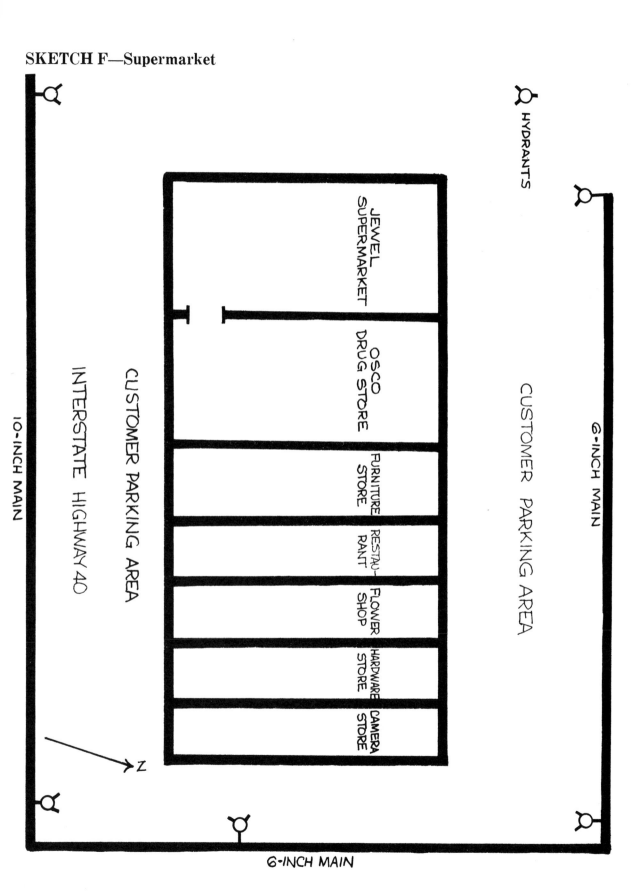

335

concerned with the possibility of a smoke explosion if the store is not properly vented.

Location and extent of fire: The drugstore rear utility area is well-involved in fire. There are ample combustibles to feed the fire. Rear or side doors are difficult to force. Entry to such fires is almost always a one sided approach from the front only—men have to advance directly into the heat and smoke. In fact, one of the classic errors made by many fire departments is that they attempt forcible entry through the rear service doors. The resulting delay usually allows the fire to involve the hanging ceiling space and from there the rest of the store.

Efforts should be made to get the rear doors open but not at the expense of neglecting hose line advancement via the front entrance. This is commonly misunderstood. Because there is evidence the fire is in the rear, efforts are concentrated at getting the rear doors open. This reasoning is wrong. First, the doors are substantial, barred and designed to keep people out. At times it takes more than 10 minutes to force such doors. Meanwhile, the fire inside is gaining headway. Second, since the fire is in the rear, there are only two places towards which it can progress. One is the hanging ceiling space, the other is the front of the store. Concentrating your efforts at the rear provides no attack to head the fire off from moving towards the main body of the store.

It makes far more sense to cut the roof over the hot spot for ventilation; to pull the smoke and gases on up and out, thereby limiting lateral involvement. Then force entrance via the front doors (easily done with little damage) and advance toward the fire. If the fire is in the hanging ceiling, use long pike poles to pull the ceiling; or use piercing nozzles into the ceiling space. If it is difficult to hold your position, break out the show windows to ventilate the store and create a draft which will help carry the combustion products out the roof hole. (See Figure 203.)

If the heat and smoke are too intense, try using a heavy stream appliance from the doorway to force up the ceiling squares which will expose the fire to attack from below.

The general strategy is to move against the fire travel; to head it off from involving any more of the structure than is already on fire. If the reverse method is used where hose lines are brought to play on a fire from behind, the fire may continue to spread forward, feeding on combustibles in its path as well as spreading the heat and smoke ahead of the fire.

Exposures:

North: None.

South: None.

East: The row of stores may be involved via the common hanging ceiling if fire gets into the hanging ceiling space of the furniture store. This has to be guarded against by placing hose lines in the furniture store and on the roof.

West: The supermarket via the open space between the stores and the common hanging ceiling.

Auxiliary appliances: Sprinklers in the rear utility areas of the supermarket and drugstore must be supplied by a pumper through the fire department siamese connection.

Water supply: The hydrants on the north side of the stores are on 6-inch dead-ended mains and should not be expected to supply more than one 1,000 GPM pumper at the far end. If a pumper is connected to the hydrant at the northeast corner of the parking area, it probably will draw the water from the pumper at the northwest end and in turn starve the sprinkler supply. The major water supply should come from the hydrants on Highway 40 (off 10-inch main) but will require police assistance to block traffic on major highway to avoid injury to firemen and damage to fire hose.

Weather, wind: According to the description, the weather is hot. This means men may easily become exhausted because of arduous fire duty and encumbered by heavy clothing. Other than this, the weather and wind have no effect on the strategy.

SKETCH G—Supermarket sizeup

SKETCH G—Supermarket sizeup

200 feet deep

concrete block

JEWEL SUPERMARKET

utility areas both stores

steel truss roof both stores

heavy smoke build up.

fire dept. Siamese

OSCO DRUG STORE

spklr.

No cellars

panapet wall

800 feet long concrete block

FURNITURE STORE

RESTAU-RANT

FLOWER SHOP

HARDWARE STORE

CAMERA STORE

These stores have flat roofs

wood sheathed

front is all show window

HYDRANTS

FIRE AREA

CUSTOMER PARKING AREA

6-INCH MAIN

10-INCH MAIN

INTERSTATE HIGHWAY 40

CUSTOMER PARKING AREA

6-INCH MAIN

N

337

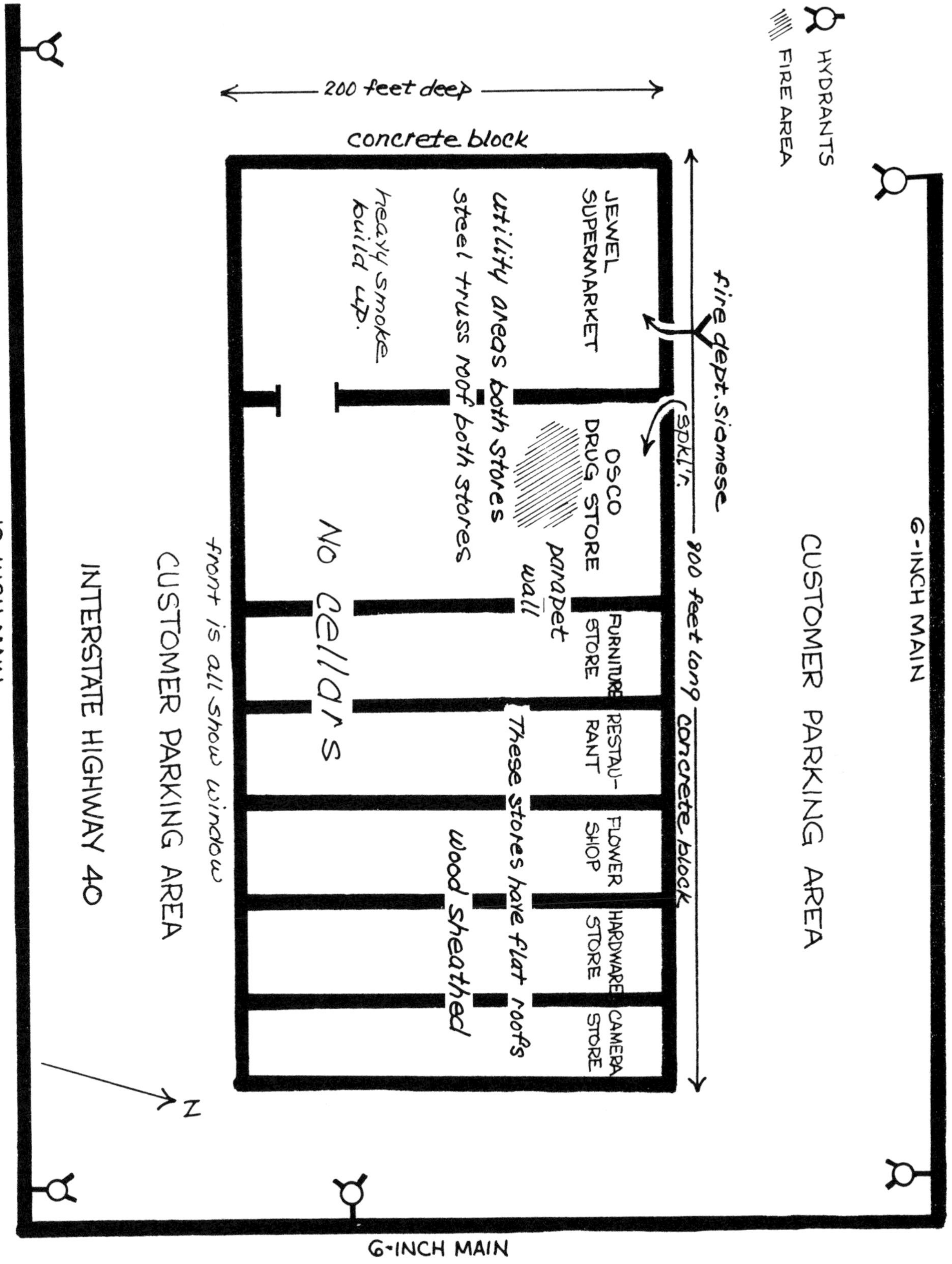

Apparatus: The two engine companies and one ladder company are completely insufficient for this fire. Sufficient help will be called to accomplish what will be specified under the handling of the fire.

Communications: A command center will be established at the front of the fire building. Communications will be maintained by mobile truck radios and portable handie talkie units carried by officers.

Salvage: Will be instituted as soon as fire is under control.

Special Matters:

1. These fires have a sorry loss record and generally result in complete collapse. Every effort must be made to effect control before roof collapse because once the roof falls in it is literally impossible to extinguish the fire burning in the stock below.

2. Great care must be exercised in sending men to open truss roofs such as these because of the early collapse potential.

3. The major water supply will have to come from across a busy highway, though traffic should be light at this hour. If hose lines are not guarded against cars and trucks running over the lines, they may break, with resulting loss of water to crucial hose lines.

4. Call for lighting trucks, rescue units, medical aid, other city departments such as building department, water department, electrical department, health department (food store involved), public utilities (gas company), and extra police to handle traffic and spectators.

5. Expansion of metal structural members (girders, beams) enough to cause walls to push out, causing collapse of roof and/or walls.

6. Large metal signs attached to roof and/or side walls which may weaken and fall onto men below or pull side walls as they fall.

7. Collapse of roof while men are working on it. As a precautionary measure, lay a long ladder across the working area. Should the roof start to give, men can step onto the ladder bridging the sagging area. Another method is to work from or tied to an ele-

vating platform basket. But where the roof is really suspect, don't send men on to it. Records of past fires show these roofs have little fire resistance because of the unprotected metal structural members. Gypsum roofs commonly used now on supermarkets are fire-resistant but this can be a dangerous disadvantage to firemen. This roof has high insulating value; if fire is burning in the hanging ceiling space it will not vent itself by burning through as it would with wood-sheathed roofs. Instead of dissipating, the heat will accumulate and bank up, attacking the unprotected steel members. The men working on the roof may be completely unaware of their danger until it suddenly collapses under them.

8. Be careful of overhead electric lines burning through and falling onto men below.

9. Ventilation is limited to the roof (by cutting), rear doors, and show windows. If the store has been closed for the night and the fire has been burning for several hours, hot combustible gases will have been distilled off. All that may be missing for an explosion is oxygen. Indiscriminate breaking of the front show windows or forcible entry from the rear may supply this missing ingredient. Men should guard against indiscriminate forcible entry advancing quickly into the body of the store. In this manner they may advance just far enough to be caught in the middle of a terrible explosion. Trained men will observe this precaution. When approaching such supermarket fires, don't rush to force entrance or break the front show windows. Feel the plate glass with your BARE hand. If the glass is burning hot, don't break it—don't force entrance yet. Get men to the roof with power saws and cut over the hot spot—cut *one* large hole, at least eight feet square. A hole this size will permit the gases to escape upwards. If they explode, the force and flame will be directed up in the air where they will do no harm. If manpower and time permits, you should have a protective hose line on the roof before starting to cut. Once roof ventilation has been effected, get the men off the roof. Then the front windows should be broken out completely and jagged pieces of glass that may fall and injure men

FIGURE 203. *If a fire breaks through the roof and is not exposing buildings or people, it constitutes a distinct help to firefighters. The combustion products will not readily spread laterally inside the building, and with adequate ventilation below, men and hose lines can advance to attack the fire from within. Yet, it is common to see hose lines performing as the one in this photograph. The stream is not accomplishing anything constructive and at the same time it is robbing water from other crucial areas where it is probably needed.*

If the stream was able to beat down the fire coming from the roof, in all probability it would also drive the combustion products back into the building and eventually make conditions so severe that men inside the building would be forced to retreat. Such streams should be shut down and the manpower and water used where it will be effective. There are, however, legitimate uses for

heavy exterior streams at fires which are coming through the roof. Here are some of them:

1. To protect exposed areas.

2. To knock down flying firebrands.

3. To drive a stream into the fire building in an attempt to cool and darken down a serious large body of fire AFTER the roof has partially or fully collapsed and it is impossible or dangerous to move men inside. In such cases, exterior heavy streams pouring down onto the fire are a proper weapon.

Some other instances for proper use of heavy streams pouring onto a fire from above are these:

1. Large open fires such as lumberyards.

2. Railroad yards.

3. Freight depots.

4. Rows of combustible shacks, sheds, or small frame dwellings which present a conflagration potential.

cleanly removed. But don't break the windows in the conventional manner. From a distance of about 20 feet and to the side of the store, direct your stream, with good pressure, at the heated window. The cold water on the heated glass will break it. Wait for a half minute or so to give the oxygen a chance to mix with the rich heated gases. If it is going to explode, you want it to do so before you move into the store.

Many firemen are overly concerned about the cost of replacing broken glass windows. But once fire has heated stained glass in a hot fire, the glass has to be replaced regardless. Where fire conditions are not severe, it is still cheaper to gain access by breaking out the door window rather than damaging the door, lock, or door frame. But be careful to remove all pieces of broken glass to avoid injury to men. The injury potential with jagged pieces of glass is the major objection to glass breakage.

Note: Whenever a roof is opened as mentioned above, an additional precaution must be taken—that is, to push down the ceiling inside the store.

**Extinguishing Process
(See Sketch G)**

Line 1. Two and a half inch into drugstore via front entrance. Advance towards rear utility area to keep fire from advancing or involving hanging ceiling space. This line is also crucial in keeping fire from involving Jewel Supermarket by unprotected opening at front of store.

Line 2. Three inch into sprinkler siamese at rear of supermarket to supply sprinkler. One reason the sprinklers apparently are failing to keep the fire in check is either poor water supply (small connection off 6-inch dead-end main) or too many heads have opened again, reducing effective flows.

Line 3. Two and a half inch to back up line. 1.

Line 4. Two and a half inch to Jewel Supermarket via front entrance. Wye off into two 1½-inch lines to cover the entire store

should fire come across into hanging ceiling space from drugstore.

Line 5. Two and a half inch to cellar nozzle onto roof of drugstore to operate through roof onto fire below.

Line 6. Two and a half inch to rear of drugstore in event door was forced to operate onto fire in utility area.

Line 7. Two and a half inch to furniture store and wyed off into two 1½-inch lines to be ready should fire pass dividing wall in hanging ceiling space.

Line 8. Two and a half inch to roof of furniture store should fire eventually start to burn through roof of drugstore.

Line 9. Two and a half inch to roof of Jewel Store should fire eventually start to burn through roof of drug store.

Line 10. If the involved area was large enough, it might be necessary to use two cellar nozzles on the roof. If so, line 10 would be used for such purpose. Then another line would be laid to the roof of the Jewel Store.

Two engine company crews would be kept on standby as a reserve in case fire did begin to involve the supermarket or if it became necessary to set up a heavy stream appliance to operate into the supermarket or drugstore from the store entrances. Since there are no exposures listed in the surrounding areas, a spark and brand patrol would not be needed. If the fire involves the drugstore roof to considerable extent, additional hose lines would have to augment lines 8 and 9 to prevent roof ignition by direct flame contact or flying brands.

Ladder company assignments

First ladder company (or available unit)

1. Ladder the fire building at the rear first because this is the closest point to where men will be operating on the roof and presents the quickest retreat, if necessary.

2. Cut the roof over the hot spot but see that line is available before opening should

fire blow out and involve roof surfaces.

3. Force entrance to both stores via front doors for line advancement and examination. Don't open if windows are very hot to touch — see "special matters" under sizeup, item 9.

Second ladder company (or available unit)

1. Ladder roof at front.

2. Start to force rear doors.

3. Open ceilings in Jewel Store alongside drugstore to see if fire has entered hanging ceiling space. Make sure charged line is available before opening.

Third ladder company (or available unit)

1. Force entrance at front of furniture store to check for possible involvement via defective parapeted wall between drugstore and furniture store by putting small holes in ceiling of furniture store toward the rear, alongside drugstore division wall. Have charged line available before opening.

2. Ladder roof of furniture store.

3. Set up emergency lighting.

4. Spread salvage covers in drugstore first, then Jewel Store, then furniture store.

When the primary functions of the ladder companies have been completed, they move in to the routine tasks of opening ceilings and sidewalls to expose any hidden fire travel. They check gas and electricity, and overhaul burnt or suspect materials.

Now let us take the same fire but make it 2 P.M. on a shopping day. These would be the major differences in strategy.

Life: Hazard is severe to shoppers and store help, as well as to firemen, particularly if the fire got into and spread throughout the cockloft. This might cause ceilings to drop in main body of store, exposing the shoppers to fire. People will panic, rushing to get out the way they came in, and may pile up against the doors. Remember, one door opens inward, and if people try to get out this way, they will pile up against it. People also may be trapped by a flash fire which can sweep across the main body of the store in the flimsy combustible stock, large flammable displays, hanging paper signs, etc.

Time: 2 P.M. on a normal shopping day would probably mean a crowded store —

women with small children on shopping carts, blocked aisles, loaded shopping carts turned over in panic rush, serving to increase the hazard. Parking lots filled with cars, blocked hydrants, impediment to apparatus maneuvers. The hour of the day makes it evident there will be adequate light except in utility areas even if electricity fails. This is fortunate because a nighttime fire in a busy store would compound the problem, indicating a potential for a greater life loss.

Height, area, construction: Will be similar to the first fire, however it is reasonable to say all the problems at the second fire will be magnified because of severe life hazard.

Location, extent of fire: Probably will not be as difficult to spot or as extensive because, since the store was occupied, discovery of the fire should be quicker unless the employees were attempting to fight the fire themselves without alerting the shoppers. This kind of delay may allow the fire to get into the hanging ceiling space without the employees knowing it.

Should the fire break out into the open, regardless whether it be from the utility area or the hanging ceiling, the people will rush in mad panic to get out through the front entrance. If the firemen try to bring hose lines in from the front via these same doors, they will block its use for the people trying to get out. In such case, the stream should be directed at the ceiling over the heads of the people. This will put a protective water curtain between the threatened shoppers and the fire.

The rear service doors are frequently open, or if closed they will not be barred and can be readily opened. Any streams operated from the rear onto the fire should be directed towards the ceiling, which will deflect the water over a wide area. Such technique will not drive the combustion products towards the store proper.

Ventilation: As in the first fire, get a large hole in the roof over the hot spot to help rid the store of the heated smoke and gases. It should also help localize the fire by drawing the fire up and through the roof, tending to prevent greater lateral involvement. Do not break out show windows until lines are in position to cover in case fire flares up because of added draft.

All other factors under "Hazards and Problems" remain the same. Because of the probability of injuries to people, summon additional ambulances and doctors.

Line 1: Two and a half inch hand line into store through broken-out center show window, directing a stream over heads of people towards the ceiling to put a water curtain between the trapped shoppers and the fire. Directing stream towards ceiling will deflect stream downward over a wide area and give far greater coverage than spot delivery. Do not advance this line far into store to avoid blocking aisles because people will be rushing to get out and may trip over the hose lines. As soon as the store is clear of people, advance this line rapidly toward the rear.

Line 2. Two and a half inch hand line into store alongside Line 1 to cover a wide frontal area. These two lines operating together will give maximum protection to trapped occupants.

Note: Such a placement would not prevent the people from getting out because they would leave by the doors and the broken-out show window at the opposite end. For this reason lines 1 and 2 penetrate store via broken-out center show windows and do not advance too far into store until people are out.

Line 3. Three inch hose line into sprinkler siamese connection and pump into same.

Line 4. Two and a half inch hose line to cellar nozzle on roof of drugstore and operate through hole cut into roof onto fire below.

Line 5. Two and a half inch line to Jewel Supermarket via front entrance. This line would be wyed off into two 1½-inch lines and operate as in the night-time fire. These lines would also help protect occupants of the Jewel Store.

Line 6. Two and a half inch line to the rear entrance of the drugstore and operate onto the fire by directing stream up towards ceiling rather than driving combustion products towards front of the store.

Line 7. If the involved area in the drugstore is sufficiently large, it may be necessary to use two cellar nozzles on the roof; if so, line 7 would be used for this purpose.

Line 8. Two and a half inch to the furniture store and wyed off into two 1½-inch lines and operated as in the night-time fire.

Line 9. Two and a half inch to roof of furniture store to guard against contingency of fire burning through roof of drugstore and involving combustible surfaces of other roofs.

Line 10. Two and a half inch to roof of Jewel Store for reasons similar to line 9. Two engine companies would be held in reserve as in the night fire.

Ladder company assignments:
First ladder company (or available unit)
1. Chock open front doors.
2. Go in and assist trapped occupants in both stores.
Second ladder company (or available unit)
1. Assist first ladder company in getting people out.
2. Where need to get people out of store more rapidly is apparent, break out one show window at opposite end to door, remove large pieces of glass, clear stock from inside of show-window ledge, and help remove people via this emergency means. Then break out other show windows between the door and the emergency window exit for line entrance and penetration into body of store. Hose line would have been called for and standing by in case fire flared up.
Third ladder company (or available unit)
1. Aid ladder 2 in search and removal of victims.
2. Force rear doors.
3. Cut roof for ventilation and/or insertion of cellar nozzle.

Fourth ladder company (or available unit)

1. Check for fire extension via hanging ceiling space from drugstore to Jewel Store by opening ceilings (wait until charged lines are available).

2. Perform the same operation in the furniture store.

3. Set up emergency first-aid equipment, inhalators, etc., to treat victims.

If ladder No. 4 reported in for assignment and people were still being removed, this company would have been ordered to assist in the search and removal. Then the company would cover the extension factor in the adjoining stores.

Normally, such a store would be evacuated in about five minutes, but because of severity of fire, people trapped or overcome, etc., the time required would vary. That is why the ladder company crews were used exclusively at the start to search for and remove any people trapped. The potential of fire spread and exposure protection is subordinate to the need to protect life. Once the people are evacuated, the ladder company crews would perform their normal functions of opening up to expose hidden fire travel, ventilation, overhaul, etc.

Note that there is a difference in operational strategy because of the difference in time, even though the fire takes place in exactly the same area. In the fire at 2 P.M. when the store was occupied, all efforts were concentrated on life safety at the expense of fire spread.

While we did advance lines in through the front, note that Lines 1 and 2 would not impede the egress of the people in that they were escaping via the normal doors and the broken-out windows at the opposite end. It is for this reason that Lines 1 and 2 penetrate store via broken-out center show windows and do not advance too far into store until people are out.

Members operating hose lines would be cautioned to avoid sweeping display counters with streams, thereby dislodging canned goods all over the floor, where they would trip people and operating forces.

With the fire occurring at 2 P.M. on a shopping day, line placement was directed to provide maximum protection for the trapped shoppers. Ladder company assignments followed the same reasoning. The primary objective in any fire is to save human life before concentrating efforts on saving property.

Example 6
Furniture Factory

A fire occurs at 3 A.M. in an old furniture factory built in 1914. It has exterior brick walls, wood-joisted floors, open wooden stairs. By the time the fire department arrives, fire has possession of the Adams Street side of the first and second floors. (See Sketch H.)

The arriving fire units go to work quickly and efficiently. Engine Company 1 lays two 2½-inch lines into the entrance on Main Street corner of Adams; one line is taken to the first floor, the second line to the second floor.

Engine Company 2 lays two 3-inch lines into the fire department siamese connection to the sprinkler system and pumps in at 150 pounds. Engine Company 3 lays two 3-inch lines into the elevating platform which was set up on Adams Street and swept the first and second floors with a heavy 2-inch stream.

Engine Company 4 lays a single 2½-inch line up the fire escape on Segal Street to the third floor.

The two ladder companies that respond are assigned to help the engine companies lay hose lines.

The fire is brought under control in 20 minutes, with damage confined to the first and second floors.

Though this fire was quickly extinguished, there were several basic errors in the total strategy. Can you point them out? In this problem you should use general terms rather than pointing out perhaps a question of improper pumper or nozzle operation.

Answers to example 6: furniture factory

There were two basic errors.

Note that there were no lines placed at any time to head off the fire from involving most of the fire building. Had the interior hand lines been unable to move in or had the elevating platform stream been obstructed by a partition, this fire would undoubtedly have involved the third and fourth floors via the open inside stairs and would have spread to the rest of the floor area. In this case, the elevating platform should have been set up on Main Street, where it could have cut off the fire from involving the rest of the floor area. Additional help should have been called immediately, two lines sent up the rear stairs on Main Street to cover the first, second, and third floors, and more lines sent up the fire escape in the alley.

The ladder company men should have been used to force entrance and ventilate the roof and windows immediately. If they had completed these assignments and there were no ceilings or sidewalls to open, they could have been used to help the engine company crews.

SKETCH H—Furniture factory

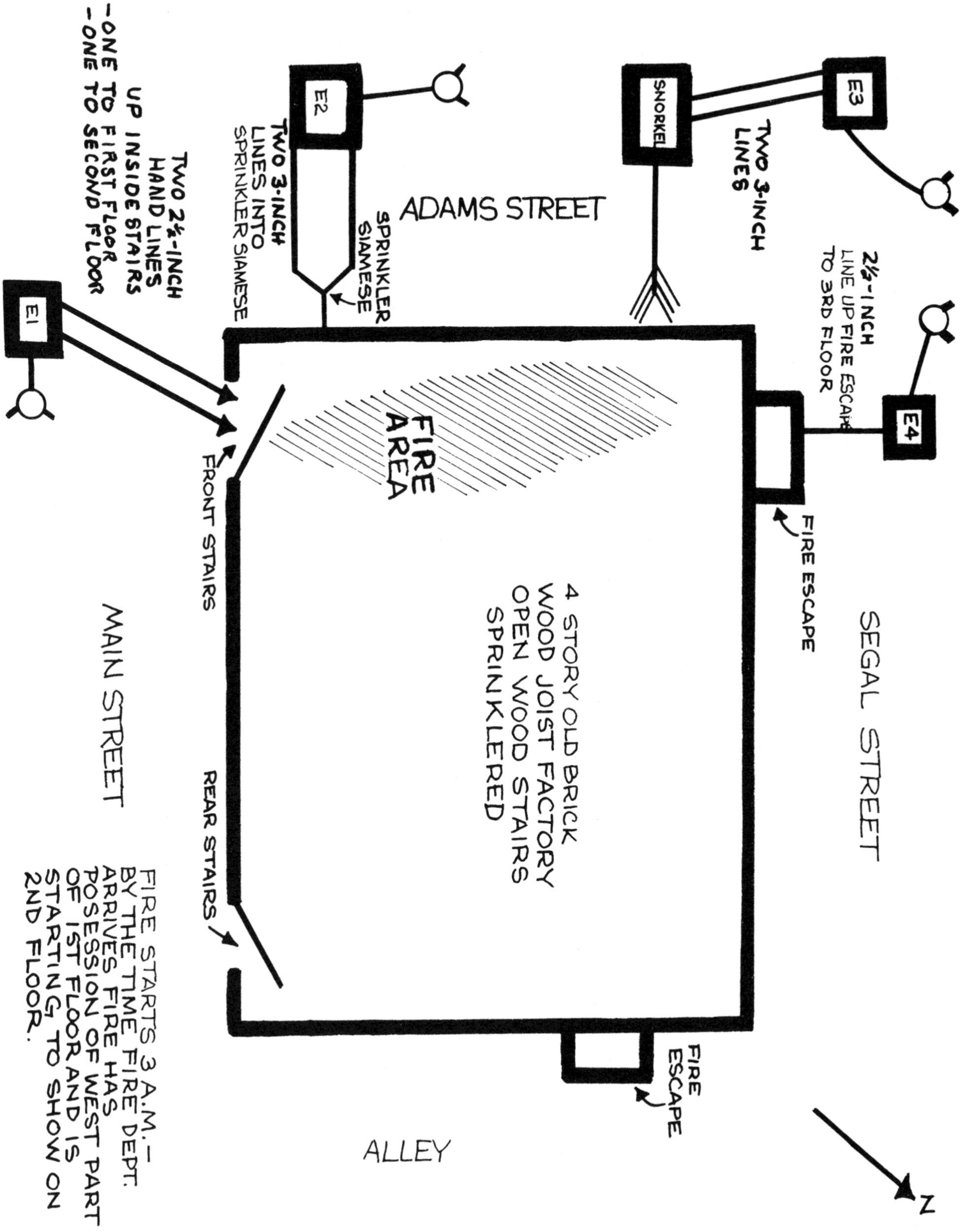

UP INSIDE STAIRS
TWO 2½-INCH HAND LINES
– ONE TO FIRST FLOOR
– ONE TO SECOND FLOOR

E1

E2
TWO 3-INCH LINES INTO SPRINKLER SIAMESE

SPRINKLER SIAMESE

SNORKEL

E3
TWO 3-INCH LINES

E4
2½-INCH LINE UP FIRE ESCAPE TO 3RD FLOOR

ADAMS STREET

FIRE AREA

FRONT STAIRS

4 STORY OLD BRICK
WOOD JOIST FACTORY
OPEN WOOD STAIRS
SPRINKLERED

FIRE ESCAPE

MAIN STREET

REAR STAIRS

SEGAL STREET

FIRE ESCAPE

FIRE STARTS 3 A.M.—
BY THE TIME FIRE DEPT.
ARRIVES FIRE HAS
POSESSION OF WEST PART
OF 1ST FLOOR AND IS
STARTING TO SHOW ON
2ND FLOOR.

ALLEY

N

Example 7
Furniture Factory-Warehouse

There is a high one-story factory complex with 1,200 feet of frontage on Robbins Street. Built originally around 1924 as a warehouse, it had stood vacant for years and later was altered to make it a complete furniture factory, from storage of raw lumber to turning out finished products of both upholstered and bedroom type furniture. In order to conform to their needs, the furniture factory partitioned the once-open warehouse space to a lumber storage area at the extreme east end of the building. Immediately to the left of the lumber storage and separated by a substantial fire wall was the factory itself with its vast array of woodworking machinery.

From here the process moved (separated by another fire wall) to the paint spray area. From the paint spray area, separated by an open interior court, again cut off by fire walls, the rest of the complex was used as a finished furniture warehouse and display area. There were two office areas on the north and south ends of the open court. The warehouse had a loading dock on the south end. The woodworking factory and paint spray area were covered by an automatic sprinkler system supplied by a 6-inch main off the city water system. There were two yard hydrants also supplied by this same main just inside the entrance gate to the plant. (See Sketch I.)

At 2 P.M. on a Sunday, fire was noticed by the plant watchman in the south part of the woodworking factory. He tried to hold the fire with an extinguisher but was driven out. He then phoned in the alarm. When the fire department arrived, some fire was showing out the front windows of the woodworking plant.

The first engine company connected to the yard hydrant inside the gate and laid a 2½-inch line to the front door of the woodworking plant but could not advance because of heavy smoke. The second engine company connected to the other yard hydrant in the

plant and laid a 2½-inch line to the lumber storage area. They, too, had difficulty moving in. Within minutes after the two hand lines were in operation, the fire seemed to grow in intensity. Help was called immediately and additional hose lines were placed as follows:

Line 3. A 2½-inch line to back up Line 1.

Line 4. A 2½-inch line to the rear entrance of the woodworking factory.

Line 5. A heavy stream appliance set up on Robbins Street to sweep the lumber yard and woodworking factory area.

Suddenly fire began to show heavily in the paint-spraying part of the plant, and before additional help arrived (by now a fourth alarm had been called), the fire had jumped the open area and was starting to involve the finished furniture warehouse. By the time lines were laid into the warehouse, the entire complex was in flames and went for a total loss. The fire department was relegated to covering exposures and chasing down incipient fires caused by flying brands.

Properly handled, this fire should have been contained to the original area of involvement. What went wrong here?

Answers to example 7: furniture factory-warehouse

There were a number of major errors in the handling of this fire. The first two engine companies, by connecting to the two hydrants inside the plant, robbed the sprinkler system of the water which was evidently holding the fire in check. Note that the fire suddenly grew in intensity when the hose lines from these engines were put into play. One of the first hose lines should have been placed into the sprinkler siamese to augment the supply.

The second hose line should have gone to the entrance of the woodworking plant but the third line should have moved into the paint-spraying area to cut off the fire in case it did move into here, as it did. Note that in each case line placement was such that it followed the fire, waiting until fire showed and then frantically trying to get a line into place to extinguish. Such tactics are almost

SKETCH I—Furniture factory-warehouse

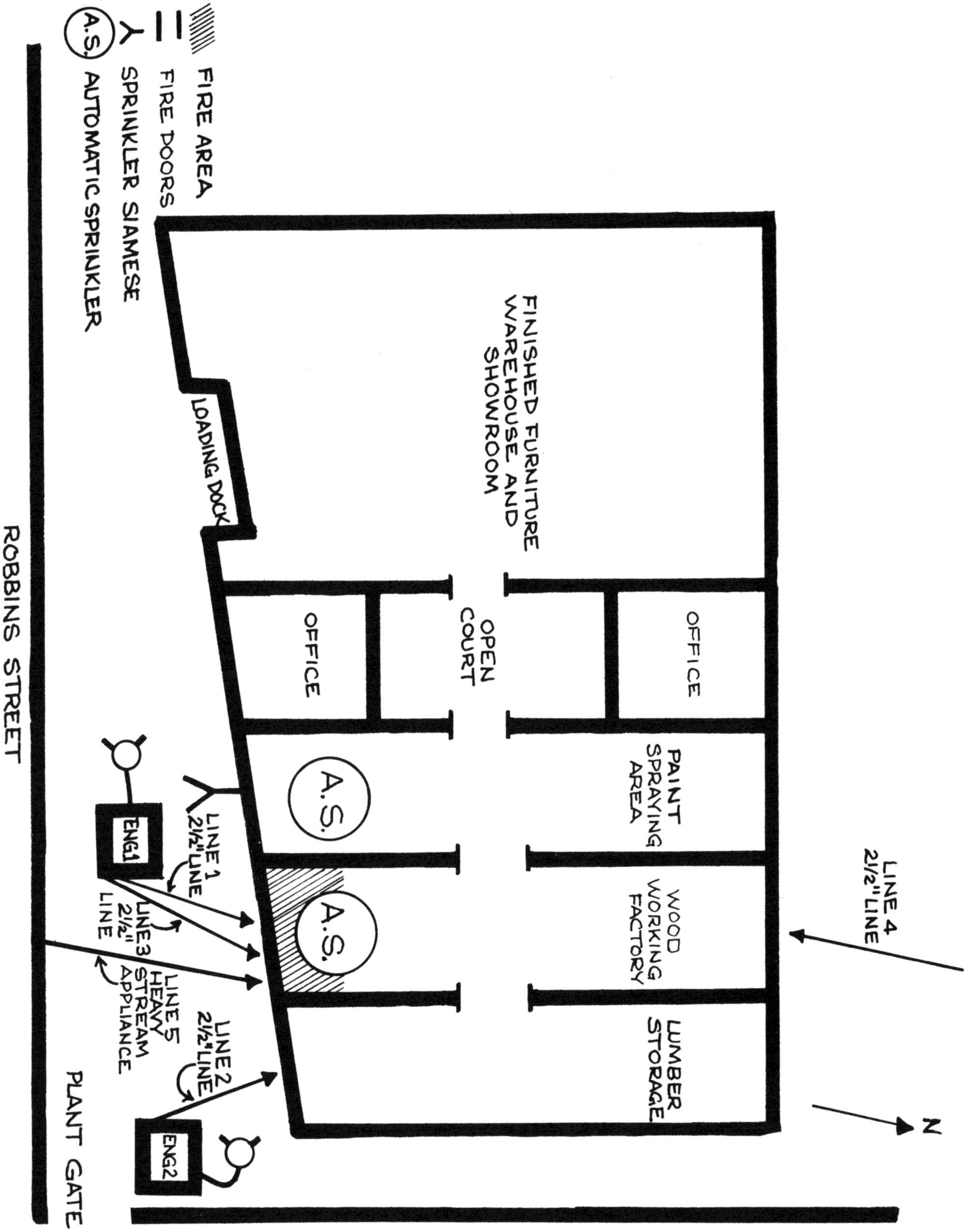

Legend:
- A.S. AUTOMATIC SPRINKLER
- SPRINKLER SIAMESE
- FIRE DOORS
- FIRE AREA

Labels in sketch:
- ROBBINS STREET
- PLANT GATE
- LOADING DOCK
- FINISHED FURNITURE WAREHOUSE AND SHOWROOM
- OFFICE
- OPEN COURT
- OFFICE
- PAINT SPRAYING AREA
- WOOD WORKING FACTORY
- LUMBER STORAGE
- A.S.
- A.S.
- ENG.1
- ENG.2
- LINE 1 2½" LINE
- LINE 3 2½" LINE
- LINE 5 HEAVY STREAM APPLIANCE
- LINE 2 2½" LINE
- LINE 4 2½" LINE
- N

347

always too late. It takes time to move hose line into position. If this is attempted only after fire shows up in an area, the attempt to combat will almost always be too late.

In this fire, heavy stream appliances should have been placed in the doorway from the open court to the paint-spray area as a stop-gap if flames did come across. Under cover of the protection of the heavy streams, hand lines could have moved in from the paint area towards the woodworking factory behind the natural cover of the fire walls. Once this extension problem was solved, lines could have been moved into the lumber storage area to hold the fire from involving this part. If a choice had to be made as to where to stop the spread, it should have been made at the fire wall between the paint area and the woodworking plant, not at the lumber storage.

There is one more major, glaring error. If the fire moved from the woodworking factory to the paint-spray area in spite of fire walls with fire doors, it must be obvious that the fire doors were blocked open. An attempt should have been made to get the doors closed, segregating the woodworking plant from the lumber storage and paint-spray area.

Had this door been closed, the sprinkler siamese supplied early, and the roof over the fire area opened, this fire would have been confined to its original area.

Chapter 29

Miscellaneous problems you may face

MAJOR PROBLEMS and the most common problems a firefighter faces have been dealt with, along with solutions to them, in the preceding chapter. There are miscellaneous problems, too, that do not fit neatly into any one category. These are the problems I will concern myself with in this chapter, to guide you in your answers to simpler examination questions.

The problem:

You respond to a second alarm and you are in charge of a ladder company. The chief directs you to ventilate the fire building at the roof.

A. What precautions would you take?

B. How would you ventilate?

Here are the answers:

A. Precautions

1. Take to the roof a roof rope, hose roller, life belt, power saw, axe, pike pole, hand lights, short ladder (to push down ceiling below or to use in gaining access to adjoining roof, etc.), and radio.

2. Lower rope at selected point to be ready to hoist hose and tools or to provide a means of escape.

3. Provide a safe retreat from roof to adjoining building or raise aerial to most protected point.

4. If vision is limited, provide adequate light for safe operations.

5. Avoid venting at points where severe exposures are formed to adjoining buildings or members operating. If exposure protectors are open, close them where necessary.

6. In opening or cutting up roof, take care not to open in line of travel.

7. Operate with back to wind and to point of retreat.

8. If conditions indicate that venting may cause exposure, delay same until charged line is available unless life in danger.

B. Ventilation

1. Take all precautions outlined above.

2. Remove all movable covers, skylights, scuttle covers over stairs, etc.

3. Don't remove those that may cause exposure hazards.

4. If ceiling below hole made in roof indicates it, push it down.

5. If openings are not large enough for adequate ventilation, enlarge them.

6. Venting at top floor also may be accomplished by pushing down or breaking windows from roof or fire escape.

7. Advise officer when you've finished. He may need your help elsewhere.

The problem:

Name five conditions necessary for a dust explosion.

Here are the answers:

1. Dust must be combustible.

2. Must be finely divided.

3. There must be a proper mixture of air and dust.

4. There must be a spark or flame or temperature sufficient to ignite.

5. There will be an absence of excessive humidity.

The problem:

State in detail how you would ventilate the cellar of a private dwelling well-involved in fire at night.

Here is the answer:

1. Divide the company into squads.

2. Force entrance as needed.

3. Send a man to the rear to open windows in basement.

4. Do the same in front of the building.

5. Assign men to move into the basement. Open doors to create circulation and relieve smoke once people above have been safely evacuated.

6. Vent upper floors by doors and windows.

7. If conditions are severe, cut floor above cellar near a window so smoke and heat will pass to outer air.

8. Use tools or short ladders to push down ceilings after cutting floor.

9. Do no venting where same would intensify fire unless charged lines are ready.

10. Do no venting where same would involve exits or lines of travel or where men may be cut off.

11. Men trying to advance down cellar stairs with lines may be helped by opening a riser in stair above.

12. When ventilating, search places for anyone overcome and remove if found.

13. Shut gas and electricity, if indicated.

14. If extension of fire is noted, call for line and notify chief if help is needed.

15. When finished, report to chief on action taken and follow further orders.

The problem:

Discuss the effect of weather on the extension of fire.

Here are the answers:

1. Heavy damp weather results in:
   a. Delayed discovery at night.
   b. Delayed alarms resulting in greater involvement.
   c. Delayed response due to poor visibility, wet streets (accident potential).
   d. Ventilation is less effective because smoke hangs low.
   e. Advance on fire is slowed because of ineffective ventilation.

2. Clear, cold weather:
   a. Discovery faster.
   b. Smoke easily noticed.
   c. Response faster.
   d. Operations of venting more effective because smoke and heat lift, making for more rapid advance, search, and extinguishment.

3. Stormy, snowy weather:
   a. Same as for heavy damp weather except that response is still slower, because of need for heavy clothing (accident potential).
   b. Operations at fires are slowed because working on roofs, fire escapes, off ladders is more hazardous.
   c. Forcible entry is needed because of closed doors, windows.
   d. Snow on roofs helps prevent the spark and brand hazard.

4. Clear hot weather:
   a. Discovery and response is more rapid.
   b. There will be greater exposure hazard to adjoining and adjacent buildings because of open doors and windows.
   c. Life hazard in slum areas is greater because of B above.
   d. Excessive water consumption in hot weather may reduce water pressure.

The problem:

Name three general conditions where the use of water should be avoided, if possible, and cite three specific instances under each general condition.

Here are the answers:

1. General condition—Where such may favor progress of chemical reaction. Examples:

   a. Unslaked lime combines with water with evolution of much heat (800° F.)— formation of dust clouds—extremely slippery.

b. Calcium carbide with water forms acetylene gas—highly inflammable—explosive range of 3 percent to 82 percent.

c. Finely ground metals on fire break down water and liberate hydrogen.

2. General condition—Where it may assist in spreading fire in oils and liquids not miscible with water or liquids that react violently with water. Examples:

a. Fires in tanks containing mineral oils.

b. Varnish vats, dip tanks, tempering tanks.

c. Large amounts of sulphuric acid.

3. General condition—Where careless use of water may cause great structural damage. Examples:

a. Highly heated unprotected metal structural members, sudden cooling causing contraction and possible collapse.

b. Where absorbents are present, increasing the live load on floors.

c. Electrical transformer vaults causing arcing, burning, and generating of flammable or explosive gases.

The problem:

Name three structural defects that exist in buildings and their effect on operations at fires.

Here are the answers:

1. Unprotected vertical openings are the worst defect in building construction.

a. Drafts created by flue effect intensify fire in story of origin.

b. Greater amount of materials, both structural and contents, exposed to fire.

c. The rapid displacement of heat and gases of combustion rising and banking at top causes mushrooming and develops conditions favorable to back draft.

d. Where such openings are stairs or elevators, the means of exit are quickly cut off.

e. Where such stairs are combustible, they weaken quickly at the top.

f. Where sprinklers are present, they make for a less efficient operation of same.

2. Large undivided areas:

a. To a lesser degree than unprotected vertical openings, they expose only the floor area and its contents to fire.

b. Access to interior is difficult because of smoke and heat conditions.

c. Streams from exterior ineffective due to lack of penetration because of great distance to interior of area.

d. Delay in surrounding fire—long stretches necessary.

e. Large areas require supporting columns and girders—such are usually not insulated.

3. Unprotected metal structural members:

a. They weaken quickly with rise in temperature.

b. In cases of only moderate fires, failures have resulted.

c. Sudden contraction by cooling has resulted in failures of members.

d. The degree of danger, of course, depending on the live and dead loads.

The problem:

State briefly why fires in large unbroken areas develop severe conditions and are so hard to handle.

Here are the answers:

1. Large amounts of fuel, both structural and content.

2. Entire areas exposed to a single fire.

3. Drafts, both existing and created, are greater than in smaller areas.

4. Displacement of heat and gases intensifies fire to greater degree.

5. Temperatures are higher and may seriously endanger structural stability.

6. In sprinklered buildings, heat will not bank down as quickly, delaying operation of sprinklers. Finally, many heads go off at once with loss in pressure and increased damage.

7. Greater delay in surrounding fire; longer stretches.

8. Fire in center of floor out of reach of exterior streams.

9. Location of fire more difficult because of smoke and heat conditions.

10. More difficult to reach to extinguish because of smoke and heat conditions.

Conclusion

Chapter 30

Command at fires

THROUGHOUT THIS BOOK I have dealt with the techniques of handling various fire problems. But to successfully handle any complex fire, a knowledge of command structure is required. This chapter summarizes some of the important facets of command, its strengths and weaknesses.

The efficiency of command generally varies with the size of the department. The efficiency of the commander varies with his experience and expertise. Frequently there is little standardization in the duties carried out by designated rank. It is not unusual to see a chief doing a firemen's work; it is common to see an entire sector of an operation under the command of a fireman or lieutenant (or no command at all). This does not in any way intend to belittle the firemen or lieutenant. He may be, and probably is, capable, but he is compelled to assume duties for which he has not been trained.

In far too many situations specific assignments to positions at fires are not given. An inevitable result of such neglect is that incoming companies tend to assign themselves. This may be described as the "free enterprise" system of firefighting. Why does this occur?

Problem with small department

First let us examine the small department. A critical analysis of past fires in smaller cities might reveal that the chief really performs the functions of a company officer and in fact often reports in on the first arriving unit.

Because the incidence of major fires in complicated structures is low, he is unprepared to handle complex problems. A lack of organization to cope with serious fires is often manifest. Frequently, manpower is so short and the urgency of the task so great, he must help connect the pumper to the hydrant, lay lines, supervise the line operation, or raise ladders (an experience many of us in the small municipality have faced).

Only when additional incoming units arrive can he rightfully assume the duties he should perform. But when the incoming units arrive where is our chief—in on the line? On the roof? Examining the building next door? To whom do the arriving units report? How are they to know what points are covered and which are in dire need of attention? It is here that the free enterprise system comes in. Each incoming officer decides which piece of the action he will take.

Now let us discuss our commander. Assume he is a volunteer and the arriving mutual aid companies are commanded by paid lieutenants. Is he reluctant to give a paid fire officer an order? In many cases he is.

But is this chief at fault? Or is he a victim of a system whereby a man may be a garage mechanic or a real estate salesman the year round. He becomes proficient at his work by experience and repetition. But when the rare, serious fire occurs he must instantly switch roles. He must become the fire chief trying to control a serious fire.

How many major fires of a similar nature

has this man had in his community? Has he ever before been inside the building which is on fire? Think back to the last time your wife moved the furniture around while you were out playing poker. You come home late, don't want to disturb the wife so you sneak into the bedroom—or try to! The chances are you will break your neck tripping over a couch that was not there when you left the house. Your own family home has suddenly become an obstacle course. You can't find your way safely in the dark in your own house—without a fire, no heat, no smoke, no tension, no excitement, no heart-pounding decisions to make. Can you then expect to direct men to operate more efficiently at a fire in a strange building? It is remarkable we do as well as we do. How efficient can such an operation be? What can we do about it?

First, if you don't know the structural layout and the contents, admit you are conducting a great guessing game. Then inspect every structure in which you can expect a serious fire until you (and everyone else too) can find your way in the dark.

Second, how do we give this chief some command experience? There has to be a better way to get this vital learning.

How do doctors and lawyers learn their profession? They go through a period of on-the-job training and learning by doing. In a number of years, due to constant repetition, they become expert in their field. We don't have this luxury. Fortunately, the number of challenging fires in most communities is too infrequent to amass this build-up of knowledge. In most cases men never gain sufficient expertise in this manner. But there are additional means of increasing our knowledge. Some such ways are:

1. Go to a large city where you can act as an observer for as long as you can.

2. Attend fire schools in large cities.

3. Critique all large fires in your own and neighboring towns.

4. Hold realistic drills in buildings of concern.

5. Burn for training, buildings that present learning capabilities.

6. Hope that training aids such as the simulator will help fill in the gaps.

Problem with large department

Now let us examine the larger paid departments. In my opinion they suffer from a serious disease I call "needed vacancies". Most people want to move ahead in their chosen profession. Firemen are no different. Consciously or unconsciously we attempt to justify the need for more officer personnel. Many large departments have too many officers in the upper ranks. This has a deleterious effect. It stifles initiative and decision making on the part of junior officers. They never get the luxurious experience of making decisions and mistakes and profiting by both.

What lieutenant dares to make a decision knowing a chief is on his way? What battalion chief dares to send a second alarm knowing the division chief is on his way? As a result men arrive at battalion chief's rank unable to make an important decision. Does this frustration, lack of experience in decision making, and fear of making mistakes (he never made any because he never said anything crucial) grow within him as he advances in his career? Does he carry this with him to the top job?

There is a terrible temptation on the part of a chief (particularly where he feels he can do the job more quickly than to order it done) to order a crucial line in to a position and then supervise it for a while. It is wrong to do it this way. If you do this, admit you haven't trained the junior officers enough so they would have been able to do it as well.

The command structure

Now before we get out onto the fireground lets dispel the mystery of the command structure. In our effort to professionalize our status we sold ourselves the same propaganda we have been feeding the public for years. Like most people we tend to go from one extreme to the other. For years and years it was automatically assumed that the man who rose to the top slot in the firefighting end of the job automatically was a top notch manager as well. Let's look at a sample budget of a 100 man department with five stations. Consider average salaries of $10,000 each for a personnel budget of over $1,000,000. Salaries are at least 90 percent of the cost of a fire department. The total budget should be about $1,100,000 for salaries, supplies, etc. Now consider five stations worth about $50,000 each (conservative). Then add seven pumpers, two ladders, one elevating platform, chief's car, etc., and you have an inventory worth over $500,000. Add this to an annual budget of over $1,100,000 and you begin to see that you are running a fair sized business.

Where was the justification to saying because a man could fight fires he could also handle a large business employing over 100 men, $500,000 worth of inventory with a payroll of over $1,100,000 annually? Nothing in his training really qualified him for this. We can see why some chiefs have trouble running an efficient department.

Now the pendulum has swung to the other extreme (as most pendulums will). With the emphasis on management, no chief (who came up the hard way) is considered to be capable of running his department. If he has no string of degrees after his name he is simply not a "qualified leader".

The personnel people (the new quiz kids of our trade) drew up new rules—set the guidelines—and woe to the chief who fails to nod in complete somnambulistic agreement. Part of our trouble is that we are so burdened by guilt complexes we believe it all eagerly, almost pathetically.

The day of the iron fist is gone (and good riddance). The era of the velvet glove approach is in full bloom. In my opinion both schools are pure bunk. There is a happy medium and many chiefs who came up the hard way are capable, competent people. Let us plot a sensible midway course.

There is nothing mysterious about running a fire department. Yes, you should become knowledgeable about management skills. The chances are you have a great deal of them already or your organization would function much more poorly than it does.

Command at the fire scene

Command on the fireground is a demanding task for the officer. To improve our ability to handle the situation, we have to concede certain basic faults that we find in ourselves. Admit these probabilities:

1. You are going to get excited.
2. You will yell.
3. You will make mistakes.
4. You will lose buildings.
5. Back in quarters the next day you will be brilliant in your diagnosis.
6. You will wonder whether you really know enough to be chief.

Stop worrying. Every other chief felt the same way at some time.

Now look at the fire scene. What is your job? It is this: To manage your men and equipment so as to best handle the situation.

To do this you will need lots of men and equipment. They will be operating beyond your sight and direct command. This is necessary because you want to surround the situation in order of urgency. Since you must be where you can be reached and where you can coordinate the operation, you will take a conspicuous frontal position.

To insure the total strategy, to insure that competent orderly procedures will be carried out at places you cannot personally see and reach, you will use help. This help has been previously trained so that it is not necessary for you to personally instruct them in their job at the fire.

In your command structure, avoid having more than four or five people reporting directly to you. Your span of control becomes limited beyond this number and efficiency will suffer.

You should have prearranged running cards which show responses and change companies. Assignment cards should be made up on which may be recorded particular areas of operation for units. In other words, everything you may need at the fire, from blankets to nozzles, should be prearranged and written down for quick reference. (See Pages 46-53.)

Placing your companies

Now what about this business of placing companies. First, chances are when you arrive at the fire scene you will be confronted with a committed plan. The companies will be at work, there will be noise and confusion.

Don't jump out of your car and start shouting orders. Find the officer in charge and ask him what the problem is, what he has done, what help he has now, and what help is on its way.

What you must now determine based on the information you receive is this:

1. Are people trapped and in danger?

2. Will people be in danger if the fire spreads?

3. Is the fire confined or is there serious potential for further involvement?

4. Is there enough manpower and equipment to cope with the situation?

5. If companies are relegated to simply protecting exposures can they be reassigned to a more positive attack and still protect exposed points?

Your general plan of attack should be as follows: The initial line placement heads off the fire spread. Then, the sprinkler system should be supplied. Place additional lines so as to surround the entire fire area. Back up those hose lines in heavily involved areas or where men may be in danger. Fill in the supply to elevating platforms, ladder pipes, standpipe and sprinkler connections. Assign a spark and brand patrol if needed.

In your day-to-day operations of the department you must accumulate a knowledge of personnel capability. That is to say, you have to know your employee strengths and weaknesses. If, for example, your subordinates report back to you that they will hold the fire at a certain point, you must know whether such positive assurance can be relied upon. If not, you could get into serious difficulty.

You must have enough belief in your own capabilities to say with authority to a young chief or company officer, "Get a line into the next building to the top floor and stop the fire from moving by way of the hanging ceiling." You must know whether or not this is a practical order that your men can carry out. By your positive order, the job assumes manageable proportions.

Chapter 31

A final word

THIS HAS BEEN a book on tactics; the art of combating fires which have already occurred. Note that I use the term art, rather than science. Firefighting is not a science; it lacks the precise results one expects of the research laboratory (even though these results may be long in coming). There are few exact procedures based on research and experimentation which can be used over and over again with similar predictable results.

The simple fact is that few communities experience large, complex fires with sufficient frequency to develop an expertise which justifies the connotation of a scientific approach. Firefighters, having been taught to expect the extinguishing process to almost come out of a test tube, are dismayed—and many times frightened—when they face their first severe test. The smoke is choking and blinding, the heat searing; the punishment while advancing hose lines or examining floors for trapped victims is torturous. This is when one wishes there were a more scientific approach. To say there is, is misleading and untrue.

Firefighting is an art and a very skillful one at that. It is learned in many ways. There are books, fire schools, special courses, and you can learn by doing. Most desirable is a combination of these. If I had to place a priority on either I would say read and learn. But to learn your art well, you must do what you have read about. You must do it over and over again until you are as familiar with

it as the back of your hand. The words *hot, smoky, punishing,* all apply to firefighting, but they are relative terms. You have to experience them yourself to be able to judge what is really *hot, smoky* and *punishing.*

There is a crying need for the genius of science in our work. Look at our tools, equipment, and clothing. How much different is it than when I started as a probationary fireman in May of 1936? In fact, most of the equipment is identical. We need research which can improve our equipment and help us in our work.

Let me touch on another sensitive area; the rapidly increasing cost of fire protection. If we look at our work, in its very broadest sense, it is to minimize losses in life and save on fire losses. If this is correct, we must consider the total cost of fire protection and this includes more than just the cost of running the fire department.

In 1970 there were 2,475,000 fires in this country. These fires took 12,200 lives and destroyed $2,800,000,000 in property. Horrible as these figures are they don't begin to tell the full story.

Many thousands were seriously hurt or burned (how many is anyone's guess—few departments keep and publish records, other than their own personnel, of people injured at fires). The cost of their medical bills, the loss of earned income because of absence from work, the small one-man business that closed because the injured person couldn't

359

TABLE VI

Salary Costs for Large Departments

	Total Budget	Percent for Salaries
Chicago	$ 41,750,000	94
Detroit	$ 16,097,000	90
Los Angeles	$ 36,298,000	96
New York City	$134,313,000	97
Philadelphia	$ 20,168,000	95

*1966 budgets. Figures do not show money set aside to pay pensions.

be there are all very real losses even though not tabulated.

Communities with one major industry have become ghost towns due to the "ripple effect". First there is the initial direct fire loss of plant, structure, and its contents. Next comes the loss of wages because people cannot find temporary employment. With a loss in earning power, there is curtailment of purchasing power. Over a period of time the unemployed worker buys less food, clothes, cars, TV. Soon the local shopkeepers feel the pinch. They in turn buy less from their sources of supply. The losses fan out like the widening ripples in a pool when a stone is tossed into the water.

The industry which suffered the fire finds its customers went to other areas of supply. There is a loss of future business due to unfulfilled contracts. The old customers, over a period of many months, are satisfied with the new arrangements made during the plant's shutdown. They may not wish to return if the plant does rebuild.

With vital records destroyed, old customers gone for good, management is reluctant to chance rebuilding and goes out of business.

Then comes the final insidious effect. The taxable income for the city has been seriously reduced to where it may be difficult to maintain the essential services which would attract new industry. The cycle is now complete.

The last costly item to consider is the fire department budget. This is minimal in the all volunteer departments. But in the fully paid department, salaries constitute over 90 percent of the budget. (See Table VI.)

Inflationary trends are skyrocketing these costs, and the end is not in sight.

In addition, fire losses are increasing yearly. This is due to a combination of inflation (it costs more to rebuild because prices are higher) and the increased hazards of modern industry.

The modern fire chief must take a hard look at his costs. Even the sacred cow of manpower must be re-examined in the light of these heavy costs. I do not question the increased fire duty being performed in the slum sections of our major cities, and the resulting vital need for manpower. This is a social phenomenon which eventually will be solved. But is it not the time to determine our objectives in the fire service?

If we look at fire departments in other parts of the world, we soon notice their losses are substantially lower than ours. One may conclude they excel in manpower and equipment. Yet this is not so. To the contrary, their fire departments are not manned nearly as well, their stations are fewer in number, and they have less equipment.

Fire departments all over the world have the same purpose: to provide good fire protection. But what do we mean by good fire protection? Are our standards the same? If not, how can we compare? The obvious conclusion is that until we define our objective clearly no one can really say what is good or poor fire protection.

Standards for fire protection in this country are generally established by the fire insurance industry. They have elaborate charts and statistics stating how far a fire company can be from a point in town, how many men are needed to man this company, how many companies are required for certain size towns, etc. Who is to say that these standards are correct? There is no statistical proof to show whether these standards provide either inferior protection or overprotection. This is not to condemn the insurance industry. Without them the fire service would not be where it is today.

One reason given for the close spacing of fire companies is the five minute myth. This says that the first five minutes of a fire are crucial and make the difference between successful containment and holocaust. This is utter nonsense. At some stages of a fire, five minutes can be critical. But in many cases fires start small and remain so, slowly growing in some concealed part of the structure or its contents for hours. The answer is efficient, automatic, early detection instruments that will detect the fire before it ever reaches dangerous proportions, and not more fire companies. It is time to look at the problem as it should have been seen some years ago.

What is there to burn?

Economically speaking, how much of what burns shall we aim at controlling? We know buildings can be constructed that will not burn down. Yet we continue to have destructive fires. Why? Look at McCormick Place in Chicago. In 1967 this building suffered the greatest single fire loss in history. The building was steel and masonry. These materials do not burn, but they are subject to destruction by the effects of large, hot fires. Does it not seem obvious then to:

1. Build a structure of materials that will not burn (the technology of such construction is well understood).

2. Limit severely the fire loading. If we do not put materials which can burn with temperatures high enough to cause serious structure failures into a building, we will have no collapse.

The problem therefore is radically simple. We know how to build with fire safe materials. We know how to make furniture, clothing, materials relatively resistant to ignition by fire. All we have to do is insist on combining the techniques. If enough people object strongly, we can have fire-safe buildings. We can even use wood, if properly treated. Using our present knowledge, it is possible to build cities in which buildings will not burn and people will not die from fires.

Hazards of industry

We have not discussed the hazards of industry. It is impossible in many instances to limit the use of combustibles (some highly hazardous) in manufacturing processes. Despite adequate laws and regulations of these industries, we will continue to have accidents and serious fires in such occupancies. But there are answers here too. One is zoning. Insist these hazardous industries are located in remote areas of the city with ample separation from other structures. Provide sufficient fire detection systems and automatic venting to rid the building of smoke and heat. Couple this with an automatic sprinkler which will extinguish the fire in its early stage and then shut itself off to prevent water damage. Sprinkler systems have a remarkable record of efficiency. They successfully extinguish 96 percent of all fires before the fire department even arrives. There are special extinguishing systems designed to handle fires on which water should not be used.

Most responsible fire officials will admit (privately) that once some buildings become seriously involved, fire will continue to burn despite the best efforts of the fire department. This is due to built-in structural conditions combined with the storage of hazardous materials. In such large fires, the fire department usually winds up in a containing action, simply surrounding the fire with large hose streams to prevent spread and allowing the fire to consume its combustible contents.

Here then is the crux of the situation. Regardless of the size and efficiency of the fire department some fires cannot be extinguished.

Fire departments are not organized to handle simple fires. Quite the reverse is true. They are arranged to handle not one but a number of larger fires. But if it is true in most cases they resort to a containing action in large fires, why then organize on a basis of extinguishing the large fires? This requires much larger forces and equipment.

Are then some of our fire departments organized with an overprotective factor which is not economically justified? I think yes.

What lies ahead?

The fire department of the future will little resemble the massive operations of today. Cities like New York and Chicago will operate with less than a quarter of their present strength. They will be manned by small teams of highly trained specialists—aided by highly sophisticated instruments and built-in equipment.

New extinguishing agents are on the way which will be radically different from anything we now have. There will be energy waves which can control flame action as well as flame destroying catalysts. There will be heat sensors in walls, floors, and ceilings which will be able to detect the energy of a fire before it is visible. These sensors will direct automatic extinguishing equipment to the hot spots where a discharge of a flame-killing chemical will stop the fire cold.

The fire chief responding to a fire call will receive a punched message on his car computer, fed by a memory bank at the central office. It will give him information such as size, construction features, dangerous storages, interior layout, exits, stairs, and where the fire is in the building. It will tell him which units are available and traffic conditions enroute.

In short, before he even reaches the building, he will be in possession of important knowledge needed to operate efficiently. He will be constantly advised of conditions not only at this fire, but in other areas as well.

It is undeniably true that existing fire traps and buildings built with conventional materials will be with us for some time to come. But with our massive urban renewal programs, and the flood of new home construction started, and expected for the future, isn't it time we started now? With the competition so fierce for the tax dollar and so little area to cut, doesn't it make sense to save huge sums of money and increase our safety from fire at the same time?

I say, let us start now!

Illustration acknowledgments

The photographs, illustrations, and drawings listed here are through the courtesy of the following individuals and publications:

FIGURE 2: Chicago Heights Star Publications, Inc.

FIGURE 7: *WNYF*, magazine of the New York City Fire Department.

FIGURE 15: Chicago Heights Star Publications, Inc.

FIGURE 16: Chicago Heights Star Publications, Inc.

FIGURE 17: E. C. Beckwith, Park Forest (Illinois) Fire Department.

FIGURE 18: *WNYF*, magazine of the New York City Fire Department.

FIGURE 20: Gilbert Fushi, Chicago Heights (Illinois) Fire Department.

FIGURE 21: Gilbert Fushi, Chicago Heights (Illinois) Fire Department.

FIGURE 22: Gilbert Fushi, Chicago Heights (Illinois) Fire Department.

FIGURE 26: E. C. Beckwith, Park Forest (Illinois) Fire Department.

FIGURE 32: Gilbert Fushi, Chicago Heights (Illinois) Fire Department.

FIGURE 33: Gilbert Fushi, Chicago Heights (Illinois) Fire Department.

FIGURE 35: Leo Musch, Hinsdale (Illinois) Fire Department.

FIGURE 47: Leo Musch, Hinsdale (Illinois) Fire Department.

FIGURE 48: *New York News.*

FIGURE 49: *New York News.*

FIGURE 50: *New York News.*

FIGURE 51: Alex Donchin, New York City.

FIGURE 52: Bob Schroeder, *Fairmont Daily Sentinel*, Fairmont, Minnesota.

FIGURE 53: E. C. Beckwith, Park Forest (Illinois) Fire Department.

FIGURE 54: *Fort Wayne News Sentinel*, Fort Wayne, Indiana.

FIGURE 71: Gilbert Fushi, Chicago Heights (Illinois) Fire Department.

FIGURE 72: Leo Musch, Hinsdale (Illinois) Fire Department.

FIGURE 73: Gilbert Fushi, Chicago Heights (Illinois) Fire Department.

FIGURE 84: *Fire Chief Magazine.*

FIGURE 93: Leo Musch, Hinsdale (Illinois) Fire Department.

FIGURE 96: Gilbert Fushi, Chicago Heights (Illinois) Fire Department.

FIGURE 107: Gilbert Fushi, Chicago Heights (Illinois) Fire Department.

FIGURE 108: Chief Fire Marshal Curtis Volkamer, Chicago Fire Department.

FIGURE 109: Chief Fire Marshal Curtis Volkamer, Chicago Fire Department.

FIGURE 110: *WNYF*, magazine of the New York City Fire Department.

FIGURE 114: Leo Musch, Hinsdale (Illinois) Fire Department.

FIGURE 115: Leo Musch, Hinsdale (Illinois) Fire Department.

FIGURE 120: *WNYF*, magazine of the New York City Fire Department.

FIGURE 121: *WNYF*, magazine of the New York City Fire Department.

FIGURE 122: *WNYF*, magazine of the New York City Fire Department.

Index